D1534744

To Bruce Householder
from
Grandad
and
Grandma

Mrs. Wiggs
of the Cabbage Patch

By
ALICE
HEGAN
RICE

Illustrated by

Norma and Dan Garris

WHITMAN PUBLISHING COMPANY
Racine, Wisconsin

Contents

1

Mrs. Wiggs's Philosophy

"In the mud and scum of things
Something always, always sings!"

My, but it's nice an' cold this mornin'! The ther-
mometer's done fell up to zero!"

Mrs. Wiggs made the statement as cheerfully
as if her elbows were not sticking out through the
boy's coat that she wore, or her teeth chattering
in her head like a pair of castanets. But, then,
Mrs. Wiggs was a philosopher, and the sum and
substance of her philosophy lay in keeping the
dust off her rose-colored spectacles. When Mr.
Wiggs traveled to eternity by the alcohol route,
she buried his faults with him, and for want of

9

better virtues to extol she always laid stress on the fine hand he wrote. It was the same way when their little country home burned and she had to come to the city to seek work; her one comment was: "Thank God, it was the pig instid of the baby that was burned!"

So this bleak morning in December she pinned the bedclothes around the children and made them sit up close to the stove, while she pasted brown paper over the broken windowpane and made sprightly comments on the change in the weather.

The Wiggses lived in the Cabbage Patch. It was not a real cabbage patch, but a strange neighborhood, where ramshackle cottages played hopscotch over the railroad tracks. There were no streets, so when a new house was built the owner faced it any way his fancy prompted. Mr. Bagby's grocery, it is true, conformed to convention, and presented a solid front to the railroad track. But Miss Hazy's cottage shied off sidewise into the Wiggses' yard, as if it were afraid of the big freight trains that went thundering past so many times a day, and Mrs. Schultz's front room looked directly into the Eichorns' kitchen. The latter was not a bad arrangement, however, for Mrs. Schultz had been confined to her bed for ten years, and her sole interest in life consisted in watching what took place in her neighbor's family.

The Wiggses' house was the most imposing in the neighborhood. This was probably due to the fact that it had two front doors and a tin roof. One door was nailed up, and the other opened outdoors, but you would never guess it from the street. When the country house burned, one door had been saved. So Mrs. Wiggs and the boys brought it to the new home and skillfully placed it at the front end of the side porch. But the roof gave the house its chief distinction; it was the only tin roof in the Cabbage Patch. Jim and Billy had made it of old cans which they picked up on the commons.

Jim was fifteen and head of the family; his shoulders were those of a man, and were bent with work, but his body dwindled away to a pair of thin legs that seemed incapable of supporting the burden imposed upon them. In his anxious eyes was the look of a breadwinner who had begun the struggle too soon. Life had been a tragedy to Jim: the tragedy that comes when a child's sensitive soul is forced to meet the responsibilities of manhood, yet lacks the wisdom that only experience can bring.

Billy Wiggs was differently constituted; responsibilities rested upon him as lightly as the freckles on his nose. When occasion or his mother demanded he worked to good purpose, with a tenacity that argued well for his future success, but for the most part he played and fought and got into trouble with the aptitude characteristic of the average small boy.

It was Mrs. Wiggs's boast that her three little girls had geography names; first came Asia, then Australia. When the last baby arrived, Billy had stood looking down at the small bundle and asked anxiously, "Are you goin' to have it fer a boy or a girl, Ma?" Mrs. Wiggs had answered, "A girl, Billy, an' her name's Europena!"

On this particular Sunday morning Mrs. Wiggs

bustled about the kitchen in unusual haste.

"I am goin' to make you all some nice Irish pertater soup fer dinner," she said, as she came in from the parlor, where she kept her potatoes and onions. "The boys'll be in soon, an' we'll have to hurry and git through 'fore the childern begin comin' to Sunday school."

For many years Sunday afternoon had been a trying time in the neighborhood, so Mrs. Wiggs had organized a Sunday school class at which she presided.

"If there don't come Chris an' Pete a'ready!" said Asia, from her post by the stove. "I bet they've had their dinner an' jes' come early to git some of ours!"

"Why, Asia!" exclaimed Mrs. Wiggs. "That ain't hospit'le, an' Chris with one leg, too! 'Tain't no trouble at all. All I got to do is to put a little more water in the soup, an' me and Jim won't take but one piece of bread."

When Jim and Billy came in they found their places at the table taken, so they sat on the floor and drank their soup out of teacups.

"Gee!" said Billy, after the third helping, "I've drinken so much that when I swallers a piece er bread I can hear it splash!"

"Well, you boys git up now, an' go out and bring me in a couple of planks to put acrost the cheers fer the childern to set on."

By two o'clock the Sunday school had begun. Every seat in the kitchen, available and otherwise, was occupied. The boys sat in the windows and on the table, and the girls squeezed together on the improvised benches. Mrs. Wiggs stood before them with a dilapidated hymnbook in her hand.

"Now, you all must hush talkin', so we kin all sing a hymn. I'll read it over, then we'll all sing it together.

'When upon life's billers you are
    tempest tossed,
When you are discouraged thinkin'
    all is lost,
Count yer many blessin's, name 'em
    one by one,
An' it will surprise you what the Lord
    hath done!' "

Clear and strong rose the childish voices in different keys and regardless of time, but with a genuine enthusiasm that was in itself a blessing. When they had sung through three stanzas Mrs. Wiggs began the lesson.

"What did we study 'bout last Sunday?" she asked.

No response, save a smothered giggle from two of the little girls.

"Don't you all remember what the Lord give Moses up on the mountain?"

A hand went up in the corner, and an eager voice cried, "Yas'm, I know! Lord give Moses ten tallers, an' he duveled 'em."

Before Mrs. Wiggs could enter into an argument concerning this new version of sacred history, she was hit in the eye with a paper wad. It was aimed at Billy, but when he dodged she became the victim. This caused some delay, for she had to bathe the injured member, and during the interval the Sunday school became riotous.

"Mith Wiggs, make Tommy thop thpittin' terbaccer juice in my hat!"

"Miss Wiggs, I know who hit you!"

"Teacher, kin I git a drink?"

It was not until Mrs. Wiggs, with a stocking tied over her eye, emerged from the bedroom and again took command that order was restored.

"Where is Bethlehem?" she began, reading from an old lesson paper.

"You kin search *me*!" promptly answered Chris.

She ignored his remark, and passed to the next, who said, half doubtfully, "Ain't it in Alabama?"

"No, it's in the Holy Land," she said.

A sudden commotion arose in the back of the room. Billy, by a series of skillful maneuvers, had succeeded in removing the chair that held one of the planks, and a cascade of small, indignant girls were tobogganing sidewise down the incline. A fight was imminent, but before any further trouble occurred Mrs. Wiggs locked Billy in the bedroom and became mistress of the situation.

"What I think you childern need is a talk about fussin' an' fightin'. There ain't no use in me teachin' what they done a thousand years ago, when you ain't got manners 'nough to listen at what I am sayin'. I recollect one time durin' the war, when the soldiers was layin' 'round the camp, tryin' they best to keep from freezin' to death, a preacher come 'long to hold a service. An' when he got up to preach he sez, 'Friends,' sez he, 'my tex' is Chilblains. They ain't no use a-preachin' religion to men whose whole thought is set on their feet. Now, you fellows git some soft soap an' pour it in yer shoes, an' jes' keep them shoes on till yer feet gits well, an' the nex' time I come 'round yer minds'll be better prepared to receive the word of the Lord.' Now, that's the way I feel 'bout this here Sunday school. First an' fo'most, I am goin' to learn you all manners. Jes' one thought I want you to take away, an' that is, it's sinful to fuss. Ma use' to say livin' was like quiltin' —you orter keep the peace an' do 'way with the scraps. Now, what do I want you to remember?"

"Don't fuss!" came the prompt answer.

"That's right. Now we'll all sing 'Pull fer the Shore.' "

When the windows had ceased to rattle from the vibrations of the lusty chorus, Mrs. Wiggs lifted her hands for silence.

"O Lord!" she prayed earnestly, "help these here childern to be good an' kind to each other, an' to their mas an' their pas. Make 'em thankful fer whatever they've got, even if it ain't but a little. Show us all how to live like you want us to live, an' praise God from whom all blessin's flow. Amen."

As the last youngster scampered out of the yard, Mrs. Wiggs turned to the window where Jim was standing. He had taken no part in the singing and was silent and preoccupied. "Jim," said his mother, trying to look into his face, "you never had on yer overcoat when you come in. You ain't gone an' sold it?"

"Yes," said the boy heavily. "But 'tain't 'nough fer the rent. I got to figger it out some other way."

Mrs. Wiggs put her arm about his shoulder, and together they looked out across the dreary commons.

"Don't you worry so, Jimmy," said she. "Mebbe I kin git work tomorraw, or you'll git a raise, or somethin'. They'll be some way."

Little she guessed what the way was to be.

2

Ways and Means

"Ah! well may the children weep before you!
    They are weary ere they run;
They have never seen the sunshine, nor the glory
    Which is brighter than the sun."

The cold wave that was ushered in that December morning was the beginning of a long series of days that vied with each other as to which could induce the mercury to drop the lowest. The descent of the temperature seemed to have a like effect on the barrel of potatoes and the load of coal in the Wiggses' parlor.

Mrs. Wiggs's untiring efforts to find employment had met with no success, and Jim's exertions were redoubled. Day by day his scanty earnings became less sufficient to meet the demands of the hungry family.

On Christmas Eve they sat near the stove, after the little ones had gone to bed, and discussed the situation. The wind hurled itself against the house in a very frenzy of rage, shaking the icicles from the window ledge and hissing through the patched panes. The snow that sifted in through the loose sash lay unmelted on the sill. Jim had a piece of old carpet about him and coughed with almost every breath. Mrs. Wiggs's head was in her hands, and the tears that trickled through her crooked fingers hissed as they fell on the stove. It was the first time Jim had ever seen her give up.

"Seems like we'll have to ast fer help, Jim," she said. "I can't ast fer credit at Mr. Bagby's; seems like I'd never have the courage to pull agin a debt. What do you think? I guess it looks like mebbe we'll have to apply to the organization."

Jim's eyes flashed. "Not yet, Ma!" he said firmly. "It 'ud be with us like it was with the Hornbys. They didn't have nothin' to eat, and they went to the organization an' the man asted 'em if they had a bed or a table, an' when they said yes, he said, 'Well, why don't you sell 'em?'

No, Ma! As long as we've got coal I'll git the vittles some way!" He had to pause, for a violent attack of coughing shook him from head to foot. "I think I can git a night job next week; one of the market men comes in from the country ever' night to git a early start nex' mornin', an' he ast me if I'd sleep in his wagon from three to six an' keep his vegetables from bein' stole. That 'ud gimme time to git home an' git breakfast, an' be down to the fact'ry by seven."

"But, Jimmy boy," cried his mother, her voice quivering with anxiety, "you never could stan' it night an' day, too! No, I'll watch the wagon. I'll—"

A knock on the parlor door interrupted her. She hastily dried her eyes and smoothed her hair. Jim went to the door.

"I've a Christmas basket for you!" cried a cheery voice.

"Is this Christmas?" Jim asked dully.

The girl in the doorway laughed. She was tall and slender, but Jim could only see a pair of sparkling eyes between the brim of the hat and

her high fur collar. It was nice to hear her laugh, though. It made things seem warmer somehow. The colored man behind her deposited a large basket on the doorstep.

"It's from the church," she explained. "A crowd of us are out in the bus distributing baskets."

"Well, how'd you ever happen to come here?" cried Mrs. Wiggs, who had come to the door.

"There is one for each of the mission school families; just a little Christmas greeting, you know."

Mrs. Wiggs's spirits were rising every minute. "That certainly is kind an' thoughtful like," she said. "Won't you—" then she hesitated. The room she had just left was not in a condition to receive guests, but Mrs. Wiggs was a Kentuckian. "Come right in an' git warm," she said cordially. "The stove's died down some, but you could git thawed out."

"No, thank you, I can't come in," said the young lady with a side glance at Jim who was leaning against the door. "Have you plenty of coal?" she asked in an undertone.

"Oh, yes'm, thank you," said Mrs. Wiggs, smiling reassuringly. Her tone might have been less confident but for Jim's warning glance. Every fiber of his sensitive nature shrank from asking help.

The girl was puzzled. She noticed the stamp of poverty on everything in sight except the bright face of the little woman before her.

"Well," she said doubtfully, "if you ever want —to come to see me, ask for Miss Lucy Olcott at Terrace Park. Good night, and a happy Christmas!"

She was gone, and the doorway looked very black and lonesome in consequence. But there was the big basket to prove she was not merely an apparition, and it took both Jim and his mother to carry it into the house. Sitting on the floor, they unpacked it. There were vegetables, oatmeal, fruit, and even tea and coffee. But the surprise was at the very bottom! A big turkey, looking so comical with his legs stuck in his body that Jim laughed outright.

"It's the first turkey that's been in this house

fer many a day!" said Mrs. Wiggs delightedly, as she pinched the fat fowl. "I 'spect Europena'll be skeered of it, it's so big. My, but we'll have a good dinner tomorra! I'll git Miss Hazy an' Chris to come over an' spend the day, an' I'll carry a plate over to Mrs. Schultz an' take a little o' this here tea to ole Mrs. Lawson."

The cloud had turned inside out for Mrs. Wiggs, and only the silver lining was visible. Jim was doing a sum on the brown paper that came over the basket, and presently he looked up and said slowly, "Ma, I guess we can't have the turkey this year. I kin sell it fer a dollar seventy-five, and that would buy us hog meat fer a good while."

Mrs. Wiggs's face fell, and she twisted her apron string in silence. She had pictured the joy of a real Christmas dinner, the first the youngest children had ever known. And she had already thought of half a dozen neighbors to whom she wanted to send "a little snack." But one look at Jim's anxious face recalled their circumstances.

"Of course we'll sell it," she said brightly. "You have got the longest head fer a boy! We'll sell it in the mornin' an' buy sausage fer dinner, an' I'll cook some of these here nice vegetables an' put a orange an' some candy at each plate, an' the childern'll never know nothin' 'bout it. Besides," she added, "if you ain't never et turkey meat you don't know how good it is."

But in spite of her philosophy, after Jim had gone to bed she slipped over and took one more look at the turkey.

"I think I wouldn't 'a' minded so much," she said wistfully, "ef they hadn't sent the cramberries, too!"

For ten days the basket of provisions and the extra money made by Jim's night work and Mrs. Wiggs's washing supplied the demands of the family. But by the end of January the clouds had gathered thicker than before.

Mrs. Wiggs's heart was heavy one night as she tramped home through the snow after a hard day's work. The rent was due, the coal was out, and only a few potatoes were left in the barrel. But these were mere shadow troubles, compared to Jim's illness. He had been too sick to go to the factory that morning, and she dared not think what changes the day may have brought. As she lifted the latch of her rickety door the sobbing of a child greeted her; it was little Europena, crying for food. For three days there had been no bread in the house, and a scanty supply of potatoes and beans had been their only nourishment.

Mrs. Wiggs hastened to where Jim lay on a cot in the corner. His cheeks were flushed and his thin, nervous fingers picked at the old shawl that covered him.

"Jim," she said, kneeling beside him and pressing his hot hand to her cheek, "Jim, darlin', lemme go fer the doctor. You're worser than you was this mornin', an'—an'—I'm so skeered!" Her voice broke in a sob.

Jim tried to put his arm around her but something hurt him in his chest when he moved, so he patted her hand instead.

"Never mind, Ma," he said, his breath coming short. "We ain't got no money to buy the medicine, even if the doctor did come. You go git some supper, now. An', Ma, don't worry. I'm goin' to take keer of you all! Only—only," he added wearily, "I guess I can't sleep in the wagon tonight."

Slowly the hours passed until midnight. Mrs. Wiggs had pulled Jim's cot close to the stove, and applied vigorous measures to relieve him. Her efforts were unceasing, and one after another the homely country remedies were faithfully administered. At twelve o'clock he grew restless.

"Seems like I'm hot, then agin I'm cold," he said, speaking with difficulty. "Could you find a little somethin' more to put over me, Ma?"

Mrs. Wiggs got up and went toward the bed. The three little girls lay huddled under one old quilt, their faces pale and sunken. She turned away abruptly and looked toward the corner where Billy slept on a pallet. The blankets on his bed were insufficient even for him. She put her hands over her face, and for a moment dry sobs convulsed her. The hardest grief is often that which leaves no trace. When she went back to the stove she had a smile ready for the sick boy.

"Here's the very thing," she said. "It's my dress skirt. I don't need it a mite, settin' up here so clost to the fire. See how nice it tucks in all 'round!"

For a while he lay silent, then he said, "Ma, are you 'wake?"

"Yes, Jim."

"Well, I bin thinkin' it over. If I ain't better in the mornin', I guess—" the words came reluctantly, "I guess you'd better go see the Christmas lady. I wouldn't mind her knowin' so much. 'Twon't be fer long, nohow, cause I kin take keer of you all soon—soon's I kin git up."

The talking brought on severe coughing, and he sank back exhausted.

"Can't you go to sleep, honey?" asked his mother.

"No, it's them ole wheels," he said fretfully, "them wheels at the fact'ry. When I git to sleep they keep on wakin' me up."

Mrs. Wiggs's hands were rough and knotted, but love taught them to be gentle as she smoothed his hot head.

"Want me to tell you 'bout the country, Jim?"

Since he was a little boy he had loved to hear of their old home in the valley. His dim recollection of it all formed his one conception of heaven.

"Yes, Ma. Mebbe it will make me fergit the wheels," he said.

"Well," she began, putting her head beside his on the pillow, so he could not watch her face, "it was all jes' like a big front yard without no fences. An' the flowers didn't belong to folks like they do over on the avenue, where you dassent pick a one. They was God's, an' you was welcome to all you could pull. An' there was trees where you could climb up an' git big red apples, Jim. An' when the frost 'ud come they'd be persimmons that 'ud jes' melt in yer mouth. An' you could look 'way off 'crost the meaders an' see the trees a wavin' in the sunshine, an' up over yer head the birds 'ud be singin' like they was never goin' to stop. An' yer pa an' me 'ud take you out at the harvestin' time, an' you 'ud play on the haystacks. I kin remember jes' how you looked, Jim—a fat little boy, with red cheeks, a-laughin' all the time."

Mrs. Wiggs could tell no more, for the old

memories were too much for her. Jim scarcely knew when she stopped. His eyes were half closed and a sweet drowsiness was upon him.

"It's nice an' warm in the sunshine," he murmured. "The meaders an' trees—laughin' all the time! Birds singin', singin', singin'."

Then Jim began to sing, too, softly and monotonously, and the sorrow that had not come with years left his tired face, and he fearlessly drifted away into the Shadowy Valley where his lost childhood lay.

3

The "Christmas Lady"

"The rosy glow of summer
    Is on thy dimpled cheek,
While in thy heart the winter
    Is lying cold and bleak.

"But this shall change hereafter,
    When years have done their part,
And on thy cheek the winter,
    And summer in thy heart."

Late the next afternoon a man and a girl were standing in the Olcott reception hall. The lamps had not been lighted but the blaze from the back-log threw a cozy glow of comfort over the crimson curtains and on the mass of bright-hued pillows in the window seat.

Robert Redding, standing with his hat in his hand, would have been gone long ago if the "Christmas Lady" had not worn her violet gown. He said it always took him half an hour to say

33

good-by when she wore a rose in her hair, and a full hour when she had on the violet dress.

"By Jove, stand there a minute just as you are! The firelight shining through your hair makes you look like a saint. Little Saint Lucinda!" he said teasingly, as he tried to catch her hand. She put it behind her for safekeeping.

"Not a saint at all?" he went on, in mock surprise. "Then an iceberg—a nice, proper little iceberg."

Lucy Olcott looked up at him for a moment, in silence. He was very tall and straight, and his face retained much of its boyishness, in spite of the firm, square jaw.

"Robert," she said, suddenly grown serious, "I wish you would do something for me."

"All right, what is it?" he asked.

She timidly put her hand on his and looked up at him earnestly.

"It's about Dick Harris," she said. "I wish you would not be with him so much."

Redding's face clouded. "You aren't afraid to trust me?" he asked.

"Oh, no! It isn't that," she said hurriedly. "But, Robert, it makes people think such wrong things about you. I can't bear to have you misjudged."

Redding put his arm around her and together they stood looking down into the glowing embers.

"Tell me about it, little girl. What have you heard?" he asked.

She hesitated. "It wasn't true what they said. I knew it wasn't true, but they had no right to say it."

"Well, let's hear it, anyway. What was it?"

"Some people were here last night from New Orleans and they asked if I knew you—said they knew you and Dick the year you spent there."

"Well?" said Redding.

Lucy evidently found it difficult to continue. "They said some horrid things then, just because you were Dick's friend."

"What were they, Lucy?"

"They told me that you were both as wild as could be; that your reputation was no better than his; that—forgive me, Robert, for even repeating it. It made me very angry, and I told them it was not true—not a word of it; that it was all Dick's fault; that he—"

"Lucy," interrupted Redding peremptorily, "wait until you hear me! I have never lied to you about anything, and I will not stoop to it now. Four years ago, when those people knew me, I was just what they said. Dick Harris and I went to New Orleans straight from college. Neither of us had a home or people to care about us, so we went in for a good time. At the end of the year I was sick of it all, braced up, and came here. Poor Dick, he kept on."

At his first words the color had left Lucy's face, and she had slipped to the opposite side of the fire. She stood watching him with horrified eyes.

"But you were never like Dick!" she protested.

"Yes," he continued passionately, "and but for God's help I should be like him still. It was an awful pull, and Heaven only knows how I struggled. I never quite saw the use of it all, until I met you six months ago; then I realized that the past four years had been given me in which to make a man of myself."

As he finished speaking he saw, for the first time, that Lucy was crying. He sprang forward but she shrank away. "No, no, don't touch me! I'm so terribly disappointed, and hurt, and—stunned."

"But you surely don't love me the less for having conquered these things in the past?"

"I don't know, I don't know," she said with a sob. "I honored and idealized you, Robert. I can never think of you as being other than you are now."

"But why should you?" he pleaded. "It was only one year out of my life. Too much, it's true, but I have atoned for it with all my might."

The intensity and earnestness of his voice were beginning to influence her. She was very young, with the stern, uncompromising standards of girlhood. Life was black or white to her, and time had not filled in the canvas with the myriad grays that blend into one another until all lines are effaced and only the Master Artist knows the boundaries.

She looked up through her tears. "I'll try to

forgive you," she said tremulously. "But you must promise to give up your friendship for Dick Harris."

Redding frowned and bit his lip. "That's not fair!" he said. "You know Dick's my chum; that he hasn't the least influence over me; that I am about the only one to stand by him."

"I am not afraid of his influence but I don't want people to see you together. It makes them say things."

"But, Lucy, you wouldn't have me go back on him? Dick has a big heart and he's trying to brace up—"

"Oh, nonsense!" cried Lucy impatiently. The fire in her eyes had dried the tears. "He could straighten up if he wanted to. He likes to drink and gamble, so he does it. You only encourage him by your friendship. Are you choosing between us?" she demanded angrily.

Redding's face was clouded and he spoke slowly. "You wouldn't ask this of me, Lucy, if you understood. Dick and I have been chums since we were boys. He came to Kentucky three months ago, sick and miserable. One day he came into the office and said, 'Bob, you've pulled through all right. Do you think it's too late for me to try?' What would you have said?"

"What you did, probably," answered Lucy, "but I would have profited by the one experience, for he has hardly drawn a sober breath since." She looked out of the window across the snowy landscape, and in her face was something of the passionless purity of the scene upon which her eyes rested.

"You are mistaken," he cried fiercely. "Because you have seen him several times in that condition, you have no right to draw such a conclusion. He is weak, nobody denies it; but what can you know of the struggle he makes, of his eagerness to do better, of the fight that he is constantly making with himself?"

His words fell on deaf ears.

"Then you choose Mr. Harris?"

"Lucy, this is madness! It is not like you in the least!"

The girl was cold with anger and excitement.

"It is bad enough," she said, "to know that my defense of you last night was worse than useless, but to have you persist in a friendship with a man who is beneath you in every way is more than I can stand." She slipped a ring from her finger and held it toward him. "I could never marry a man of whom I was ashamed."

The shot went home. There was a white line about Redding's mouth as he turned away.

"I would not ask you to," he said, with simple dignity, as he opened the door.

"Please, ma'am, is this Miss Olcott's?" asked a trembling voice on the piazza. A shabby woman stood looking at them with wild eyes. Her gray hair had escaped from the torn shawl that was pinned over her head, and stray locks blew across her face.

Lucy did not recognize her. "I will speak to you in a moment," she said.

An awkward pause followed, each waiting for the other to speak.

"I will come when you send for me," said Redding without looking at her and, turning abruptly, he strode down the steps and out into the dusk.

Lucy caught her breath and started forward; then she remembered the woman.

"What is it?" she asked listlessly.

The woman stepped forward and put out a hand to steady herself against the door. Her face was distorted and her voice came in gasps.

"You said I was to come if I needed you. It's Jimmy, ma'am—he's dead!"

It may be experience of suffering makes one especially tender to the heartaches of others; at any rate, the article that Lucy Olcott wrote for the paper that night held the one touch of nature that makes the whole world kin. She had taken Aunt Chloe, the old colored servant, and gone home with Mrs. Wiggs, relieving as far as possible the immediate needs of the family. Then she had come home and written their story, telling it simply, but with the passionate earnestness of one who, for the first time, has come into contact with poverty and starvation. She told of the plucky struggle made by the boy; of his indomitable courage; of his final defeat. She ended by asking help of any kind for the destitute family.

A week later she sat at her desk bewildered. Her article, written on the impulse of the moment, with the one thought of making people understand, had fulfilled its mission. For seven days she had done nothing but answer questions and notes and receive contributions for the Wiggs family. Money had arrived from all over the state and from every class of society. Eichenstine Brothers sent fifty dollars, and six ragged newsboys came to present thirty cents. A lavender note, with huge monogram and written in white ink, stated that some of the girls of the "Gay Burlesque Troupe" sent a few dimes to the "kid's" mother. The few dimes amounted to fifteen dollars. Mrs. Van Larkin's coachman had to wait with her note while Lucy answered the questions of a lame old Negro who had brought a quarter.

"Maria done tole me what was writ in de papah 'bout dat pore chile," he was saying. "I sutenly do feel sorry for his maw. I ain't got much, but

I jus' tole Maria I guess we could do without somethin' to gib a quahter."

So it continued. Old and young, rich and poor, paid their substantial tribute of respect to Jimmy Wiggs.

Lucy counted up the long line of figures. "Three hundred and sixty-five dollars!" she exclaimed. "And food, clothes, and coal enough to last them a year!"

It was like a direct answer to her prayer, and yet this poor little suppliant, instead of being duly exalted, put her head on the desk and wept bitterly. Now that the need of the Wiggs family had been met, another appeal, silent and potent, was troubling her heart.

Redding had neither come nor written, and she was beginning to realize the seriousness of their misunderstanding.

4

The Annexation of Cuby

"They well deserve to have,
That know the strongest and surest way to get."

Almost a year rolled over the Cabbage Patch and it was nearing Christmas again. The void left in Mrs. Wiggs's heart by Jim's death could never be filled, but time was beginning to soften her grief, and the necessity for steady employment kept her from brooding over her trouble.

It was still necessary to maintain the strictest economy, for half the money which had been given them was in Miss Olcott's keeping as a safeguard against another rainy day. Mrs. Wiggs had gotten as much washing as she could do; Asia helped about the house, and Billy did odd jobs wherever he could find them.

The direct road to fortune, however, according to Billy's ideas, could best be traveled in a kindling wagon, and, while he was the proud possessor of a dilapidated wagon, sole relic of the late Mr. Wiggs, he had nothing to hitch to it. Scarcely a week passed that he did not agitate the question, and, as Mrs. Wiggs often said, "When Billy Wiggs done set his head to a thing, he's as good as got it!"

So she was not surprised when he rushed breathlessly into the kitchen one evening about suppertime and exclaimed in excited tones, "Ma, I've got a horse! He was havin' a fit on the commons an' they was goin' to shoot him, an' I ast the man to give him to me!"

"My land, Billy! What do you want with a fit-horse?" asked his mother.

" 'Cause I knowed you could cure him. The man said if I took him I'd have to pay fer cartin' away his carcass, but I said, 'All right, I'll take him, anyway.' Come on, Ma, an' see him!" and Billy hurried back to his new possession.

Mrs. Wiggs pinned a shawl over her head and

ran across the commons. A group of men stood around the writhing animal, but the late owner had departed.

"He's 'most gone," said one of the men, as she came up. "I tole Billy you'd beat him fer takin' that ole nag offen the man's han's."

"Well, I won't," said Mrs. Wiggs stoutly. "Billy Wiggs's got more sense than most men I know. That hoss's carcass is worth somethin'. I 'spect he'd bring 'bout two dollars dead, an' mebbe more livin'. Anyway, I'm goin' to save him if there's any save to him!"

She stood with her arms on her hips and critically surveyed her patient. "I'll tell you what's the matter with him," was her final diagnosis. "His lights is riz. Billy, I'm goin' home fer some medicine. You set on his head so's he can't git up, an' Ma'll be right back in a minute."

The crowd which had collected to see the horse shot began to disperse, for it was suppertime, and there was nothing to see now but the poor suffering animal, with Billy Wiggs patiently sitting on its head.

When Mrs. Wiggs returned she carried a bottle and what appeared to be a large marble. "This here is a calomel pill," she explained. "I jes' rolled the calomel in with some soft, light bread. Now, you prop his jaw open with a little stick an' I'll shove it in. An' then hole his head back while I pour down some water an' turkentine outen this bottle."

It was with great difficulty that this was accomplished, for the old horse had evidently seen a vision of the happy hunting ground, and was loath to return to the sordid earth. His limbs were already stiffening in death and only the whites of his eyes were visible. Mrs. Wiggs noted these discouraging symptoms and saw that violent measures were necessary.

"Gether some sticks an' build a fire quick as you kin. I've got to run over home. Build it right clost to him, Billy. We've got to git him het up."

She rushed into the kitchen, and, taking several cakes of tallow from the shelf, threw them into a tin bucket. Then she hesitated for a moment. The

kettle of soup for supper was steaming away on the stove. Mrs. Wiggs did not believe in sacrificing present need to future comfort. She threw in a liberal portion of pepper, and, seizing the kettle in one hand and the bucket of tallow in the other, staggered back to the bonfire.

"Now, Billy," she commanded, "put this bucket of tallow down there in the hottest part of the fire. Look out! Don't tip it—there! Now, you come here an' help me pour this soup into the bottle. I'm goin' to git that ole hoss so het up he'll think he's havin' a sunstroke! Seems sorter bad to keep on pestering him when he's so near gone, but this here soup'll feel good when it once gits inside him."

When the kettle was empty the soup was impartially distributed over Mrs. Wiggs and the patient. But a goodly amount had "got inside," and already the horse was losing his rigidity.

Only once did Billy pause in his work and that was to ask, "Ma, what do you think I'd better name him?"

Giving names was one of Mrs. Wiggs's chief

accomplishments and usually required much thoughtful consideration. In this case, however, if there was to be a christening it must be at once.

"I'd like a jography name," suggested Billy, feeling that nothing was too good to bestow upon his treasure.

Mrs. Wiggs stood with the soup dripping from her hands and earnestly contemplated the horse. Babies, pigs, goats, and puppies had drawn largely on her supply of late, and geography names especially were scarce. Suddenly a thought struck her.

"I'll tell you what, Billy! We'll call him Cuby! It's a town I heared 'em talkin' 'bout at the grocery."

By this time the tallow was melted and Mrs. Wiggs carried it over by the horse. She put each of his hoofs into the hot liquid while Billy rubbed the legs with all the strength of his young arms.

"That's right," she said. "Now you run home an' git that piece of carpet by my bed an' we'll kiver him up. I'm goin' to git them fence rails over yonder to keep the fire goin'."

Through the long night they worked with their patient. And when the first glow of morning appeared in the east, a triumphant procession wended its way across the Cabbage Patch. First came an old woman bearing sundry pails, kettles, and bottles and next came a very sleepy little boy leading a trembling old horse, with soup all over its head, tallow on its feet, and a strip of rag carpet tied about its middle.

And thus Cuba, like his geographical namesake, emerged from the violent ordeal of reconstruction with a mangled constitution, internal dissension, a decided preponderance of foreign element, but a firm and abiding trust in the new power with which his fortunes had been irrevocably cast.

5

A Reminiscence

"It is easy enough to be pleasant
  When life flows along like a song,
But the man worth while is the one who will smile
  When everything goes dead wrong."

When Miss Hazy was awakened early that morning by a resonant neigh at the head of her bed, she mistook it for the trumpet of doom. Miss Hazy's cottage, as has been said, was built on the bias in the Wiggses' side yard, and the little lean-to, immediately behind Miss Hazy's bedroom, had been pressed into service as Cuba's temporary abode.

After her first agonized fright, the old woman ventured to push the door open a crack and peep out.

"Chris," she said in a tense whisper to her sleeping nephew, "Chris, what on airth is this here hitched to our shutter?"

Chris, usually deaf to all calls less emphatic than cold water and a broomstick, raised a rumpled head from the bedclothes.

"Where at?" he asked.

"Right here!" said Miss Hazy, still in a terrified whisper, and holding fast the door, as if the specter might attempt an entrance. Chris did not stop to adjust his wooden leg, but hopped over to the door and cautiously put an eye to the opening.

"Why, shucks, 'tain't nothin' but a hoss!" he said, in disgust, having nerved himself for nothing less than a rhinoceros, such as he had seen in the circus.

"How'd he git there?" demanded Miss Hazy. Chris was not prepared to say.

All through breakfast Miss Hazy was in a flutter of excitement. She had once heard of a baby being left on a doorstep, but never a horse. When the limit of her curiosity was about reached, she saw Mrs. Wiggs coming across the yard carrying a bucket. She hastened to meet her.

"Mornin'," called Mrs. Wiggs brightly, in spite of her night's vigil. "Ain't we got a fine hoss?"

Miss Hazy put the ash barrel between herself and the animal and hazarded a timid inspection, while Mrs. Wiggs made explanations and called attention to Cuba's fine points.

"Can't you come in an' take a warm?" asked Miss Hazy, as she concluded.

"Well, I b'lieve I will," said Mrs. Wiggs. "I ain't been over fer quite a spell. The childern kin clean up, bein' it's Saturday." From seven to nine in the morning were the favorite calling hours in the Cabbage Patch.

Mrs. Wiggs chose the chair which had the least on it and leaned back smiling affably. She remarked, "We're used to hosses. This here's the second one we've had."

"My," said Miss Hazy, "you muster been well to do!"

"Yes," continued Mrs. Wiggs, "we was—up to the time of the fire. Did I ever tell you 'bout how Jim brought our other hoss to town?"

Miss Hazy had heard the story a number of

times, but she knew the duties of a hostess.

"It was this a-way," went on Mrs. Wiggs, drawing her chair closer to the fire and preparing for a good, long talk. "You see, me an' the childern was comin' on the steam-car train but ther' wasn't no way to git the hoss here, 'ceptin' fer somebody to ride him. Course Jim said he'd do it. Poor Jim, always ready to do the hard part!" She paused to wipe her eyes on her apron and Miss Hazy wept in sympathy.

"Never min', Miss Wiggs. Don't cry. Go on an' tell me what you done next."

"Well," said Mrs. Wiggs, swallowing the lump in her throat, "Jim said he'd go. He never had been to the city, an' he was jes' a little shaver, but I knowed I could trust him."

"I don't see how you could stand to risk it!" exclaimed Miss Hazy.

"Oh, I reckon whatever you *got* to do, you *kin* do. I didn' see no other way. So one mornin' I put a old patch quilt over the hoss, tied a bucket of oats on behin', an' fixed some vittles fer Jim, an' started 'em off. It was a forty-mile ride to the city, so I calkerlated to start Jim so's he'd git to Dr. White's 'bout nightfall."

"Dr. White was your old doctor, wasn't he?" prompted Miss Hazy.

"Yes'm, he used to 'tend Mr. Wiggs before we moved over into Bullitt County. You know Mr. Wiggs was a widow man when I married him. He had head trouble. Looked like all his inflictions gethered together in that head of hisn. He uster go into reg'lar transoms!"

Miss Hazy was awe-struck, but more dreadful revelations were to follow.

"I guess you knew I killed him," continued Mrs. Wiggs calmly. "The doctor an' ever'body said so. He was jes' gitten over typhoid, an' I give him pork an' beans. He was a wonderful man! Kept his senses plumb to the end. I remember his very las' words. I was settin' by him, waitin' fer the doctor to git there, an' I kep' sayin', 'Oh, Mr. Wiggs! You don't think you are dyin', do you?' an' he answered up jes' as natural an' fretful-like, 'Good lan', Nancy! How do I know? I ain't never died before.' An' them was the very las' words he ever spoke to anybody."

"Was he a church member, Miss Wiggs?" inquired Miss Hazy.

"Well, no, not exactly," admitted Mrs. Wiggs reluctantly. "But he was what you might say a well-wisher. But, as I was tellin' you, Dr. White was a old friend, an' I pinned a note on Jim's coat tellin' who he was an' where he was goin', an' I knowed the doctor would have a eye on him when he got as fur as Smithville. As fer the rest of the trip I wasn't so certain. The only person I knowed in the city was Pete Jenkins, an' if there was one man in the world I didn't have no use fer, it was Pete. But when I don't like folks I try to do somethin' nice fer 'em. Seems like that's the only way I kin weed out my meanness. So I jes' sez to Jim, 'You keep on astin' till you git to Number Six Injun House, an' then you ast fer Pete Jenkins. You tell him,' sez I, 'you are Hiram Wiggs's boy, an' as long as he done so much harm to yer pa, mebbe he'd be glad to do a good turn by you an' keep you an' the hoss fer the night, till yer ma comes fer you.' Well, Jim started off lookin' mighty little settin' up on that big hoss, an' I waved my apron long as I could. Then I hid behin' a tree to keep him from seein' me cry. He rode all that day an' 'bout sundown he come to Dr. White's. Pore little feller, he was so tired an' stiff he couldn't hardly walk, but he tied the hoss to the post an' went 'round to the back door an' knocked real easy. Mrs. White come to the door an' sez, real cross, 'No, doctor ain't here,' an' slammed it shut agin. I ain't meanin' to blame her. Mebbe her bread was in the oven, or her baby cryin', or somethin', but seems to me I couldn't have treated a dog that a-way!

"Pore Jim, he dragged out to the road agin, an' set there beside the hoss, not knowin' what to do nex'. Night was a-comin' on, he hadn't had no supper, an' he was dead beat. By an' by he went to sleep an' didn't know nothin' till somebody shuck his shoulder an' sez, 'Git up from here! What you doin' sleepin' here in the road?' Then he went stumblin' 'long, with somebody holdin' his arm, an' he was took into a big, bright room, an' the doctor was lookin' at him an' astin' him questions. An' Jim said he never did know what he answered but it must 'a' been right, fer the doctor grabbed holt of his hand an' sez, 'Bless my soul! It's little Jimmy Wiggs, all the way from Curryville!'

"Then they give him his supper, an' Mrs. White sez, 'Where'll he sleep at, Doctor? There ain't no spare bed.' Then Jim sez the doctor frowned like ever'thin' an' sez, 'Sleep? Why, he'll sleep in the bed with my boys. An' they orter be proud to have sech a plucky bedfeller!'

"Jim never did fergit them words. They meant a good deal more to him than his supper.

"Early the nex' mornin' he started out agin, the doctor pointin' him on the way. He didn't git into the city till 'long 'bout four o'clock, an' he sez he never was so mixed in all his life. All my childern was green about town. It made ever' one of 'em sick when they first rode on the streetcars. An' Europena was skeered to death of the newsboys 'cause she thought they called 'Babies,' 'stid of 'Papers.' Jim kep' right on the main road like he was tole to, but things kep' a-happenin' 'round him so fast, he said he couldn't do no more'n jes' keep out o' the way. All of a suddint a ice wagon come rattlin' up behin' him. It was runnin' off, an' 'fore he knowed it a man hit it in the head an' veered it 'round towards him. Jim said his hoss turned a clean somerset, an' he was th'owed up in the air, an'——"

"Ma!" called a shrill voice from the Wiggses' porch. "Australia's in the rain barrel!"

Mrs. Wiggs looked exasperated. "I never was havin' a good time in my life that one of my children didn't git in that rain barrel!"

"Well, go on an' finish," said Miss Hazy, to whom the story had lost nothing by repetition.

"Ther' ain't much more," said Mrs. Wiggs, picking up her bucket. "Our hoss had two legs an' his neck broke, but Jim never had a scratch. A policeman took him to Number Six Injun House an' Pete Jenkins jes' treated him like he'd been his own son. I was done cured then an' there fer my feelin' aginst Pete."

"Ma!" again came the warning cry across the back yard.

"All right, I'm comin'! Good-by, Miss Hazy. You have a eye to Cuby till we git our shed ready. He ain't as sperited as he looks."

And with a cordial hand shake Mrs. Wiggs went cheerfully away to administer chastisement to her erring offspring.

6

A Theater Party

"The play, the play's the thing!"

Billy's foreign policy proved most satisfactory, and after the annexation of Cuba many additional dimes found their way into the tin box on top of the wardrobe. But it took them all, besides Mrs. Wiggs's earnings, to keep the family from the awful calamity of "pulling agin a debt."

One cold December day Billy came in and found his mother leaning wearily on the table. Her face brightened as he entered, but he caught the tired look in her eyes.

"What's the matter?" he asked.

"Ain't nothin' the matter, Billy," she said, trying to speak cheerfully. "I'm jes' wore out, that's all. It'll be with me like it was with Uncle

63

Ned's ole ox, I reckon. He kep' a-goin' an' a-goin' till he died a-standin' up. An' even then they had to push him over."

She walked to the window and stood gazing absently across the commons. "Do you know, Billy," she said suddenly, "I've got the craziest notion in my head. I'd jes' give anythin' to see the show at the Opery House this week."

If she had expressed a wish for a diamond necklace Billy could not have been more amazed, and his countenance expressed his state of mind.

Mrs. Wiggs hastened to explain, "Course, I ain't really thinkin' 'bout goin' but them show bills started me to studyin' 'bout it an' I got to wishin' me an' you could go."

"I don't 'spect it's much when you git inside," said Billy, trying negative consolation.

"Yes, 'tis, Billy Wiggs," answered his mother impressively. "You ain't never been inside a theayter, an' I have. I was there twict, an' it was grand! You orter see the lights, an' fixin's, an' all the fine ladies an' their beaux. First time I went they was a man in skin tights a-walkin' on a rope h'isted 'way up over ever'body's head."

"What's skin tights?" asked Billy, thrilled in spite of himself.

"It's spangles 'round yer waist an' shoes without no heels to 'em. You see, the man couldn't wear many clothes 'cause it would make him too heavy to stay up there in the air. The band plays all the time an' folks sing an' speechify, an' ever'-body laughs an' has a good time. It's jes' grand, I tell you!"

Billy's brows were puckered and he sat unusually quiet for a while looking at his mother. Finally he said, "You might take my snow money from las' week."

Mrs. Wiggs was indignant. "Why, Billy Wiggs!" she exclaimed. "Do you think I'd take an' go to a show when Asia an' Australia ain't got a good shoe to their backs?"

Billy said no more about the theater. But that afternoon when he was out with the kindling he pondered the matter deeply. It was quite cold and sometimes he had to put the reins between his knees and shove his hands deep into his pockets to get the stiffness out of them. It really seemed as if everybody had just laid in a supply of kindling. The shadowy little plan he had been forming was growing more shadowy all the time.

"I 'spect the tickets cost a heap," he thought ruefully, as he drew himself up into a regular pretzel of a boy. "But then, she never does have no fun an' never gits a thing fer herself." And because Billy knew of his mother's many sacrifices, and because he found it very hard to take Jim's place, a lump lodged in his throat and gave him so much trouble that he forgot for a while how cold he was.

About this time he came within sight of the Opera House. Tantalizing posters appeared advertising the GREATEST EXTRAVAGANZA OF THE CENTURY. He pulled Cuba into a walk and sat there absorbing the wonders depicted. Among the marvels were crowds of children dressed as butterflies, beautiful ladies marching in a line, a man balancing a barrel on his feet, and—yes, there was the man in "skin tights" walking on the rope!

A keen puff of wind brought Billy back to his senses, and as his longing eyes turned from the gorgeous show bills they encountered the amused look of a gentleman who had just come out of the Opera House. He was so tall and fine-looking that Billy thought he must own the show.

"Some kindlin', sir?"

The gentleman shook his head. The posters still danced before Billy's eyes. If his mother could only see the show! The last chance seemed slipping away. Suddenly a bold idea presented itself. He got out of the wagon and came up on the step.

"Couldn't you use a whole load if I was to take it out in tickets?"

The man looked puzzled. "Take it out in tickets?" he repeated.

"Yes, sir," said Billy, "theayter tickets. Don't you own the show?"

The gentleman laughed. "Well, hardly," he said. "What do you want with more than one ticket?"

There was a certain sympathy in his voice,

in spite of the fact that he was still laughing, and before Billy knew it he had told him all about it.

"How many tickets could yer gimme fer the load?" he asked, in conclusion.

The gentleman made a hurried calculation. "You say you have three sisters?" he asked.

"Yep," said Billy.

"Well, I should say that load was worth about five tickets."

"Gee whiz!" cried the boy. "That 'ud take us all!"

He followed the gentleman back to the ticket office and eagerly watched the man behind the little window count out five tickets and put them in a pink envelope.

"One for you, one for your mother, and three for the kids," said his friend, as Billy buttoned the treasure in the inside pocket of his ragged coat.

He was so excited that he almost forgot his part of the bargain but as the gentleman was turning away he remembered.

"Say, mister, where must I take the kindlin' to?"

"Oh, that's all right. You can sell it tomorrow," answered the man.

Billy's face fell instantly. "If you don't take the kindlin', I'll have to give you back the tickets. Ma don't 'low us to take nothin' that way."

"But I don't need the kindling. I haven't any place to put it."

"Ain't you got no home?" asked Billy incredulously.

"No," answered the man shortly.

The idea of any one, in any walk of life, not having any use for kindling was a new one to Billy. But he had no time to dwell on it for this new complication demanded all his attention.

"Ain't there nobody you could give it to?" he asked.

The gentleman was growing impatient. "No, no, go along. That's all right."

But Billy knew it would not be all right when he got home, so he made one more effort. "How'd you like to send it out to Miss Hazy?" he inquired.

"Well, Miss Hazy, not having the pleasure of my acquaintance, might object to the delicate attention. Who is she?"

"She's Chris's aunt. They ain't had no fire fer two days."

"Oh!" said the man heartily. "Then take it to Miss Hazy, by all means. Tell her it's from Mr. Bob who is worse off than she is, for he hasn't even a home."

An hour later there was wild excitement under the only tin roof in the Cabbage Patch. Such scrubbing and brushing as was taking place!

"It's jes' like a peetrified air castle," said Mrs. Wiggs, as she pressed out Asia's best dress. "Here I been thinkin' 'bout it, an' wantin' to go, an' here I am actually gittin' ready to go! Come here, child, and let me iron out yer plaits while the iron's good an' hot."

This painful operation was performed only on state occasions. Each little Wiggs laid her head on the ironing board, a willing sacrifice on the altar of vanity, while Mrs. Wiggs carefully ironed out five plaits on each head. Europena was the only one who objected to being a burnt offering. But when she saw the frizzled locks of the others her pride conquered her fear, and, holding tight to Billy's hand, she bent her chubby head to the trying ordeal.

"Now, Billy, you run over to Mrs. Eichorn's an' ast her to loan me her black crepe veil. Mrs. Krasmier borrowed it yesterday to wear to her pa's funeral, but I guess she's sent it back by this time. An', Billy—Billy, wait a minute—you be sure to tell 'em we're goin' to the show." Mrs. Wiggs vigorously brushed her hair with the clothesbrush as she spoke. Australia had thrown the hairbrush down the cistern the summer before.

"Asia, you go git the alpaca from behind the chest an' sorter shake it out on the bed."

"Who's goin' to wear it, Ma?" The question came in anxious tones, for the blue alpaca had been sent them in a bundle of old clothes, and though it failed to fit either of the girls, the wearing of it was a much coveted privilege.

"Well, now, I don't know," said Mrs. Wiggs,

critically surveying the children. "It won't button good on you and it swags in the back on Australia."

"Lemme wear it, Ma!"

"No, lemme!" came in excited tones.

Mrs. Wiggs had seen trouble before over the blue alpaca. She knew what anguish her decision would bring to one or the other.

"It really looks best on Asia," she thought, "but if I let her wear it Austry'll have a cryin' spell an' git to holdin' her breath an' that'll take up too much time." So she added aloud, "I'll tell you what we'll do. Asia, you kin wear the skirt an' Austry kin wear the jacket."

But when she had pinned the skirt over one little girl's red calico dress and buttoned the blue jacket over the clean pinafore of the other, she looked at them dubiously. "They do look kinder mixed," she admitted to herself, "but I reckon it don't matter, so long as they're both happy."

Just then Billy came in with the veil in one hand and a bunch of faded carnations in the other hand.

"Look, Ma!" he exclaimed, holding up his trophy. "I swapped 'em with Pete fer a top an' a agate. He got 'em outen a ash barrel over on the avenue."

"Well, now, *ain't* that nice?" said Mrs. Wiggs. "I'll jes' clip the stems an' put 'em in a bottle of water. By the time we go they'll be picked up right smart. I wisht you had something to fix up in, Billy," she added. "You look as seedy's a rasbury."

Billy did look rather shabby. His elbows were out and two of the holes in his pants were patched and two were not. Mrs. Wiggs was rummaging in the table drawer.

"I wisht I could find somethin' of yer pa's that would do. Here's his white gloves he wore the time he was pallbearer to ol' Mr. Bender. Seems to me they do wear white gloves to the theayter, but I disremember."

"Naw! I ain't a-goin' to wear no gloves," said Billy firmly.

Mrs. Wiggs continued her search. "Here's yer grandpa's watch fob but I'm skeered fer you to wear it. You might lose it. It's a family remnant—been handed down two generations. What about this here red comforter? It would sorter spruce you up an' keep you warm, besides. You know you've had a cold fer a week an' yer pipes is all stopt up." So it was decided, and Billy wore the comforter.

At seven o'clock they were ready, and, the news having spread abroad that the Wiggses were going to a show, many of the neighbors came in to see how they looked and to hear how it happened.

"Some of you shake down the stove an' pull the door fer me. I am jes' that skeered of hurtin' Mrs. Eichorn's veil I'm 'fraid to turn my head," said Mrs. Wiggs nervously as she stepped off the porch.

The little procession had left the railroad tracks far behind when Mrs. Wiggs stopped suddenly.

"Fer the land's sakes alive! Do you know what we've gone an' done? We have left the theayter tickets to home!"

At this Australia began to cry and a gloom settled upon the party.

"Billy, you run back fast as yer legs kin carry you an' look in that tin can behind the clock. We'll wait right here fer you." Mrs. Wiggs wrapped Europena in her shawl and tried to keep up the spirits of the party as they huddled on the curbing to await Billy's return.

"Look how pretty it looks, all them lights a-streamin' out the winders on the snow. Looks like a chromo Ma used to have."

But the young Wiggses were in no frame of mind to appreciate the picturesqueness of the scene.

It was very cold and even the prospect of the show was dimmed by the present discomfort. By and by Australia's sobs began anew.

"What's the matter, honey? Don't cry. Billy'll be back in a little while an' then we'll git in where it's good an' warm."

"I want my supper!" wailed Australia.

Then it dawned on Mrs. Wiggs for the first time that, in the excitement of preparation, supper had been entirely overlooked.

"Well, if that don't beat all!" said she. "I had jes' 'bout as much idea of supper as a goat has of kid gloves!"

But when Billy came flying back with the tickets, and the party had started once more on the long walk to the Opera House, the enticing posters began to appear and supper and the cold were forgotten.

7

"Mr. Bob"

"If his heart at high floods
Swamped his brain now and then,
'Twas but richer for that
When the tide ebbed again."

A large audience assembled that night to witness
THE GREATEST EXTRAVAGANZA OF THE CENTURY.
The Opera House was a blaze of light and color.

From the recesses of one of the boxes Redding
made a careful survey of the faces beneath him.
First nights usually found him there with the
same restless, eager look in his eyes. Tonight he
evidently failed to find what he sought and was
turning listlessly away when he stopped suddenly,
bent forward, then smiled broadly. He had caught
sight of Billy's red comforter.

The boy's hair was plastered close to his head

and his face was transformed by soap and happiness. Redding glanced quizzically at the rest of the party—at the mother's radiant countenance beaming from the dusk of her crepe veil, at the three little girls in their composite costumes, at the carnations pinned on each bosom. Then he deliberately turned his back on THE GREATEST EXTRAVAGANZA OF THE CENTURY and centered his attention on the motley group.

It was a singularly enthusiastic theater party, oblivious of surroundings and lost in wonder at the strange sights. Billy's laugh rang out frequently with refreshing spontaneity. Their enjoyment was so evident that Redding was surprised at the close of the first act to see them put on their wraps and march solemnly out of the theater. He hastened to the lobby and touched Billy on the shoulder.

"Didn't you like the show?" he asked.

"You bet!" said Billy, his eyes shining and his cheeks flushed.

Mrs. Wiggs was hopelessly entangled in the crepe veil but her ideas of etiquette were rigid.

She disengaged one hand and said with dignity, "I 'low this is Mr. Bob, Billy's friend. Happy to meet yer acquaintance. Asia, speak to the gentleman—Australia—Europena!" with a commanding nod at each.

Three small hands were thrust at Redding simultaneously and he accommodated them all in his broad palm.

"But why are you going home?" he asked, looking from one to the other.

"Where else would we go to?" asked Mrs. Wiggs in amazement.

"Why not stay and see the play out? That was only the first act."

"Is there some more, Ma?" asked Asia eagerly.

"Why, of course," explained Redding, "lots more. Now, go back and stay until everybody has left the theater, and then you will be certain it's over."

So back they went, furnishing an amusing between acts diversion for the impatient audience.

After the curtain descended on the final scene,

Redding waited in the lobby while the stream of people passed. The Wiggses had obeyed instructions and were the very last to come out. They seemed dazed by their recent glimpse into fairyland. Something in their thin bodies and pinched faces made Redding form a sudden resolve.

"Billy," he said gravely, "can't you and your family take supper with me?"

Billy and his mother exchanged doubtful glances. For the past three hours everything had been so strange and unbelievable that they were bewildered.

"You see, we will go right over to Bond's and have something to eat before you go home," urged Redding.

Mrs. Wiggs was in great doubt, but one of the little girls pulled her skirt and said in pleading tones, "Ma, let's do!" And Billy was already casting longing eyes at the big restaurant across the way. She had not the heart to refuse. As they were crossing the street Asia stopped suddenly and cried, "Ma, there's the 'Christmas Lady' gittin' in that cab! She seen us! Look!"

But before they could turn, the cab door had slammed.

Redding took them into a small apartment curtained off from the rest of the café so only the waiters commented on the strange party. At first there was oppressive silence. Then the host turned to Europena and asked her what she liked best to eat.

A moment of torture ensued for the small lady, during which she nearly twisted her thumb from its socket, then she managed to gasp, "Green pups!"

Mr. Bob laughed. "Why, you little cannibal!" he said. "What on earth does she mean?"

"Cream puffs," explained Mrs. Wiggs airily. "She et 'em onct at Mrs. Reed's, the Bourbon Stock Yard's wife, an' she's been talkin' 'bout 'em ever sinct."

After this the ice, while not broken, at least had a crack in it, and by the time the first course was served Redding was telling them a funny story and three of the audience were able to smile. It had pleased him to order an elaborate supper and he experienced the keenest enjoyment over the novelty of the situation. The Wiggses ate as he had never seen people eat before. "For speed and durability they break the record," was his mental comment. He sat by and, with consummate tact, made them forget everything but the good time they were having.

As the supper progressed Mrs. Wiggs became communicative. She still wore her black cotton gloves and gestured with a chicken croquette as she talked.

"Yes," she was saying, "Jim was one o' them handy childern. When he was eight years old he could peddle as good as you could! I guess you heard 'bout our roof. Ever'body was talkin' 'bout it. Billy is takin' right after him. Do you know what that boy has gone an' done? He's built his pa a monumint!"

"A monument!" exclaimed Redding.

"Yes, sir, a tombstun monumint! I was allers a-wishin' that Mr. Wiggs could have a monumint, and Billy never said a word but he set his head to it. One day he come home with a lot of these here tiles what they had throwed out from the tile fact'ry. Some of 'em was jes' a little nicked an' the others was jes' as good as new. Well, he kep' on gittin' 'em ever' day or two till he had a consider'ble pile. Ever' night he used to set on the floor an' fool with them things, a fittin' 'em here an' crackin' 'em off there, but I never paid no 'tention to him. One night, when I come in from Mrs. Eichorn's, what did I see on the floor but a sure-'nough tombstun slab. An' spelt out in little blue tiles down the middle was:

'Pa. Gone, but not forgotten.'

I was jes' that pleased I set down an' bust out cryin'. We made a sorter box to hold it, an' chinked it up with cement, an' las Sunday me an' the childern took it out an' fixed it up on Mr. Wiggs's grave. Some day we're goin' to make Jimmy one; you know Jimmy's my boy that's dead." Her eyes filled and her lips trembled. Even the sunshine of her buoyant nature could not dispel one shadow that always lay across her heart.

At this moment Billy, doubtless thrilled at being the topic of conversation, upset his glass of water, and the deluge descended full upon Australia, drenching the jacket of the blue alpaca. Such a wail as arose! Threats and persuasion were alike unavailing. She even refused to be mopped off, but slid in a disconsolate heap under the table. Redding attempted to invade the citadel with an orange as a flag of truce, but his overtures were ineffectual and he was compelled to retreat under fire.

"I'd leave her be, Mr. Bob," advised Mrs. Wiggs placidly, as she spread her salad on a piece of bread. "She'll git to holdin' her breath if you notice her."

The shrieks gradually diminished to spasmodic sobs which in turn gave place to ominous silence.

"Billy," said Redding, taking Mrs. Wiggs's advice and ignoring the flood sufferer, "how would you like to be my office boy?"

"I'd like it a heap," answered Billy promptly.

Redding turned to Mrs. Wiggs. "You see, it's a newspaper office, and while the pay isn't much at first, still it's better than peddling kindling, and there would be a chance for promotion as he got older."

"Oh, yes," answered Mrs. Wiggs complacently, "there wouldn't be no trouble 'bout Billy promotin'. I 'spect he could take to writin' newspapers right away if you could hold him down to it. He's jes' like his pa—the very spittin' image of him! Mr. Wiggs was so educated—the most fluent man in jography I ever seen!"

"I'm goin' to be like Mr. Bob when I grow up," said Billy stoutly. His recollection of his paternal parent was not the sort ideals are made of.

Just here the waiter appeared with the final course and Asia lifted the tablecloth and whispered, "Say, 'Straly, we've got ice cream." No answer. Then little Europena, with baby wisdom, put her towhead under the cloth and said, " 'Traly, it's pink!" and Australia emerged, tear-stained but smiling, and finished her supper on Mr. Bob's knee.

When the limit of capacity had been tested to the fullest and Billy had declared that "he couldn't swaller no more, he was jes' chawin','" Redding filled their pockets with candy and, when Mrs. Wiggs was not looking, put a quarter in each hand. Then he rang for a carriage, and in spite of Mrs. Wiggs's protestations he put them in and repeated Billy's directions as to the exact location of the Cabbage Patch.

"My, my, ain't this nice!" said Mrs. Wiggs, leaning back against carriage cushions for the first time in her life, while Redding lifted Europena in beside her.

"We've seed a good time fer onct in our lives," said Asia. It was the first time she had spoken since they left the theater.

"Lemme ride up on top, Ma!" demanded Billy, eagerly.

"Lemme, too, lemme!" came from the sleepy Australia who did not know what new attraction was being offered but was resolved not to miss anything.

"All right, Billy. But, Austry, you must stay with Ma. Good-by, Mr. Bob, and thanks—thanks fer one an' all!"

Redding stood on the corner where they had left him, and the smile died out of his face. Within a block was a jolly crowd and a hearty welcome; across the street was the big apartment house where his dark and cheerless window promised him nothing. For a moment he stood irresolute. "There is certainly nobody to care where I go," he thought gloomily; then suddenly the smile came back. "But if I'm to be Billy Wiggs's model I guess I'd better go to bed." He ran lightly across the street and up the broad stone steps.

8

Mrs. Wiggs At Home

"She had a sunny nature that sought, like
a flower in a dark place, for the light."

On Christmas day Lucy Olcott stood by the
library window and idly scratched initials on the
frosty pane. A table full of beautiful gifts stood
near, and a great bunch of long-stemmed roses on
the piano filled the room with fragrance. But Lucy
evidently found something more congenial in
the dreary view outside. She was deep in thought
when the door opened and Aunt Chloe came in
with a basket and a note.

The old woman grinned as she put the basket
on the floor. "You might 'a' knowed it wuz

fum dem Wiggses," she said.

Lucy opened the note and read:

Dear miss Lucy the basket of cloths and vittles come. We or so mutch obliged, and asia wore the read dress to the soshul and enjoyed her selph so. Mutch I wish you could a went. Billy liked his hock and ladar and romcandons. Me and the childern want to send you a crismas mess of some of all we lade in for to live on. They is pertaters 2 kines, onions, termaters, a jar of vinegar and a jar perservs. I boughten the peeches last summer, they was gitting a little rotting so I got them cheep. Hope you will Enjoy them. I send some of all we got but Cole and Flower. Thankes thankes to you for your kind fealings.

From yours no more

MRS WIGGS.

"Bless her old heart!" cried Lucy. "That's the biggest widow's mite I ever saw. Put the basket there with my other presents, Aunt Chloe. It's worth them all."

She went over to the fire and held her hands to the friendly blaze. There was a restless, discontented look in her eyes that proved only too plainly that her Christmas was not a happy one.

"I wish it was night," she said. "I hate Christmas afternoon! Mother is asleep and it's too early for callers. I believe I'll go down to the Cabbage Patch."

Aunt Chloe stuck out her lip and rolled her eyes in deprecation.

"Don' you do it, honey. What you wanter be foolin' 'round wif dat po' white trash fer? Why don' you set heah by de fiah an' bleach yer han's fer de party tonight?"

"Bother the old party!" said Lucy impatiently.

Fifteen minutes later she was tramping through the snow, her cheeks glowing and her spirits rising. The Wiggses, while always interesting, had of late acquired a new significance. Since seeing them in the theater lobby with Robert Redding she had found it necessary to make several visits to the Cabbage Patch. The chief topic of conversation had been Mr. Bob: how he had taken them to the show; had made Billy his office boy; had sent them a barrel of apples and was coming to see them some day. To which deluge of information Lucy had listened with outward calmness and inward thrills.

Today as she entered the Wiggses' gate a shout greeted her. Billy let himself down from the chicken-coop roof and ran forward.

"Them Roman candles wasn't no good!" he cried. "One of 'em busted too soon and 'most blowed my hand off."

"Oh, no, it didn't, Miss Lucy!" said Mrs. Wiggs who had hastened out to meet her. "Them Roman candons was fine. Billy's hand wasn't so bad hurt he couldn't shoot his gum-bow shooter and break Miss Krasmier's winderpane. I'll be glad when tomorra comes an' he goes back to the office! Come right in," she continued. "Asia, dust off a cheer fer Miss Lucy. That's right. Now, lemme help you off with yer things."

"Lemme hold the muff!" cried Australia.

"No—me—me!" shrieked Europena.

A center rush ensued during which the muff was threatened with immediate annihilation. The umpire interfered.

"Australia Wiggs, you go set in the corner with yer face to the wall. Europena, come here!" She lifted the wailing little girl to her lap and looked her sternly in the eye. "If you don't hush this minute, I'll spank your doll!"

The awful threat was sufficient. Mrs. Wiggs had long ago discovered the most effectual way of punishing Europena.

When peace was restored Lucy looked about her. In each window was a piece of holly tied with a bit of red calico, and on the partly cleared table she saw the remains of a real Christmas dinner.

"We had a grand dinner today," said Mrs. Wiggs, following her glance. "Mr. Bob sent the turkey. We et all we wanted an' got 'nough left fer the rest of the week, countin' hash an' soup an' all. Asia says she's goin' to hide it, so as I can't

give no more away. By the way, do you notice what Asia's doin'?"

Lucy went to the window where Asia was busily working. This taciturn little girl, with her old, solemn face and clever fingers, was her favorite of the children.

"What are you making?" she asked, as the child dipped a brush into one of three cans which stood before her.

"She's paintin' a picture," announced Mrs. Wiggs proudly. "Looked like she was jes' crazy 'bout picture painting, an' I said, 'Well, Asia, if you have made up yer mind to be a artist, guess you'll have to be one.' Seems like when folks kin do pianner playin' an' picture paintin' it ain't right to let 'em wash dishes an' clean up all the time. So I went to a store an' ast fer some paint to make pictures with, and they wanted seventy cents fer a little box full. Ain't that a mighty heap, Miss Lucy, jes' fer plain paint, 'fore it's made up into flowers an' trees an' things? Well, anyway, I couldn't git it but I come home an' got me three tin cans an' took 'em 'round to Mr. Becker's paint shop. An' he poured me a little red an' yaller an' blue an' only charged me a nickel an' throwed in a brush. Asia's painted a heap with it. I'll show you some of her things."

It was not necessary, for in every direction Lucy looked her eyes were greeted with specimens of Asia's handiwork. Across the footboard of the bed was a spray of what might have passed for cauliflower. The tin boiler was encircled by a wreath of impressionistic roses, and on the windowpane a piece of exceedingly golden goldenrod bent in an obliging curve in order to cover the crack in the glass.

"It's perfectly wonderful!" said Lucy, with entire truthfulness.

"Ain't it?" said Mrs. Wiggs, with the awed tone one uses in the presence of genius. "Sometimes I jes' can't believe my eyes when I see what my childern kin do! They inherit their education after Mr. Wiggs. He was so smart an' b'longed to such a fine fambly. Why, Mr. Wiggs had real Injun blood in his veins. His grandpa was a squaw —a full-blood Injun squaw!"

Lucy made an heroic effort to keep a solemn face as she asked if Asia looked like him.

"Oh, my, no!" continued Mrs. Wiggs. "He was a blunette—real dark complected. I remember when he fus' come a-courtin' me folks thought he was Italian. Pa wasn't, to say, well off in them days." Mrs. Wiggs never applied superlatives to misfortunes. "He had a good many of us to take keer of, an' after Mr. Wiggs had been keepin' company with me fer 'bout two weeks he drove up one night with a load of coal an' kindlin' an' called Pa out to the fence. 'Mr. Smoot,' sez he, 'as long as I am courtin' your daughter I think I orter furnish the fire to do it by. Ef you don't mind,' sez he, 'I'll jes' put this wagonload of fuel in the coal house. I 'spect by the time it's used up Nance'll be of my way of thinkin'.' An' I was!" added Mrs. Wiggs, laughing.

Ordinarily Lucy found endless diversion in listening to the family reminiscences but today another subject was on her mind.

"How is Billy getting along?" she asked.

"Jes' fine!" answered Mrs. Wiggs. "Only he

comes home at night 'most dead. I give him money to ride, but ever' day last week he et up his nickel."

"Who—who has charge of him now?" Lucy blushed at her subterfuge.

"Mr. Bob," said Mrs. Wiggs. "He's the gentleman that took us to supper. He's got money. Asia said he give the waiter a quarter. Billy is jes' crazy 'bout Mr. Bob. Says he's goin' to be jes' like him when he grows up. He will, too, if he sets his head to it! Only he never kin have them big brown eyes an' white teeth Mr. Bob's got. Why, when Mr. Bob smiles it jes' sort of breaks up his whole face."

Lucy's eyes were fixed on the mammoth butterfly upon whose iridescent wings Asia was putting the finishing touches but her thoughts were far away.

"I jes' wish you could see him!" went on Mrs. Wiggs enthusiastically.

"I wish I could!" said Lucy, with such fervor that Mrs. Wiggs paused on her way to answer a knock at the outside door.

There was a scraping of feet in the passage.

"I have been driving all over the country looking for you," said a man's voice. "I have some Christmas presents for the kids."

Lucy rose hastily and turned just as Redding entered.

"Mr. Bob, this is Miss Lucy," announced Mrs. Wiggs triumphantly. "She was jes' 'lowin' she'd like to see you."

If a blue-eyed angel straight from the peaks of paradise had been presented to him, Redding could not have been more astounded nor more enraptured.

But to Lucy it was a moment of intense chagrin and embarrassment. During the long silence of the past year she had persuaded herself that Redding no longer cared for her. To be thrust upon him in this way was intolerable. All the blood in her veins rushed to her face.

"Do you know where my muff is, Mrs. Wiggs?" she asked, after a formal greeting.

"Oh! You ain't a-goin'?" asked the hostess, anxiously. "I wanted you all to git acquainted."

"Yes, I must go," said Lucy hurriedly, "if you will find my muff."

She stood nervously pulling on her gloves while Mrs. Wiggs searched for the lost property. There was a deafening tumult in her heart, and though she bit her lips to keep from laughing, the tears stood in her eyes.

"Austry's under the bed," announced Europena, who had joined in the quest.

"I ain't!" came in shrill, indignant tones as Mrs. Wiggs dragged forth the culprit and restored the muff.

"May I drive you over to the avenue? I am going that way." It was Redding's voice, but it sounded queer and unnatural.

"Oh, no! No, thank you," gasped Lucy, hardly knowing what she said. Her one idea was to get away before she broke down completely.

Redding held the door open as she passed out. His face was cold, calm, inscrutable; not a quiver of the mouth, not a flutter of the lids, but the light went out of his eyes and hope died in his heart.

Mrs. Wiggs stood watching the scene in perplexity.

"I dunno what ailed Miss Lucy," she said, apologetically. "Hope it wasn't the toothache."

9

How Spring Came to the Cabbage Patch

"The roads, the woods, the heavens, the hills
    Are not a world today—
But just a place God made for us
    In which to play."

When the last snow had melted and the water
was no longer frozen about the corner pump,
the commons lost their hard, brown look and a
soft green tinge appeared instead. There were
not many ways of telling when spring came to
the Cabbage Patch. No trees shook forth their
glad little leaves of welcome, no anemones and
snowdrops brought the gentle message. Even the
birds that winged their way from the southland
hurried by without so much as a chirp of greeting.

But the Cabbage Patch knew it was spring,
nevertheless; something whispered it in the air.
A dozen little signs gave the secret away; weeds

were springing up in the fence corners, the puddles which a few months ago were covered with ice now reflected bits of blue sky, and the best token of all was the bright, warm sunshine that clung to the earth as if to love it back into beauty and life again.

One afternoon Mrs. Wiggs stood at her gate talking to Redding. It was the first time he had been there since Christmas day, for his first visit had been too painful for him to desire to repeat it.

"Yes, indeed, Billy kin go," Mrs. Wiggs was saying. "I'm mighty glad you drove him by home to git on his good coat. He never was to the fair grounds before. It'll be a big treat. How's Mr. Dick today?"

"No better," said Redding. "He coughed all night."

"He was takin' a nap o' sleep when I went to clean up this mornin'," said Mrs. Wiggs, "so I didn't disturb him. He ain't fer long, pore feller!"

"No, poor chap," said Redding sadly.

Mrs. Wiggs saw the shadow on his face and hastened to change the subject. "What do you think of Asia's fence?" she asked.

"What about it?"

"She done it herself," said Mrs. Wiggs. "That an' the pavement, too. Mrs. Krasmier's goat et up her flowers las' year, an' this year she 'lowed she'd fix it different. Chris Hazy, that boy over yonder with the peg stick, helped her dig the postholes but she done the rest herself."

"Well, she is pretty clever!" said Redding, almost incredulously, as he examined the fence and sidewalk. "How old is she?"

"Fourteen, goin' on fifteen. Asia, come here." The girl left the flower bed she was digging and came forward.

"Not a very big girl, are you?" said Redding, smiling at her. "How would you like to go up to the tile factory and learn to do decorating?"

Her serious face lit up with great enthusiasm. She forgot her shyness and said eagerly, "Oh, yes, sir! Could I?"

Before Redding could answer, Mrs. Wiggs broke in, "You'd be gittin' a artist, Mr. Bob! Them fingers of hers kin do anything. Last fall she built that there little greenhouse out of ol' planks an' kep' it full of flowers all winter. Put a lamp in durin' the cold spell. You orter see the things she's painted. And talk about mud pictures! She could jes' take some of that there mud under that hoss's feet an' make it look so much like you, you wouldn't know which was which."

Billy's appearance at this moment saved Redding from immediate disgrace.

"You come to the office with Billy in the morning," he called to Asia as they started off. "We'll see what can be done."

Asia went back to her digging with a will. The prospect of work, of learning how to do things right, and, above all, of learning how to paint, filled her with happiness.

"If I was you I'd make that bed in the shape of a star," said her mother, breaking in on her reflections. "Why don't you make it a mason star? Yer pa was a fine mason; it would be a sort of compliment to him."

"What is a mason star like?" asked Asia.

"Well, now I ain't right sure whether it's got

five points or six. Either way will do. Lands alive, I do believe there comes Miss Lucy!"

Lucy Olcott had been a frequent visitor of late. Through Mrs. Wiggs she had gotten interested in Mrs. Schultz and often stopped in to read to the bedridden old lady. Here, of course, she heard a great deal about the Eichorns, the elite of the Cabbage Patch, whose domestic infelicities furnished the chief interest in Mrs. Schultz's life. Lucy had even stood on a chair, at the invalid's earnest request, to count the jars of preserves in the Eichorn pantry. Later she had become acquainted with Miss Hazy, the patient little woman in monochrome, whose whole pitiful existence was an apology when it might have been a protest.

In fact, Lucy became an important personage in the neighborhood. She was sought for advice, called upon for comfort, and asked to share many joys. Her approach was usually heralded by a shout, "That's her a-comin'!" and she was invariably escorted across the commons by a guard of ragged but devoted youngsters. And the friendship of these simple people opened her eyes to the great problems of humanity. As she worked among them and knew life as it was, the hard little bud of her girlhood blossomed into the great soft rose of womanhood.

"Didn't you meet Mr. Bob up the street?" asked Mrs. Wiggs, as she led the way into the kitchen. "Him an' Billy have jes' left, goin' out to the fair grounds. Mr. Bob's jes' naturally the best man I ever set eyes on, Miss Lucy! Got the biggest heart, an' always doin' something kind fer folks. Jes' now talkin' 'bout gittin' Asia a place at the tile fact'ry. I don't see how you missed 'em! If he'd a sawn you with them vi'lets in yer belt, an' them roses in yer cheeks, I bet he wouldn't 'a' went."

"Oh, yes, he would!" said Lucy emphatically. "My roses don't appeal to Mr. Bob."

"Well, he likes yer eyes, anyway," said Mrs. Wiggs, determined to carry her point.

"Who said so?" demanded Lucy.

"He did. I ast him. I said they was regular star-eyes, jes' shining blue with them black eyelashes rayin' out all 'round, an' he said yes, that was the right name fer 'em—star-eyes."

There was a mist over the star-eyes as Lucy turned away.

"That's right, set right down there by the winder. It's so pretty out today it makes you feel good clean down yer back."

"I believe you always feel that way," said Lucy, pulling off her gloves. "Don't you ever worry over things?"

Mrs. Wiggs grew serious. "I'm lonesome fer Jimmy all the time," she said simply. "Some folks goes right under when trouble comes, but I carry mine fur an' easy."

"I don't mean grieving," said Lucy. "I mean worrying and fretting."

"Well, yes," admitted Mrs. Wiggs, taking a hot iron from the stove, "I've done that, too. I remember onct last winter I was tooken sick an' got to pesterin' 'bout what the children 'ud do if I died. They wasn't no money in the house an' they didn't know where to git none. All one night I laid there with my head 'most bustin' jes'

worryin' 'bout it. By an' by I was so miserable I
ast the Lord what I mus' do an' he tole me."
There was absolute conviction in her tone and
manner. "Nex' mornin'," she went on, "soon's
I could I went over to the 'spensary an' ast fer
the chief doctor.

" 'Doctor,' I sez, 'don't you buy corpses?'

" 'Yes,' sez he, lookin' kinder funny.

" 'Well,' sez I, 'I want to sell mine.'

"Then I tole him all 'bout it an' ast him if
he wouldn't take my body after I was gone an'
give the money to the childern.

" 'Will you put it in writin'?' sez he.

" 'Yes,' sez I, 'if you'll do the same.'

"So he drawed up the papers an' we both signed.
An' a man with a spine in his back an' a lady with
the rheumatiz witnessed it. So you see," concluded
Mrs. Wiggs, "I didn't die. You mark my words,
it ain't never no use puttin' up yer umbrell'
till it rains!"

Lucy laughed. "Well, you certainly practice
what you preach."

"Not always," said Mrs. Wiggs. "I'm 'feared I

use' to worry some over Mr. Wiggs. T'words the last he uster pretty often—" Here Mrs. Wiggs tipped an imaginary bottle to her lips and gave Lucy a significant wink. Even in the strictest confidence she could not bear to speak of the weakness of the late lamented.

"But no matter how bad he done, he always tried to do better. Mr. Dick sorter puts me in mind of him 'bout that."

"Who is Mr. Dick?"

"He's Mr. Bob's friend. Stays at his rooms sence he was took down."

"Is Mr. Redding sick?" asked Lucy, the color suddenly leaving her face.

"No, it's Mr. Dick. He's consumpted. I clean up his room ever' mornin'. He coughs all the time, jes' like Mr. Wiggs done. Other day he had a orful spell while I was there. I wanted to git him some whisky but he shuck his head. 'I'm on the water cart,' sez he. 'Bob's drivin' it.' He ain't no fatter 'n a knittin' needle an' weaker 'n water. You orter see him watch fer Mr. Bob! He sets by the winder, all propped up with pillars, an' never tecks his eyes offen that corner. An' when Mr. Bob comes in an' sets down by him an' tells him what's goin' on, an' sorter fools with him a spell, looks like he picks up right off. He ain't got no folks nor nothin'—jes' Mr. Bob. He shorely does set store by him —jes' shows it ever' way. That's right, too. I hold that it's wrong to keep ever'thing bottled up inside you. Yer feelin's is like rasbury vinegar. If you're skeered to use 'em an' keep on savin' 'cm, first thing you know they've done 'vaporated!"

Lucy's experience had proved the contrary, but she smiled bravely back at Mrs. Wiggs, with a new tenderness in her face.

"You have taught me lots of things!" she said impulsively. "You are one of the best and happiest women I know."

"Well, I guess I ain't the best by a long sight but I may be the happiest. An' I got cause to be: four of the smartest childern that ever lived, a nice house, fair to middlin' health when I ain't got the rheumatiz, and folks always goin' clean out of the way to be good to me! Ain't that 'nough to make a person happy? I'll be fifty years old on the Fourth of July, but I hold there ain't no use in dyin' 'fore yer time. Lots of folks is walkin' 'round jes' as dead as they'll ever be. I believe in gittin' as much good outen life as you kin—not that I ever set out to look fer happiness—seems like the folks that does that never finds it. I jes' do the best I kin where the good Lord put me at, an' it looks like I got a happy feelin' in me 'most all the time."

Lucy sat silent for a while, gazing out of the window. Mrs. Wiggs's philosophy was having its effect. Presently she rose and untied the bundle she held.

"Here is a dress I brought for Asia," she said, shaking out the folds of a soft crepe.

"Umph, umph! Ain't that grand?" exclaimed Mrs. Wiggs, coming from behind the ironing board to examine it. "It does seem lucky that your leavin's jes' fits Asia, an' Asia's jes' fits Austry. There ain't no symptoms of them bein' handed down, neither! We all model right after you but it looks like Asia's the only one that ketches yer style. Oh, must you go?" she added, as Lucy picked up her gloves.

"Yes, I promised Mrs. Schultz to read to her this afternoon."

"Well, stop in on yer way back—I'll have a little present ready fer you." It was an unwritten law that no guest should depart without a gift of some kind. Sometimes it was one of Asia's paintings, again it was a package of sunflower seed, or a bottle of vinegar, and once Lucy had taken home four gourds and a bunch of paper roses.

"I declare, I never will git no work done if this weather keeps up!" said Mrs. Wiggs, as she held the gate open. "If I wasn't so stove up an' nobody wasn't lookin', I'd jes' skitter 'round this here yard like a colt!"

10

Australia's Mishap

" 'Tis one thing to be tempted,
Another thing to fall."

Through the long afternoon Mrs. Wiggs sang over her ironing and Asia worked diligently in her flower bed. Around the corner of the shed which served as Cuba's dwelling place, Australia and Europena made mud pies. Peace and harmony reigned in this shabby Garden of Eden until temptation entered and the weakest fell.

" 'Tain't no fun jes' keepin' on makin' mud pies," announced Australia, after enough pastry had been manufactured to start a miniature bakery.

"Wish we could make some white cakes like they have at Mr. Bagby's," said Europena.

"Could if we had some whitewash. I'll tell you what's let do! Let's take some of Asia's paint she's goin' to paint the fence with an' make 'em green on top."

"Ma wouldn't like it," protested Europena. "Besides, I don't want my little pies green."

"I'm goin' to," said Australia, beginning her search for the paint can. "It won't take but a little teeny bit. They'll never miss it."

After some time the desired object was discovered on a shelf in the shed. Its high position enhanced its value, giving it the cruel fascination of the unattainable.

"Could you stand up on my soldiers, like the man at the show?" demanded Australia.

"I'd fall off," said Europena.

" 'Fraid-cat!" taunted her sister, in disgust. "Do you reckon you could hol' the chair while I climbed up on the back?"

"It ain't got no bottom."

"Well, it don't need to have no bottom if I'm goin' to stand on its back," said Australia sharply. Leaders of great enterprises must of necessity turn deaf ears to words of discouragement.

"You might git killed," persisted Europena.

" 'Twouldn't matter," said Australia loftily.
" 'Twouldn't be but the seventh time. I got three
more times to die. 'Fore you was borned I was
drownded out in the country, that was one time.
Then I fell in the ash bar'l and was dead, that's
two times. An'—an' then I et the stove polish,
that's four times. An' I can't 'member, but the
nex' time will be seven. I don't keer how much I
git killed till it's eight times. Then I'm goin' to
be good all the time 'cause when you are dead
nine times they put you in a hole an' throw dirt
on you!"

Australia had become so absorbed in her theory of reincarnation that she had forgotten the
paint, but the bottomless chair recalled it.

"Now, you lay 'crost the chair, Europena, an'
I'll climb up," she commanded.

Europena, though violently opposed to the
undertaking, would not forsake her leader at a
critical moment. She had uttered her protest,
had tried in vain to stem the current of events;

nothing was left her now but to do or die. She valiantly braced her small body across the frame of the chair and Australia began her perilous ascent.

Cuba looked mildly astonished as the plump figure of the little girl appeared above his feed-box.

"I've 'most got it!" cried Australia, reaching as high as possible and getting her forefinger over the edge of the big can.

At this juncture Cuba, whose nose had doubt-less been tickled by Australia's apron string, gave a prodigious sneeze. Europena, feeling that ret-ribution was upon them, fled in terror. The bal-last being removed from the chair, the result was inevitable. A crash, a heterogeneous combination of small girl, green paint, and shattered chair, then a series of shrieks that resembled the whis-tles on New Year's Eve!

Redding was the first to the rescue. He had just driven Billy to the gate when the screams began, and with a bound he was out of the buggy and rushing to the scene of disaster. The picture that met his eyes staggered him. Australia, screaming wildly, lay in what appeared to his excited vision to be a pool of green blood. Europena was jumping up and down beside her, calling wildly for her mother, while Cuba, with ears erect and a green liquid trickling down his nose, sternly surveyed the wreck. In a moment Redding had Australia in his arms and was mopping the paint from her face and hair.

"There, there, little sister, you aren't much hurt!" he was saying, as Mrs. Wiggs and Asia rushed in.

The damage done proved external rather than internal, so after assuring herself that no bones were broken Mrs. Wiggs constituted herself a salvage corps.

"Take off yer coat out here, Mr. Bob, an' I'll take off Austry's dress. Them's the worst, 'ceptin' her plaits. Now, we'll all go up to the kitchen, an' see what kin be did."

Now, Fate, or it may have been the buggy at the gate, decreed that just as they turned the corner of the house Lucy Olcott should be coming

up the walk. For a moment she stood bewildered
at the sight that greeted her. Redding, in his shirt
sleeves, was leading Australia by the hand. The
little girl wore a red flannel petticoat, and over
her face and hands and to the full length of her
flaxen braids ran sticky streams of bright green
paint.

Involuntarily, Lucy looked at Redding for explanation and they both laughed.

"Ain't it lucky it was the back of her head
'stid of the front?" said Mrs. Wiggs, coming up.
"It might 'a' put her eyes out. Pore chile, she looks
like a Mollygraw! Come right in, an' let's git to
work."

Billy was dispatched for turpentine. Lucy, with
an apron pinned about her, began operations on
Australia's hair, while Redding sat helplessly by,
waiting for Mrs. Wiggs to make his coat present-
able.

"I am afraid her hair will have to be cut," said
Lucy ruefully, as she held up a tangled snarl of
yellow and green.

"All right," Mrs. Wiggs said promptly. "Whatever you say is all right."

But Australia felt differently. Her sobs, suppressed for a time, broke forth afresh.

"I ain't goin' to have my hair cut off!" she wept. "Jes' leave it on this a-way."

Mrs. Wiggs commanded and Lucy entreated in vain. Finally Redding drew his chair up in front of the small girl.

"Australia, listen to me just a moment, won't you? Please!"

She uncovered one eye.

"You wouldn't want green hair, would you?"

A violent shake of the head.

"Well, if you will let Miss Olcott cut off all that ugly green hair and give the pretty curls a chance to grow back, I'll give you—let's see, what shall I give you?"

"A doll buggy an' dishes," suggested Europena, who was standing by.

"Yes," he said, "a doll buggy, and dishes, and a dollar besides!"

Such munificence was not to be withstood. Australia suffered herself to be shorn, in view of the future tempering of the wind.

"You orter been a hoss trainer, Mr. Bob," said Mrs. Wiggs admiringly, when the deed was accomplished. "Yer voice jes' makes folks do things!"

"Not everybody, Mrs. Wiggs," he said grimly.

"Where do you suppose Billy's went with the turkentine? I declare that boy would be a good one to send after trouble! Oh, you ain't goin' to try an' wear it this a-way?" she said, as Redding insisted on putting on his coat.

As he turned to the door a light hand touched his arm. Lucy unfastened the violets at her belt and timidly held them toward him.

"Will you take them—to Dick?" she faltered.

He looked at her in amazement. For a moment neither spoke, but her eyes made the silence eloquent. They told the secret that her lips dared not utter. There are times when explanations are superfluous. Redding threw discretion to the winds and, regardless of Wiggses and the consequences, took the "Christmas Lady" in his arms and kissed away the year of grief and separation.

It was not until Mrs. Wiggs saw their buggy disappear in the twilight that she recovered her speech.

"Well, it certainly do beat me!" she exclaimed, after a fruitless effort to reconstruct her standard of propriety. "I've heard of 'painters' colic,' but I never knowed it to go to the head before!"

11

The Benefit Dance

"Those there are whose hearts have a slope
   southward, and are open to the whole
   noon of Nature."

Notwithstanding the fact that calamities seldom come singly, it was not until the Fourth of July that the Cabbage Patch was again the scene of an accident.

Mrs. Wiggs had been hanging out clothes and was turning to pick up the empty basket, when Billy precipitated himself into the yard, yelling wildly.

"Chris Hazy's broke his leg!"

Mrs. Wiggs threw up her hands in horror. "Good lands, Billy! Where's he at?"

"They're bringin' him up the railroad track."

Mrs. Wiggs rushed into the house. "Don't let

126

on to Miss Hazy till we git him in," she cautioned, snatching up a bundle of rags and a bottle of liniment. "Pore chile! How it must hurt him! I'll run down the track an' meet 'em."

She was breathless and trembling from excitement as she turned the corner at Mrs. Schultz's. A crowd of boys were coming up the track, trundling a wheelbarrow, in which sat Chris Hazy, the merriest of the lot, waving a piece of his wooden leg in the air.

Mrs. Wiggs turned upon Billy.

"I never lied, Ma! I said he broke his leg," the boy gasped out as best he could for laughing, "an' you never ast which one. Oh, boys! Git on to the rags an' arniky!"

Such a shout went up that Mrs. Wiggs laughed with the rest, but only for a moment, for she spied Miss Hazy tottering toward them and she hastened forward to relieve her anxiety.

"It's his peg stick!" she shouted. "P-e-g stick!"

This information, instead of bringing relief to Miss Hazy, caused a fresh burst of tears. She sat down on the track, with her apron over her face and swayed backward and forward.

"Don't make much difference which one 'twas," she sobbed. "It would be 'bout as easy to git another sure-'nough leg as to git a new wooden one. That las' one cost seven dollars. I jes' sewed an' saved an' scrimped to git it, an' now it's—busted!"

The boys stood around in silent sympathy, and when nobody was looking Chris wiped his eyes on his coat sleeve. Miss Hazy's arrival had changed their point of view.

Mrs. Wiggs rose to the occasion.

"Boys," she said, and her voice had an inspiring ring, "I'll tell you what let's do! Let's give a benefit dance tonight an' buy Chris Hazy a new peg stick. Every feller that's willin' to help, hol' up his hand."

A dozen grimy hands were waved on high and offers of assistance came from all sides. Mrs. Wiggs saw that now was the time to utilize their enthusiasm.

"I'll go right back to the house an' git Asia to write out the tickets, an' all you boys kin sell ten apiece. Miss Hazy, you kin come over an' help me git the house ready, an' we'll put Chris to cleanin' lamp chimbleys."

Under this able generalship the work was soon under way. The boys were dispatched with the tickets and the house was being put straight—at least the parlor was. It would have required many days to restore order to the chaos that habitually existed in the house of Wiggs.

"Asia, you help me roll these here barrels out on the porch an' I'll mop up the floor," said Mrs. Wiggs. "Miss Hazy, you look 'round in the kitchen an' see if you can't find a taller candle. Seems like I put one in the sugar bowl—that's it! Now, if you'll jes' cut it up right fine it'll be all ready to put on the floor when I git done."

When the floor was dry and the candle sprinkled over it, Australia and Europena were detailed to slide over it until it became slick.

"Would you ast ever'body to bring a cheer, or would you have 'em already here?" asked Mrs. Wiggs.

"Oh, le's bring 'em ourselves!" insisted Asia,

who had been to a church social.

So a raid was made on the neighborhood, and every available chair borrowed and arranged against the parlor wall.

By noon the boys reported most of the tickets sold, and Mrs. Wiggs received the funds which amounted to six dollars.

It being a holiday everybody was glad to come to the dance, especially as the proceeds were to help little Miss Hazy.

At one time there threatened to be trouble about the music. Some wanted Uncle Tom, the old Negro who usually fiddled at the dances, but others preferred to patronize home talent and have Jake Schultz, whose accordion could be heard at all hours in the Cabbage Patch.

Mrs. Wiggs effected a compromise. "They kin take turn about," she argued. "When one gits tired the other kin pick up right where he left off, an' the young folks kin shake the'r feet till they shoes drop off. Uncle Tom an' Jake, too, is a heap sight better than them mud-gutter bands that play 'round the streets."

"Wisht we could fix the yard up some," said Asia, when there was nothing more to be done in the parlor.

"I got a Japanee lantern," suggested Miss Hazy doubtfully.

"The very thing!" said Mrs. Wiggs. "We'll hang it in the front door. Billy's makin' a jack-o'-lantern to set on the fence. Fer the land's sake! What's John Bagby a-bringin' in here?"

The grocery boy, staggering under the weight of an ice-cream freezer and carrying something wrapped in white paper, came up the path.

"It's fer you," he said, grinning broadly. John was cross-eyed, so Miss Hazy thought he looked at Mrs. Wiggs, and Mrs. Wiggs was sure he was looking at Miss Hazy.

However, the card on the freezer dispelled all doubt:

Fer mrs Wiggs on her 50 Birthday
compelments of The Naybors.

Under the white paper was a large, white iced cake with a **W** in cinnamon drops on top.

"How'd they ever know it was my birthday?" exclaimed Mrs. Wiggs, in delight. "Why, I'd even forgot it myself! We'll have the cake fer the party tonight. Somehow, I never feel like good things b'long to me till I pass 'em on to somebody else."

This necessitated a supply of saucers and spoons, and friends were again called upon to provide as many as possible.

The Wiggses were quite busy until seven o'clock when they stopped to get dressed for the party.

"Where's Europena?" asked Asia.

Nobody had seen her for some time. A search was made and she was discovered standing on a chair in a corner of the parlor, calmly eating the cinnamon drops off the birthday cake. Fingers and mouth were crimson, and the first stroke of the **W** was missing. Billy was so indignant that he insisted on immediate punishment.

"No, I ain't a-goin' to whip her on my birthday, Billy. She's sorry. She says she is. Besides, the cake ain't spoiled. It's jes' a 'N' now, 'stid of a

'W,' an' N stands fer Nancy jes' as good as W stands fer Wiggs!"

The first guest to arrive was Mr. Krasmier. He had paid ten cents toward the refreshments and proposed to get his money's worth. Mrs. Eichorn came early, too, but for a different reason: She was very stout and her happiness for the evening depended largely upon the size of the chair she secured.

Half the spectators had arrived before the hostess appeared. Her delay was caused by the loss of her false curls, which she had not worn since the memorable night at the Opera House. They were very black and very frizzled and had been bought at a reduced price from a traveling salesman some ten years before. Mrs. Wiggs considered them absolutely necessary to her toilet on state occasions. Hence consternation prevailed when they could not be found. Drawers were upset and boxes emptied, but with no success.

When hope was about abandoned, Asia suddenly darted out to the shed where the children kept their playthings. When she returned she triumphantly displayed a battered doll, armless and footless, with a magnificent crowning glory of black, frizzled hair.

Mrs. Wiggs waited until all the guests assembled before she made her speech of thanks for the cake and ice cream. It was a very fine speech, having been written out beforehand by Mr. Bagby. It began, "Ladies and gents, it gives me pleasure—" but before Mrs. Wiggs got half through she forgot it and had to tell them in her own way how grateful she was. In conclusion she said, "Couldn't nobody be more obliged than what I am! Looks like nice things is always comin' my way. Hope God'll bless you all! The musicianers have come, so we'll begin the party with a Virginer reel."

The young people scampered to their places, and when Mr. Eichorn made a bow to Mrs. Wiggs she laughingly took her place at the head of the line. And at the first strains of "Old Dan Tucker" she went down the middle with a grace and spirit that flatly contradicted the little red fifty on the birthday cake.

"Swing yer pahtners, balance all,
    Swing dat gal wid a waterfall.
    Skip light, ladies, de cake's all dough,
    Nebber min' de weather,
        so de win' don't blow."

Old Uncle Tom was warming up to his work, and the fun waxed furious. Asia, looking very pretty in her new crepe, cast shy glances at Joe Eichorn who had been "keeping company" of late. Billy, for whom there was no room in the reel, let off his energy in the corner by a noisy execution of the "Mobile Buck." Australia and Europena sat in the window with Chris Hazy and delightedly clapped time to the music.

When the dance ended, Mrs. Wiggs went to the door to get cool. She was completely out of breath, and her false curls had worked their way down over her eyebrows.

"Look—comin', Ma!" called Billy.

When Mrs. Wiggs saw who it was she hastened down to the gate.

"Howdy, Mr. Bob. Howdy, Miss Lucy! Can't you git right out an' come in? We're havin' a birthday party an' a benefit dance fer Chris Hazy's leg."

"No, thanks," said Redding, trying in vain not to look at Mrs. Wiggs's head. "We just stopped by to tell you the good news."

" 'Bout Asia's position?" asked Mrs. Wiggs eagerly.

"Yes, about that and something else besides. What would you say if I told you that I was going to marry the prettiest, sweetest, dearest girl in the world?"

"Why, that's Miss Lucy!" gasped Mrs. Wiggs, more breathless than ever. Then the truth flashed upon her, and she laughed with them.

"Oh, sure 'nough! Sure 'nough! I'm jes' pleased to death!" She did not have to tell them. Her eyes, though suffering a partial eclipse, fairly beamed with joy and satisfaction. "An' so," she added, "it wasn't the paint, after all!"

When they had driven away, she lingered a moment at the gate. Music and laughter came from the house behind her as she stood smiling out across the moonlit Cabbage Patch. Her face still held the reflected happiness of the departed lovers, as the sky holds the rose tints after the sun has gone.

"An' they're goin' to git married," she whispered softly to herself. "An' Billy's got promoted, an' Asia's got a place, an' Chris'll have a new peg stick. Looks like ever'thin' in the world comes right, if we jes' wait long enough!"

Whitman
CLASSICS

Mrs. Wiggs of the
Cabbage Patch

Little Women

Black Beauty

Huckleberry Finn

Heidi

The Call of the Wild

Tom Sawyer

The Little Lame Prince

Robin' Hood

The Wonderful
Wizard of Oz

Robinson Crusoe

Wild Animals I
Have Known

The War of the Worlds

Here are some of the best-loved stories of all time. Delightful ... intriguing ... never-to-be-forgotten tales that you will read again and again. Start your own home library of WHITMAN CLASSICS so that you'll always have exciting books at your fingertips.

Whitman ADVENTURE and MYSTERY Books

Adventure Stories for GIRLS and BOYS...

TIMBER TRAIL RIDERS
The Long Trail North
The Texas Tenderfoot
The Luck of Black Diamond
Mystery of the Hollywood Horse
The Mysterious Dude

POWER BOYS SERIES
The Haunted Skyscraper
The Flying Skeleton
The Million-Dollar Penny
The Burning Ocean

DONNA PARKER
In Hollywood
At Cherrydale
Special Agent
On Her Own
A Spring to Remember
Mystery at Arawak
Takes a Giant Step

TROY NESBIT SERIES
Sand Dune Pony
Indian Mummy Mystery
Mystery at Rustlers' Fort

New Stories About Your Television Favorites...

Dr. Kildare
The Magic Key

Lassie
Secret of the Summer
Forbidden Valley

The Munsters
The Great Camera Caper

Combat! The Counterattack

Walt Disney's Annette
Mystery at Smugglers' Cove
Desert Inn Mystery
Mystery at Medicine Wheel

Voyage to the Bottom of the Sea

The Beverly Hillbillies

Introducing an Exciting New Series

ROBIN KANE
The Mystery of the Blue Pelican
The Mystery of the Phantom

Cosmic Rays

McGraw-Hill Paperbacks in Physics

Arthur F. Kip   University of California, Berkeley
Consulting Editor

James J. Brophy   Semiconductor Devices
Bruno B. Rossi   Cosmic Rays
Hugh D. Young   Statistical Treatment of Experimental Data

Professor Bruno Rossi
Department of Physics
Massachusetts Institute of Technology

McGraw-Hill Book Company
New York
San Francisco
Toronto
London

Cosmic Rays

Cosmic Rays

Preface

A steady rain of charged particles, moving at nearly the speed of light, falls upon our planet at all times and from all directions. These particles, known as *cosmic rays*, are just the nuclei of ordinary atoms stripped of their electrons—for the most part nuclei of hydrogen.

The property of cosmic rays that sets the rays apart from all other kinds of radiation and accounts for the extraordinary role they have played in the development of modern physics is the very large individual energies of cosmic-ray particles. Before the discovery of cosmic rays, the particles of highest energy known to physicists were those emitted in the spontaneous decay of radioactive atoms. Some time later, largely in an effort to duplicate the effects of cosmic rays under controlled laboratory conditions, physicists began developing accelerators capable of yielding particles of higher and higher energies. Recently, man-made machines, having achieved energies about 10,000 times those characteristic of natural radioactivity, have overtaken the "average" cosmic-ray particle. But cosmic rays have a very wide range of energy, and a few of them are known to have more than a billion times the energy of the particles produced by the most powerful of our accelerators.

In this book I have tried to relate how, starting from seemingly trivial observations, physicists discovered the existence of cosmic rays; how, through half a century of hard work, they finally found out precisely what cosmic rays are; how, in the process, they discovered a host of new particles that are born out of energy and live but a minute fraction of a second, and thus opened the field of elementary-particle physics; and how, for all their labors, they now find themselves faced with a more challenging and formidable problem than any they already solved: the problem of the origin of cosmic rays.

I felt that this story might have some interest not only for the professional physicist but for any person with a curiosity about modern science and about the manner in which scientific discoveries are made. Therefore, I have tried to keep the language as simple as possible without violating scientific accuracy, and I have omitted all the technical details and mathematical developments that are not needed for understanding the essential parts of the story. I know that in doing so I have failed to give proper recognition to many distinguished scientists who made vital contributions to the development of cosmic-ray physics. It would be futile for me to apologize to them; instead, I trust in their understanding of the constraints imposed by the character of this book.

I must also warn the reader that because of my personal involvement in the subject, I could not be expected to write the story of cosmic rays as impartially as I might have had I been merely a spectator. In fact, what I have told in this book is to a large extent the story of how my understanding of cosmic-ray effects developed through the years. Therefore, it is quite possible that my own work and that of my collaborators may have been given undue prominence.

Many friends have generously helped with advice and suggestions. I am deeply grateful to all of them, but particularly to Giuseppe Occhialini and the late Francis Friedman, who took the time to read the whole manuscript and did not spare me their constructive criticism. I wish also to express my appreciation to Anthony Wiggenhorn for his most conscientious and competent editorial work.

Bruno Rossi

Contents

Cosmic Rays

The subject [of cosmic rays] is unique in modern physics for the minuteness of the phenomena, the delicacy of the observations, the adventurous excursions of the observers, the subtlety of the analysis, and the grandeur of the inferences.

Karl K. Darrow

A radiation from outer space

1

At six o'clock on the morning of August 7, 1912, a balloon ascended from a field near the town of Aussig, in Austria. In the gondola of the balloon were three men: a navigator, a meteorologist, and a physicist. During the next 2½ hours, the balloon rose to an altitude of 13,000 feet while drifting rapidly northward. For another hour it floated between 13,000 and 16,000 feet. At noon the balloon touched down near the German town of Pieskow, 30 miles east of Berlin and some 125 miles from Aussig.

The physicist and leader of the flight was Victor F. Hess. He had taken with him three electroscopes of the kind then being used to detect and measure the radiation emitted by radium and other radioactive substances. While his companions took care of the navigation and measured altitude and temperature, Hess watched his instruments and recorded their readings. A few months later, after a careful study of the data, he presented to the scientific community a conclusion of far-reaching significance. In the

November, 1912, issue of the German journal *Physikalische Zeit-schrift*, Hess summarized his work with the statement: "The results of my observations are best explained by the assumption that a radiation of very great penetrating power enters our atmosphere from above."

This was the beginning of one of the most extraordinary adventures in the history of science. Subsequent investigations of the "radiation from above" opened up the new and bewildering world of high-energy physics. Here scientists found particles of subatomic dimensions, with energies thousands, millions, billions, trillions of times greater than the energy of particles emitted by radioactive materials found on earth. Here for the first time they witnessed processes in which particles of matter are created out of energy and then promptly disappear in giving birth to other particles. Beyond this, Hess's discovery revealed new vistas in astrophysics and cosmology. The mysterious radiation was found to carry important messages concerning the physical conditions of the distant regions of space through which it had traveled on its way to the earth. And finally, in an effort to explain the origin of the radiation, physicists developed a number of novel ideas about the nature of the events that take place in stars and in the masses of dilute gas that fill interstellar space.

But in August, 1912, no one — including Hess — had any reason to suspect such developments. What then, had prompted Hess to perform his experiment? And on what evidence did he base his conclusion?

Most scientific discoveries sprout from seeds that have been lying about for a long time. Hess's discovery was no exception. For more than a century physicists had known that a gold-leaf electroscope (Fig. 1-1) or similar instrument will not hold an electric charge indefinitely. The phenomenon of loss of charge is familiar to anyone who has ever taken a high school physics course. When a charged piece of glass, for example, is touched against the metal rod of an electroscope, the two leaves suspended from the rod fly apart. This happens because both leaves have acquired the same charge (positive in this case) and like charges repel each other. The leaves remain apart for a time after the glass has been removed; but eventually, little by little, they drop to their original positions as the electric charge gradually disappears.

In an ordinary electroscope the charge escapes mainly through the insulating sleeve that separates the rod from the metal case. With special care, this leak can be reduced practically to zero; but even so, the electroscope will not retain its charge indefinitely. Nor will the use of any particular gas (instead of air) in an airtight electroscope case affect the final result.

By the end of the nineteenth century, physicists had learned enough about the structure of matter to be able to explain the spontaneous discharge of electroscopes. Briefly, they knew that matter consists of atoms, that each chemical element represents a distinct type of atom, and that the atoms of one or more elements join in various combinations to form molecules of different chemical substances. While their picture of what atoms "look like" was far from precise, they knew that atoms ordinarily contain equal quantities of positive and negative charge. To this overall balance

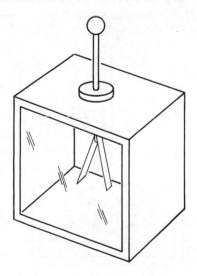

Fig. 1-1 Gold-leaf electroscope. The two gold leaves hang from a metal rod that is separated from the metal case of the electroscope by an insulating sleeve. The leaves are viewed through a glass window. Usually the case is electrically grounded.

of opposite charges they ascribed the neutral state of atoms and molecules. Moreover, they knew that the charges themselves possess a "granular structure," in other words, that they occur as simple multiples of some indivisible elementary charge. Indeed, in 1897 the English physicist J. J. Thomson had discovered a particle of very small mass — the *electron* — which he identified as the fundamental unit of negative charge.

Now according to this picture, the discharge of the electroscope was to be explained by the fact that gas molecules occasionally lose their electrical neutrality. A molecule may lose an electron and thus be left with an excess positive charge. The electron either remains free or attaches itself to a neutral molecule. A number of experiments had shown conclusively that the air or gas surrounding the electroscope leaves is always slightly *ionized*, that is, always contains a small percentage of "free" electrons and charged molecules, or *ions* as they are known. Thus, if the leaves are positively charged, they attract negative ions and repel positive ions (Fig. 1-2). The positive charge that holds the leaves apart is gradually neutralized by negative ions, and the leaves drop. Conversely, negatively charged leaves attract positive ions with the same result.

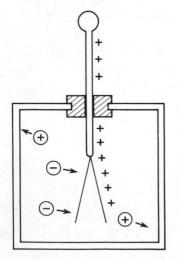

Fig. 1-2 Discharge of an electroscope by gas ions.

But what was the reason for the ever-present, if slight, ionization of gases? Physicists seeking to answer that question in the early years of the twentieth century were aware that various kinds of radiation could ionize gases. In 1895 Wilhelm Roentgen had discovered X-rays and had found that an electroscope discharged immediately when placed in front of an X-ray tube. The next year Henri Becquerel discovered radioactivity, and in 1898 Pierre and Marie Curie succeeded in isolating radium. This element and other radioactive substances also emitted ionizing rays capable of discharging an electroscope. In the light of these facts, most physicists were inclined to consider the observed ionization of gases as resulting from some sort of weak radiation rather than from a spontaneous breakup of gas molecules.

One obvious possibility was that the radiation came from small traces of radioactive substances present in the materials from which electroscopes were made. This guess turned out to be partly correct; for some of the ionization was often traced to such impurities. However, radioactive contamination of the instrument could not account for the whole effect. Experimenters were able to decrease the rate of discharge by surrounding an electroscope with lead or water; thus part of the ionizing radiation had to come from outside. At the same time, the thick layers of matter required to produce an appreciable decrease pointed to a radiation of considerable penetrating power.

For a decade the prevailing opinion attributed the source of the penetrating radiation to minute quantities of radioactive materials in the earth's crust. Clearly, one could test the assumption by comparing observations at different altitudes. If the radiation responsible for the discharge of the electroscope came from the earth, it should be strongest near the earth's surface and become progressively weaker with increasing altitude.

Several investigators, including Thomas Wulf in Germany and A. Gockel in Switzerland, undertook to put the hypothesis to an experimental test. By that time, electroscopes were much more refined and reliable than the old-fashioned gold-leaf type. Par-

ticularly suitable as a radiation meter was the instrument designed
by Wulf in 1909. He replaced the gold leaves with two very thin
metal wires held under tension by a light quartz fiber (Fig. 1–3).
When charged, the two wires would repel each other, and the
separation could be measured by means of a microscope. In 1910
Wulf carried one of his electroscopes to the top of the Eiffel Tower;
in 1912 Gockel used a similar instrument in a balloon ascent.
Neither found what they had expected. The rate of discharge did
not decrease with altitude, or at least did not decrease as fast as
they had anticipated.

This was the situation when Hess became interested in the
problem and initiated a series of balloon flights that culminated in
the memorable ascent of August, 1912. His electroscopes were of
the Wulf type, constructed with particular care. Two of the three
instruments had airtight cases so that the internal air pressure
remained constant at all altitudes. Consequently, the sensitivity of
these instruments was independent of altitude. (The sensitivity

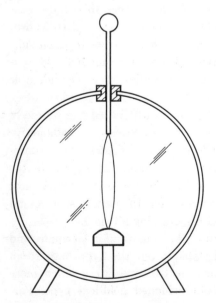

Fig. 1-3 The electroscope that was
developed by Wulf in 1909 and was
used in many of the early experiments on cosmic rays.

of a nonpressurized electroscope decreases with increasing altitude, because the number of *ion pairs* produced in a given volume of gas by a given intensity of radiation is proportional to the gas pressure. Ions are always produced — and neutralized — by twos: one positive and one negative. Hence the term *ion pair*.)

As the balloon began its ascent through the atmosphere, Hess found that the ionization became somewhat weaker at first, as indicated by a slower rate of electroscope discharge. Unquestionably, there was a radiation emanating from the earth's crust. But above 2,000 feet the trend reversed itself and the ionization began to increase gradually with altitude, as though the balloon were moving toward the source of the ionizing radiation instead of away from it. Indeed, at 16,000 feet the electroscopes were discharging about *four times faster* than they had at ground level. It was in order to explain this unexpected increase that Hess postulated a radiation falling upon the earth from somewhere beyond the atmosphere.

His assumption was certainly a bold one, and many years were to pass before it became generally accepted. First of all, other experimenters had to check the findings reported by Hess. When they did, they found that the increase of radiation strength with altitude continued well above 16,000 feet. Especially noteworthy were the daring balloon flights carried out by W. Kohlhörster of Germany between 1913 and 1919. In his flights he reached a maximum altitude of about 28,000 feet, where he found an ionizing radiation considerably stronger than that detected by Hess.

Second, it was necessary to explore all other possible — and less revolutionary — explanations for the observed ionization. C. T. R. Wilson, the inventor of the cloud chamber and one of the leading experts in ionization phenomena, suggested that the radiation was produced by thunderstorms high up in the atmosphere. Other physicists thought the atmosphere might contain small traces of radioactive gases. (Some radioactive substances, such as *radon*, element 86, were known to exist in the gaseous state.) If, for some reason, these radioactive gases had a tendency to concentrate in the upper layers of the atmosphere, they would explain the increased ionization at higher altitudes.

On both of these assumptions the intensity of the unknown radiation should vary according to weather conditions, it should change with the hour, day, and season. For thunderstorms obviously did not occur at all times, and it was hardly conceivable that the distribution of the hypothetical radioactive gases in the atmosphere would remain constant at all times of the day or year and through all changes of weather. Now, Hess had already pointed out the apparent absence of such intensity variations, and later investigations confirmed his findings. Clearly, despite disagreements and uncertainties due to the limited accuracy of the instruments in use at the time, the radiation was on the whole remarkably uniform. It came by day and by night, in summer and winter, in rain or shine, with little change from one day to the next, and with little change from one place to another at the same altitude.

The work of Millikan and Regener

Still, not all physicists were satisfied. Most skeptical among the skeptics was Robert A. Millikan, professor of physics at the California Institute of Technology. He and his collaborators decided to determine for themselves whether the experimental data reported by Hess and other workers were correct, whether there actually were compelling reasons to believe in the existence of a radiation from outer space. The result was a series of remarkable experiments carried out between 1923 and 1926, involving measurements made under water as well as at high altitudes. Millikan's experiments convinced himself and nearly everyone else in the scientific community that the radiation discovered by Hess *did* come from beyond the earth's atmosphere. And it was Millikan who gave the name *cosmic rays* to this radiation.

Millikan's last doubts about the existence of cosmic rays were apparently dispelled by an experiment performed at Muir Lake and Arrowhead Lake in the San Bernardino Range of southern California. The respective altitudes of the lakes are 11,800 and 5,100 feet. To any radiation passing vertically through the atmosphere, the additional 6,700 feet of air above Arrowhead Lake would represent an absorbing mass per unit area of lake surface equivalent to 6 feet of water. By sinking his electroscope to various depths in the two lakes, Millikan found that "within the limits of observational error, every reading in Arrowhead Lake corresponded to a reading six feet farther down in Muir Lake, thus showing that the rays do come in definitely from above and that their origin is entirely outside the layer of atmosphere between the levels of the two lakes."

A more detailed explanation of the argument on which Millikan based his conclusion appears in Fig. 1–4. As a footnote, it should be pointed out that his argument is neither foolproof nor completely correct. For reasons discussed in Chap. 8, equal masses per unit area[1] of air and water do not absorb exactly the same fraction of cosmic rays. Had the experimental data been more accurate than the state of the art permitted at the time, Millikan would have detected a difference between readings in Arrowhead Lake and readings 6 feet farther down in Muir Lake. Conceivably this finding might have prevented him from reaching the correct conclusion!

The work of Millikan's team made history not only because of the scientific results obtained but also because of the novel and ingenious techniques employed. An important innovation was the application of sounding balloons to cosmic-ray research. Hess and Kohlhörster had had to accompany their electroscopes in order to observe them. The use of unmanned balloons eliminated both the danger and the high cost of manned balloon flights. Millikan's electroscopes, masterpieces of ruggedness and sensitivity, were borne aloft by two balloons; at a certain altitude one of the balloons would burst and the other would then bring the equipment gently back to earth. During the flight, a simple device continuously

[1] See Appendix A.

recorded the electroscope readings on photographic film, to be developed and examined after recovery.

In the late 1920s and early 1930s the technique of self-recording electroscopes, carried by balloons into the highest layers of the atmosphere or sunk to great depths under water, was brought to an unprecedented degree of perfection by the German physicist Erich Regener and his group. To these scientists we owe some of the most accurate measurements ever made of cosmic-ray ionization as a function of altitude and depth (Figs. 1-5 and 1-6).

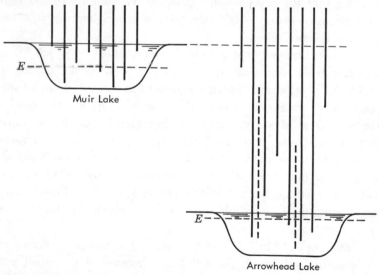

Fig. 1-4 Principle of Millikan's experiment at Muir Lake and Arrowhead Lake in Southern California. An electroscope (at level E) lies 6 feet deeper in Muir Lake than in Arrowhead Lake. Since the layer of air between the levels of the two lakes weighs as much as 6 feet of water, cosmic rays incident from above the level of Muir Lake must traverse the same total mass per unit area of absorber (air plus water) before reaching either electroscope. Millikan assumed that equal masses per unit area of air or water absorb cosmic rays equally. Thus, if no cosmic rays are created in the air layer between the two lakes, the number of such rays reaching the two electroscopes should be the same. If, however, new rays (dashed lines) were created in the air layer, then the electroscope at Arrowhead Lake would record more rays than the one at Muir Lake.

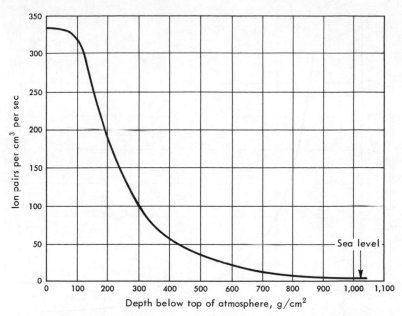

Fig. 1-5 Intensity of cosmic rays as a function of atmospheric depth, as measured by Regener and his group with balloon-borne electroscopes. The atmospheric depth plotted on the horizontal axis is the mass per unit area of the air layer above the electroscope. The vertical scale gives the number of ion pairs produced per second by cosmic rays in 1 cm³ of air at standard temperature and pressure. In these units, the cosmic-ray intensity at sea level is about 2.

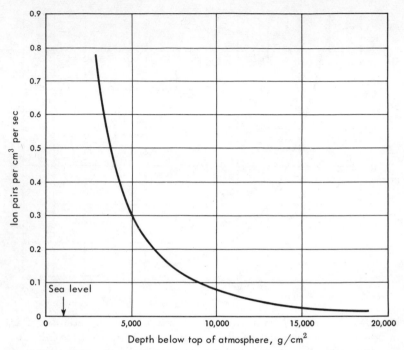

Fig. 1-6 Intensity of cosmic rays under water, as measured by Regener and others. The total mass per unit area of air and water above the electroscope is plotted on the horizontal axis. Sea level corresponds to a depth of 1,033 g/cm². The vertical scale gives the number of ion pairs produced per second in 1 cm³ of air at standard temperature and pressure.

Atoms and radiations

2

Unlikely as it may seem, no serious attempt was made to find out what cosmic rays actually are until 16 years after Hess's discovery.[1] Of course, it would have been difficult to identify the nature of cosmic rays with the comparatively crude experimental techniques then available. The methods used so successfully in studies of, for example, X-rays and radioactivity could not be applied to cosmic rays. X-rays and radioactivity came from well-defined sources and were subject to experimental control in a laboratory. Cosmic rays, on the other hand, seemed to come from everywhere. They could not be turned on and off at will as X-rays could be. And, unlike a sample of radioactive material, the source of cosmic rays was inaccessible, not to say unknown. More important, at ground level, where it would have been easiest to study them, the ionizing effects

---

[1] It was 24 years afterward, in 1936, that Hess shared a Nobel Prize in physics for his discovery.

of cosmic rays were exceedingly small compared to those caused by terrestrial radiations.

Aside from practical difficulties, however, there was little incentive to investigate the problem of the nature of cosmic rays, because most scientists believed they already knew the answer. What were the reasons for the prevailing misconceptions about cosmic rays? And what were the ideas behind the experiments, begun in 1929, that eventually led to our present understanding of their physical nature? To answer these questions, we must first recall what was known in 1929 about atoms and radiations.

Atoms

In the 16 years after Hess's discovery, physicists had achieved a much clearer understanding of atomic structure. They knew that atoms consist of a comparatively heavy, positively charged *nucleus* surrounded by a cloud of negatively charged electrons of almost negligible mass. Also, they had discovered that classical physics could provide no satisfactory description of the behavior of electrons in atoms, and they had developed a new theory — known as *quantum mechanics* — to deal with that and other atomic phenomena.

As for atomic nuclei, various investigators had measured their masses, electric charges, and approximate sizes. Very little was known about their structure, however. After the discovery of radioactivity, it was clear that at least the nuclei of heavier elements did have a structure, that is, consisted of smaller "building blocks." For example, occasionally a nucleus of radium disintegrated spontaneously into a nucleus of radon and a nucleus of helium (called an *alpha particle, α*).

Thus, the radium nucleus was not a "simple" particle. Moreover, it had been known for 10 years that high-speed α particles could break up the nuclei of certain elements such as nitrogen and cause them to eject positive particles — *protons* — identical with hydrogen nuclei. There were speculations that all nuclei were formed from the same building blocks. Indeed, since nuclear masses were known to be nearly whole-number multiples of the proton mass, it was thought that these building blocks might be the proton and the (practically massless) electron.

But scientists did not accept this hypothesis without misgivings, because they were well aware that it presented a number of serious difficulties. The puzzle of the constitution of nuclei was to be solved a few years later when the British physicist James Chadwick discovered the *neutron*. It then became clear that nuclei consist of protons and neutrons; see Appendix G.

Radiations

At the time I am speaking of, the word "radiations" referred, as it does now, to a variety of different physical phenomena having certain features in common. One of the most important characteristics of any radiation is its energy. All radiations are energy carriers, and they will give up part or all of their energy to an appropriate absorber. In many cases the added energy can be detected directly in the form of heat, as in the simple example of an object exposed to bright sunlight.

Physicists generally distinguished between two broad groups of radiations: *corpuscular* and *electromagnetic*. Corpuscular radiations included *beta rays* (β), or high-speed electrons emitted in the spontaneous decay of certain radioactive atoms; α rays, or helium nuclei, emitted in the spontaneous decay of radioactive atoms; and artificially accelerated particles such as *cathode rays*, which are electrons emitted by the negative electrode, or cathode, during the electric discharge in a vacuum tube. Electromagnetic radiations included visible light, infrared and ultraviolet rays, X-rays, and gamma rays (γ). Gamma rays are among the products of radioactive decay, and they are emitted simultaneously with β rays and α rays.

In earlier years, the main difference between the two groups of radiations appeared to be that corpuscular rays were particles and electromagnetic rays were waves. By the late 1920s, however, the development of quantum physics had brought about a drastic revision of this view. Physicists realized that all rays behave in some respects as waves and in other respects as individual particles. (Particles of electromagnetic radiations had been named *photons*.)

The concept of something that behaves both as a wave and as a particle is difficult to grasp; fortunately, however, it is not essential to our discussion. As it turns out, in fact, cosmic rays contain only photons and other particles of very high energy whose wave characteristics are never dominant. Thus, in what follows we can forget about waves and take the view that corpuscular as well as electromagnetic rays consist of individual particles, or *quanta*.

Even though, by 1929, the fundamental distinction between particles and waves had disappeared, it was still convenient — as it is now — to maintain the traditional classification between corpuscular rays and electromagnetic radiations.

All corpuscular rays are particles to which a definite *mass* can be assigned (9.11×10^{-28} gram for an electron in a β-ray beam; 6.64×10^{-24} gram for a helium nucleus in an α-particle beam).[1] The kinetic energy, or energy of motion,[2] of each particle depends on its velocity as well, of course, as on its mass; and the velocities vary considerably. Particles of the kind found in many corpuscular radiations travel at "relativistic" velocities (that is, at velocities comparable to the velocity of light).[3] According to the laws of relativistic, as opposed to classical, mechanics, no material (corpuscular) particle can ever reach the velocity of light (about 300,000 kilometers/sec in a vacuum), even though it approaches this velocity more and more closely as its kinetic energy increases.

On the other hand, the photons of electromagnetic radiations do not possess a finite mass. Although they have different energies,

---

[1] For powers of 10, see Appendix B.
[2] See Appendix D.
[3] *Ibid.*

they all travel at the velocity of light. Moreover, although particles of finite mass may still continue to exist as particles when they are "stopped" by an absorber, photons disappear altogether by, for example, transferring their energy to electrons or atomic nuclei. All electromagnetic radiations are alike in another respect: they originate from the accelerated motion of electric charges. What distinguishes one type of electromagnetic radiation from another is simply the different, individual energies of the photons. Photons of visible light are more energetic than infrared photons and less energetic than ultraviolet photons; these, in turn, are less energetic than X-ray photons; and the latter are less energetic than γ-ray photons.

Of the radiations known prior to the discovery of cosmic rays, those emitted by radioactive substances had the highest energies. In fact, the energies of individual α particles, β particles, and γ-ray photons are of the order of *millions of electron volts*. By contrast, photons of visible light have energies of the order of 10 electron volts. (One electron volt, abbreviated eV, is the kinetic energy of an electron accelerated by a potential difference of one volt.[1] Cosmic-ray physics involves much greater energies, which are measured in millions of electron volts (MeV) or billions of electron volts (BeV).

Ionization by corpuscular rays

As I have already noted, from the end of the nineteenth century it had been the common practice of physicists to detect certain radiations by their property of ionizing gases. By the late 1920s, the manner in which different types of radiation ionize gases was well understood. This matter is of fundamental importance to any treatment of cosmic-ray phenomena; for until recent years almost the only means of studying cosmic radiation was through its ionizing effects on gases. Hence, I must ask those of my readers

[1] See Appendix E.

who are already familiar with ionization in gases to bear with me through the following discussion.

Consider first a beam of charged particles (β rays, say) traversing a gas. When one of the particles passes near a molecule of the gas, its electric forces disturb the arrangement of the electrons in the molecule. If the disturbance is sufficiently violent, one of the electrons may break loose and leave behind a positively charged molecular fragment, or positive ion. The electron itself may remain free for a while and wander about in the gas as a light negative ion, or it may attach itself to a neutral molecule and form a heavy negative ion. In either case, the charged particle leaves in its wake a trail of ions.

The ion trail can be made visible in the ingenious instrument known as the *cloud chamber*, invented by C. T. R. Wilson in 1911. Wilson's original cloud chamber — or *expansion chamber*, to distinguish it from later types — is essentially a glass box with a movable wall, or piston (Fig. 2–1). The chamber contains a mixture of alcohol vapor and either air or some gas such as argon. If one suddenly enlarges the enclosed space by pulling back the piston, the gases expand and their temperature drops. If the temperature drop is great enough, the alcohol vapor condenses into droplets, which form a fog in the chamber. Proper control of the expansion, however, will produce a somewhat smaller temperature change, and

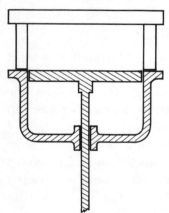

Fig. 2-1 Expansion cloud chamber. When the piston is pulled back rapidly, the gas and vapor in the chamber expand. The resulting drop in temperature is sufficient for condensation of the vapor, which, if carefully controlled, takes place around any ions present in the gas.

the vapor will condense only around ions. Consequently, a charged particle traversing the chamber at about the time of the expansion will leave a "fossil track" in the form of visible droplets that condense along the particle's trail of ions.

To be detected, the particle must traverse the chamber at some time during the so-called expansion phase. If the particle enters the chamber too soon — more than a few milliseconds prior to expansion, the ions will diffuse away before the gases are cooled. If it enters too late — more than a few milliseconds after expansion, the gases will warm up again before the ion trail is formed. Thus, the chamber is sensitive for a period of about one-hundredth of a second each time it is expanded.

Fast-moving particles with different electric charges and different velocities produce ion trails of different densities in a gas. For a given velocity, the density, or number of ions per unit length in the trail, *increases with increasing charge*. The explanation is fairly simple. The electric forces exerted on the electrons of a molecule by a particle passing nearby are proportional to the electric charge of the particle. Therefore, particles of greater charge cause more violent disturbances than particles of smaller charge, and thus they ionize a larger number of molecules while traveling a given distance in the gas.

For a given charge, the ion density *decreases with increasing velocity*. To understand the reason for this effect, consider a particle that passes near a molecule. The particle disturbs the molecule appreciably only while it is within a certain minimum distance. Hence, the time of interaction is longer for a slow-moving particle than for a fast-moving one. Obviously, the longer the period of interaction, the more effective the force will be in disrupting the molecule. Therefore, slower particles ionize more heavily than faster particles.

As I mentioned before, when the kinetic energy of a particle increases indefinitely, the velocity of the particle eventually approaches that of light. The density of the track left by such a particle at first decreases with increasing energy, but then tends to a practically constant value characteristic of a particle moving at nearly the velocity of light (Fig. 2–2). Hence, there is a lower limit to the amount of ionization produced by any charged particle. The ion trail of smallest possible density is one left by a singly charged particle (for example, an electron or a proton) moving at nearly the velocity of light. Such a particle is called by physicists a *minimum-ionizing particle.* For example, β rays with kinetic energies of the order of 1 MeV, which are singly charged and travel at about 94 per cent the velocity of light, behave very much like minimum-ionizing particles. In air at standard temperature and pressure they produce about 50 pairs of positive and negative ions per centimeter of path. On the other hand, α particles emitted in the radioactive decay of polonium have an energy of 5.3 MeV and a velocity only 5.4 per cent that of light; they carry two elementary charges and produce about 24,000 ion pairs per centimeter of path in air.[1]

Ionization processes similar to those in gases also occur when charged particles pass through liquids or solids. But whatever the substance — solid, liquid, or gas — the particles lose, in general, a very small fraction of their energy in any ionization "event" (something of the order of 30 eV in air). Yet the cumulative effects of many such events will gradually slow down a particle and eventually bring it to rest. In fact, in the late 1920s it was commonly believed that all charged particles traveling through matter lost their energy almost entirely by ionization. This belief, as we shall see, turned out to be wrong.

Ionization by photons

The discussion thus far has concerned only the ionization caused by fast-moving charged particles. But what about photons, which

---

[1] Electrons ejected from a molecule by a moving, charged particle often have sufficient energy to produce, in turn, one or several ion pairs. The ionization densities quoted here include both the ion pairs produced directly by the "primary" particle and those produced by the "secondary" electrons. Direct ionization accounts for something less than half the total.

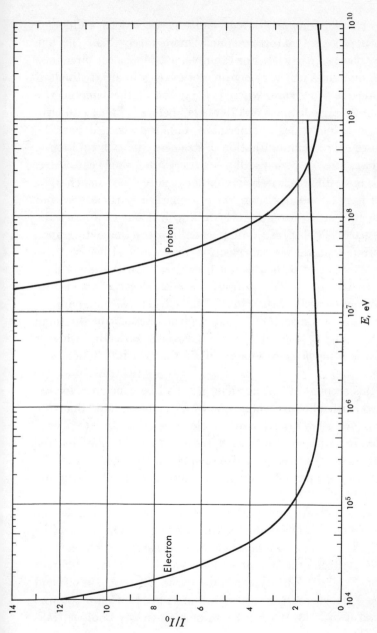

Fig. 2-2 Ion density as a function of kinetic energy along the track of an electron or a proton. The energy E, measured in electron volts, is plotted on a logarithmic scale (see Appendix C). For both electrons and protons the ion density at first decreases with decreasing energy and then remains almost constant as the particle approaches the velocity of light. Strictly speaking, the ion density passes through a minimum at a kinetic energy close to the rest energy of the particle (see Appendix D); it then increases at an extremely slow rate. The quantity plotted on the vertical axis is the actual ion density I divided by the minimum density I_0.

carry no charge? Photons too can ionize gases, but by a different process, a process that occurs much more rarely than the one involving charged particles. For example, a 2-MeV electron ionizes about 50 molecules for every centimeter of path in air at standard temperature and pressure, whereas a photon of the same energy travels an average distance of 170 meters before it knocks an electron out of a molecule. Furthermore, unlike a charged particle, which loses only a minute fraction of its energy in each collision, a photon loses most or perhaps all of its energy in a single encounter.

This basic difference in behavior between photons and charged particles is not too surprising, since a charged particle does not have to "hit" an electron directly to knock it out of a molecule. It is the particle's electrostatic repulsion or attraction acting upon the electron that shakes the electron loose, and either of these forces is effective at distances much greater than the dimensions of the particle itself. The photon, because it lacks an electric charge, is not capable of such long-range effects. Nothing happens until it makes a "direct hit" on an electron. Because of the small size of the target, such an event is naturally rare. But when it occurs, it is a much more violent affair than an interaction at a distance.

In this account of cosmic rays, we shall be concerned for the most part with photons whose energy is much greater than the minimum necessary to remove an electron from an atom or a molecule. It turns out that, with respect to these photons, the electrons behave essentially as free particles. In other words, the fact that they are part of a complex atomic or molecular structure is immaterial.

The collision of a photon with an electron closely resembles the collision of a moving billiard ball with a ball at rest. The photon (the moving ball) bounces off at an angle with its energy much reduced, while the electron (the ball at rest) is knocked off in a different direction (Fig. 2–3). This type of interaction between photons and electrons is called the *Compton effect*, after A. H. Compton, who discovered it in 1923. When a beam of high-energy photons traverses a gas, the number of molecules ionized as a result of Compton collisions is exceedingly small. The *recoil electrons* produced in these collisions, however, carry off a sizable fraction of the photon energy, and they are therefore capable of producing large numbers of ions before coming to rest. Thus photons ionize gases *indirectly*, through the few high-speed secondary electrons that they eject from gas molecules.

Absorption and energy loss

I have been speaking somewhat loosely of the absorption of corpuscular rays and photons by matter. Notice how differently the two kinds of rays behave in this respect.

Charged particles lose their energy bit by bit through a large number of ionization events. A beam of particles, all having the same mass, charge, and initial kinetic energy, will slow down at almost exactly the same rate as they travel through matter. Thus they will all come to rest after traversing the same distance. This distance, called the *range*, depends, of course, on the nature and initial energy of the particles and on the material of which the absorber is made. For the reasons explained in Appendix A, the range is often measured in grams per square centimeter rather than in centimeters.

What happens to any given photon that travels through matter, however, is largely a question of chance. It may undergo a

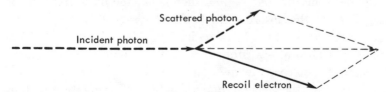

Fig. 2-3 Compton effect. A photon "collides" with an electron at rest. The photon, having given part of its energy to the electron, is scattered; the electron recoils in a different direction. The vector sum of the momenta of the scattered photon and the recoil electron equals the momentum (see Appendix D) of the incident photon.

Compton collision almost immediately or after traveling a considerable distance. Consequently, in a beam of photons that has traveled a certain distance, some photons still have the same energy they started with, while others have lost a large share of their energy in Compton collisions. The latter, moreover, will have been deflected away from the beam. In the case of a photon beam, we can predict only the *average* behavior of the particles. We can say that a certain fraction of all photons traversing a given mass of matter will be lost from the beam. This fraction depends on the thickness of the absorber, on the material in the absorber, and, if all the photons have the same energy, on the value of that energy.

If, ideally, the absorber is divided into layers of the same thickness, the same *fraction* of the incident photons is absorbed in each layer. Suppose, for example, that the fraction absorbed is 10 per cent. Starting with a million photons, after the first layer the number of photons in the beam will be 900,000 (1,000,000 − 100,000); after the second layer it will be 810,000 (900,000 − 90,000), and so on. By plotting the number of surviving photons as a function of absorber thickness, one obtains an *absorption curve*, such as that shown in Fig. 2–4. In mathematical language, a curve of this general shape is said to be *exponential*.

As we have seen, photons of a given energy travel different distances before undergoing their first collisions. The average distance is called the *mean free path*, and, like the range of particles, it is often measured in grams per square centimeter. One can prove (but I shall not attempt to do so here) that the mean free path is also equal to the absorber thickness necessary to cut down the number of photons to 1/2.7 of its initial value. (The number 2.7 is the base of natural logarithms.) Therefore, the shorter the mean free path, the steeper the absorption curve.

Such was the general understanding of the absorption of corpuscular rays and photons in 1929. Before turning to the question of cosmic rays and their physical nature, I should like to point out that this understanding rested on two important assumptions: that charged particles lose energy only by ionization and that photons lose energy only by undergoing Compton collisions. As later research was to show, however, at sufficiently high energies other absorption processes come into play. High-energy particles and photons are absorbed much more readily than the physicists of 1929 supposed. The absorption of high-energy particles and photons will be discussed in Chaps. 7 and 10.

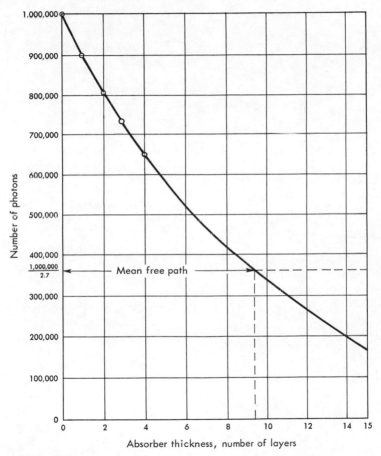

Fig. 2-4 Exponential absorption curve (see text). The intersection of the curve with the horizontal line that passes through the point at 1,000,000/2.7 on the vertical axis determines the mean free path.

The nature of
cosmic rays

3

The gamma-ray hypothesis

Most of the early workers in the field of cosmic rays were convinced that the rays were simply photons of greater energy than any previously discovered. In fact, as late as 1929, the German literature commonly referred to cosmic rays as *Ultragammastrahlung* (ultra-gamma radiation). The reason is easy to understand. Aside from cosmic rays, the most penetrating radiation known at the time consisted of γ rays from radioactive substances. The mean free path of γ-ray photons in air measured hundreds of meters, whereas β rays of comparable energies showed ranges of only several meters and the ranges of α particles were smaller still.

Moreover, theoretical computations, based on the assumption that high-energy photons were absorbed predominantly through Compton collisions, predicted an increasing mean free path with increasing photon energy. In confirmation of this prediction, it had been found experimentally that the most energetic γ rays were also the most penetrating.[1]

Now, absorption measurements in the atmosphere and under water by Hess, Kohlhörster, Millikan, Regener, and others had shown the cosmic radiation to be more penetrating than any other (see Figs. 1–5 and 1–6). It was thus natural to think that cosmic rays were of greater energy than the most energetic photons found among γ rays. Some physicists, willing to trust the theory of the Compton effect in a range of energies where it had not yet been tested experimentally, estimated the energies of the hypothetical cosmic-ray photons from the shape of their absorption curve. Cosmic rays, they concluded, were a mixture of photons with energies ranging from 20 or 30 to several hundred MeV. This estimate was the basis of a most provocative suggestion put forward by Millikan in 1928. According to Millikan, cosmic rays were born of the energy released during the synthesis of heavier elements from primordial hydrogen spread throughout the universe.

Millikan's hypothesis

As explained in Chap. 2. a beam of high-energy photons, all having the same energy and all traveling in the same direction through matter, are absorbed exponentially (Fig. 2–4). The absorption curve is characterized by a mean free path whose length, for a given absorber material, depends on the photon energy. But even if the cosmic-ray photons all carried the same energy (which is very unlikely), their absorption could not be represented by a simple exponential curve, because cosmic rays do not form a parallel beam, but instead fall on the atmosphere from all directions. It is not difficult to correct for this effect and to compute the theoretical

[1] The theory of the Compton effect was published in 1929 by Oscar Klein of Sweden and Yoshio Nishina of Japan. A preliminary and less accurate theory had been developed by P.A.M. Dirac of England in 1926.

absorption curves of photons incident from all directions and characterized by a particular mean free path.

Millikan noted that the actual absorption curve of cosmic rays did not correspond to any single curve thus computed. However, it could be represented by the *sum* of the absorption curves of three groups of photons with mean free paths of 300, 1,250, and 2,500 g/cm². Using Dirac's theory of the Compton effect (Klein and Nishina had not yet published theirs), Millikan arrived at energies of about 26, 110, and 220 MeV for the three respective groups of photons. He therefore concluded that cosmic radiation was for the most part a mixture of photons with those energies.

While searching for clues to the origin of the photons, which appeared to come in equal numbers from every region of the sky, Millikan was led to the following speculation: Interstellar space is filled with very dilute hydrogen gas. Conceivably, out of this gas the atoms of the heavier elements might continuously evolve by a spontaneous process of *fusion*. Once in a while, for example, four hydrogen atoms might meet and fuse to form a helium atom.

A helium atom weighs slightly less (about 4.8×10^{-26} gram less) than four hydrogen atoms. According to Einstein's principle of equivalence between mass and energy, this means that if a helium atom forms from four hydrogen atoms, an amount of energy equal to 4.8×10^{-26} times the square of the velocity of light is released.[1] In the usual units, the amount of released energy is 27 MeV. Now, allowing for experimental error, 27 MeV was just the energy of the first of the three groups of photons found in cosmic radiation. Consequently, Millikan concluded that these photons result from the synthesis of helium in interstellar space.

Thus encouraged, Millikan explored the possibility of finding a similar explanation for the origin of the other two groups, and he was remarkably successful. Among the most abundant elements in the universe are nitrogen and oxygen. One atom of nitrogen weighs about 1.8×10^{-25} gram less than fourteen atoms of hydrogen. From this *mass defect* one can calculate that the fusion of

[1] See Appendix D.

fourteen hydrogen atoms into one atom of nitrogen would produce about 100 MeV of energy. Similarly, the synthesis of one oxygen atom from sixteen atoms of hydrogen would release an energy of about 120 MeV.

These values are close to each other and to the estimate for the photons of Millikan's second group. Quite naturally, Millikan concluded that these photons also resulted from the synthesis of heavier elements, namely, nitrogen and oxygen. But that was not all. For, as other calculations showed, if twenty-eight hydrogen atoms fused to form one atom of silicon, another abundant element, the process would release an amount of energy very nearly equal to the energy of the photons in the third group. This set of coincidences, which turned out to be purely accidental, convinced Millikan that cosmic rays were indeed the "birth cry" of atoms being continuously created in space.

The coincidence experiments of Bothe and Kohlhörster

Of course, from time to time physicists expressed doubts about the nature of cosmic rays. But the prevailing view of cosmic rays as high-energy photons was not seriously challenged until 1929, when the German physicists Walther Bothe and W. Kohlhörster published a paper titled "Das Wesen der Hoehenstrahlung" ("The Nature of the Radiation from Above"). In this paper, Bothe and Kohlhörster related certain experiments and arrived at certain conclusions that marked a turning point in the history of cosmic-ray research. The experiments were made possible by an important technical development earlier the same year: the invention of a convenient instrument to *count* cosmic rays.

Electroscopes of the type used in earlier work on cosmic rays could detect only the combined ionizing effects of large numbers of particles over relatively long periods of time. They could not detect individual particles, because the passage of a single particle through an electroscope does not produce enough ionization to cause an observable movement of the electroscope leaves. There were, of course, instruments capable of detecting individual ionizing particles. For many years, physicists had been using the Wilson cloud chamber, which I have already described, and had been "counting" α particles by observing the tiny sparks, or *scintillations*, produced when the particles hit a fluorescent screen.

Moreover, Hans Geiger of Germany, while working in the laboratory of Ernest Rutherford at the University of Manchester from 1906 to 1912, had collaborated in the development of electrical counting devices known as *point counters*. A point counter is basically a thin, pointed rod projecting into a metal box (Fig. 3–1). A battery or other voltage source maintains the rod at a positive

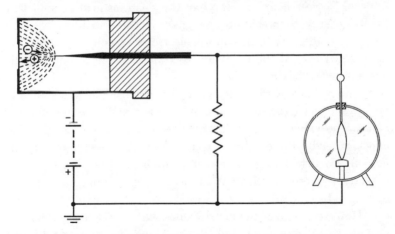

Fig. 3-1 Particle counter of the type used in early experiments on radio activity. It consists of a metal box containing a pointed rod that is held in place by an insulator. Ionizing particles enter the box through a window in front of the point. The window is covered by a thin foil so that the counter can be operated with different gases and at different pressures. The case is connected to the negative terminal of a high-voltage battery with its positive terminal grounded. The rod, connected to an electroscope, is grounded through a large resistor; thus the rod is at a positive voltage with respect to the case. When a discharge occurs in the counter, the electroscope wires undergo a sudden deflection. The wires then quickly return to their original position as the charge leaks to ground through the resistor.

electric potential with respect to the box. When the potential difference is less than a certain critical value (usually of the order of 1,000 volts, depending on the design of the counter and on the gas pressure), the electric field simply sweeps positive ions toward the negatively charged walls and negative ions (electrons) toward the positively charged point, just as ions of opposite sign are swept toward the case and the leaves of a charged electroscope.

The *drift* of the ions, toward the walls or the point, is comparatively slow because both positive and negative ions collide frequently with the gas molecules. But at potential differences above the critical value something new happens in the vicinity of the point, where the electric field is strongest. In the short time interval between collisions, some of the electrons acquire sufficient kinetic energy to break up the gas molecules with which they collide. In these collisions more electrons are ejected; they are accelerated toward the point and become capable of ionizing the gas molecules they encounter.

The result is a growing avalanche of ions. The gas suddenly acquires a very large electrical conductivity, and a discharge takes place. The value of the point counter lies in this multiplication effect, whereby the few ions produced by the passage of a single ionizing particle suffice to trigger a discharge that can easily be detected by, for example, a Wulf electroscope connected as shown in Fig. 3–1.

However, none of the instruments that I have mentioned was well suited to cosmic-ray studies. The cloud chamber was difficult to run and was sensitive for no more than a small fraction of a second at each expansion. The fluorescent material of *scintillation counters* detected only those particles capable of ionizing much more heavily than most of the particles associated with the cosmic radiation. The point counter was not very stable and could not be made sufficiently large to be of much use in the study of a radiation whose intensity was as small as that of cosmic rays.

The answer to the needs of cosmic-ray physicists came in 1929 with the invention, by Geiger and one of his students, W. Müller, of the so-called Geiger-Müller counter (or G-M counter for short). This instrument, one of the most widely used tools of experimental physics in the twentieth century, essentially consists of a metal tube with a thin metal wire stretched along its axis (Fig. 3–2). The tube is first evacuated and then filled with a gas at a pressure of about one-tenth of an atmosphere. Under operating conditions, the wire is held at a positive potential with respect to the tube.

The G-M counter works on the same principle as the point counter; that is, it makes use of the *cascade effect*, in which a single ion pair produced in the gas triggers a discharge. The operating voltage is usually between 1,000 and 1,500 volts, and the counter is sensitive over practically its whole volume. The G-M counter is comparatively easy to build, is much more reliable than the point counter, and can be made in a variety of sizes, up to several inches in diameter and several feet in length.

In their experiments, Bothe and Kohlhörster had set up two G-M counters, each connected to an electroscope, in order to observe cosmic rays. They noticed that the counters, when placed one above the other a small distance apart (Fig. 3–3), often dis-

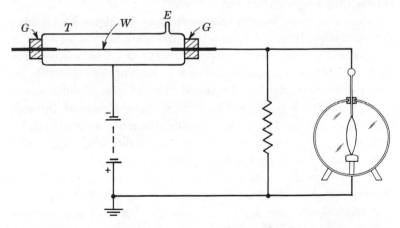

Fig. 3-2 The Geiger-Müller counter: metal tube *T;* glass insulators *G;* thin wire *W;* tube for evacuating and filling the tube *E*. Electrical connections are similar to those shown in Fig. 3-1.

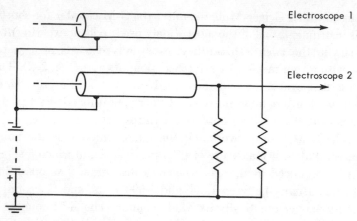

Fig. 3-3 Two G-M counters placed one above the other and connected to two electroscopes. Simultaneous deflections of the electroscope leaves indicate simultaneous discharges of the two counters, or *coincidences*.

charged simultaneously. These simultaneous discharges, or *coincidences*, could not be due to chance, or at least not entirely to chance, because they became much less frequent when the distance between the two counters was increased.

A photon could, in principle, produce a coincidence by a double Compton effect (Fig. 3–4*a*). However, the probability of a Compton collision in the wall or in the gas of a counter is very small, and the probability of two Compton collisions is quite negligible. As Bothe and Kohlhörster rightly concluded, the observed coincidences must be due to the passage of individual charged particles through both counters (Fig. 3–4*b*). Furthermore, the particles could not be ordinary α or β rays, because the counter walls (1 mm thick and made of zinc) would stop all such particles.

In itself, this result did not contradict the view that the *primary radiation*, the cosmic radiation falling on the atmosphere from outer space, consisted of high-energy photons. Since photons undergo Compton collisions in the atmosphere, the observed ionizing particles might have been the recoil electrons arising from such collisions. As I mentioned before, the energies of the hypothetical primary photons were believed to range from 20 or 30 to several hundred MeV. The recoil electrons of these photons would have more than enough energy to traverse the counter walls.

To check upon this possibility, Bothe and Kohlhörster placed a gold block 4.1 cm thick between the counters. (Gold was chosen because of its high density and correspondingly high stopping power.) Now only particles with a range greater than 4.1 cm of gold could traverse both counters and produce coincidences. The experimenters found that the rate of coincidences was still 76 per cent of what it had been without the block. In other words, 76 per cent of the charged particles present in the cosmic radiation near sea level could penetrate 4.1 cm of gold.

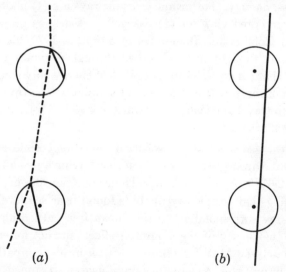

Fig. 3-4   Photon and charged-particle coincidences. (a) A photon produces a Compton electron in the upper counter and then another Compton electron in the lower counter. Typically, the probability of each Compton collision is of the order of 5 per cent. This means the number of pulses (recording Compton electrons) in each counter is about one-twentieth the number of photons that traverse the counter; the number of coincidences is therefore approximately 0.25 per cent ($1/20 \times 1/20 = 1/400$) of the number of photons that traverse both counters. (b) Every particle passing through both counters produces a coincidence.

This result was very surprising; for according to even the most generous estimates, only a small fraction of the recoil electrons found at any point in the atmosphere should have had a greater range. Bothe and Kohlhörster concluded that the then-current ideas concerning the nature of cosmic rays were probably wrong and that *the primary cosmic radiation itself consisted of charged particles rather than photons.*

Photons versus charged particles

Consider for a moment the consequences of the two contrasting hypotheses, namely, that primary cosmic rays are (1) photons, the generally accepted view, or (2) charged particles, as proposed by Bothe and Kohlhörster. Remember also that, in 1929, high-energy photons were thought to be absorbed through Compton collisions alone and charged particles supposedly lost energy only through the ionization of matter. (For the sake of simplicity, the rays may be assumed to travel vertically downward, instead of coming from all directions.)

1. Near sea level the absorption curve of cosmic radiation resembles the absorption curve of photons having a mean free path of about 300 g/cm^2 in air or water. Hence one can simplify matters by assuming that cosmic-ray photons found near sea level have a single energy corresponding to this mean free path. Calculations based on the theory of the Compton effect[1] predict an energy of approximately 60 MeV for photons with a mean free path of 300 g/cm^2 in air or water. As a further simplification, assume that when a Compton collision occurs, the photon disappears by giving up all its energy to an electron. Then each recoil electron will have an energy of 60 MeV and a corresponding computed range of 30 g/cm^2 in air or water.

[1] That is, the theory developed by Klein and Nishina. It is important to keep this distinction in mind when comparing the energy estimates quoted here and those used by Millikan (page 29).

At any point in the atmosphere (or other absorber) the radiation is, then, a mixture of photons and electrons. This is shown graphically in Fig. 3–5a, where dashed lines represent photons and solid lines represent recoil electrons. (The figure assumes the recoil electrons to be traveling in the same direction as the photons from which they received their energy.)

Now suppose the horizontal line at 0 represents sea level; the line at 100, a depth of 100 g/cm² (about 333 feet) below sea level; and the line at 200, a depth of 200 g/cm² (666 feet) below sea level. How do the so-called intensities of cosmic radiation at the three levels compare with one another? Since there are six recoil electrons at sea level and four at 100 g/cm² and three at 200 g/cm² below sea level, the intensities at the three levels (as measured with an electroscope or a single counter) are in the ratio of 6:4:3. These are approximate numbers because the figure shows only 60 photons, which is much too small a sample to serve as a basis for accurate predictions.

Using a more adequate sample — 6,000 photons, say — the ratio would be 600:430:336. These values correspond to three points on the absorption curve shown in Fig. 3–6. Note that even though this is the "absorption curve of cosmic rays," it does not actually give the number of primary photons found at the different levels; instead, it gives the number of their recoil electrons. The curve does not include photons, of course, because the discharge rate of an electroscope, as well as the counting rate of a single G-M counter, depends only on the number of *charged particles* that pass through the instrument.

2. If the primary cosmic radiation consists of charged particles, these particles must have different initial energies; for if they all had the same energy, they would also have nearly identical ranges and would all stop at the same level. In Fig. 3–5b the energy distribution has been chosen in such a way that the number of particles present at a given level is the same as the number of recoil electrons at the same level in Fig. 3–5a. For this particular energy distribution, the response of an electroscope or of a single G-M

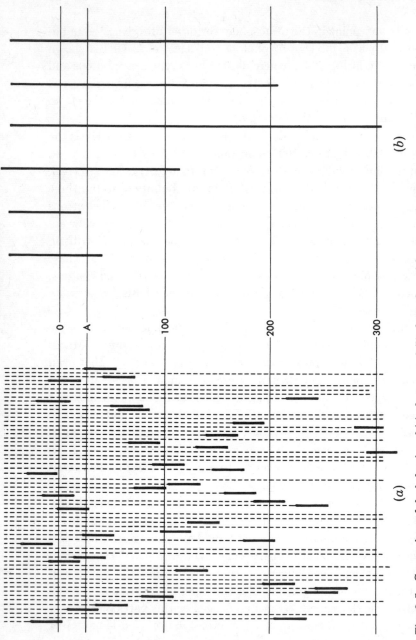

Fig. 3-5 Comparison of the behavior of (a) photons and (b) charged particles traversing matter (see text).

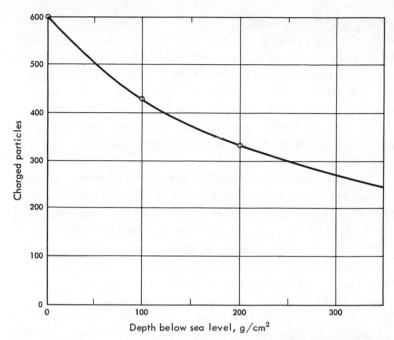

Fig. 3-6 Number of charged particles present at various depths below sea level. As explained in the text and illustrated in Fig. 3-5, this number is the same in the case of a radiation consisting of photons and in the case of a radiation consisting of charged particles with an appropriate energy distribution.

counter at any given level is the same as in case 1. In other words, the absorption curve of the corpuscular radiation, as usually measured, is identical to that of the photon radiation (Fig. 3–6).

Although the hypothesis of a primary photon radiation and the hypothesis of a primary corpuscular radiation lead to entirely different pictures of the radiation after it has passed through a layer of matter (Fig. 3–5a and b), the absorption measurements taken before 1929 provided no way of distinguishing between the two hypotheses.

The significance of the coincidence experiments of Bothe and Kohlhörster was that they afforded, for the first time, the possibility of distinguishing between the consequences of the opposing hypotheses. If all primary cosmic rays are photons of 60 MeV energy, no coincidences whatever would have been recorded with 4.1 cm of gold between the counters; 60-MeV electrons cannot travel that far through gold. But if primary cosmic rays are charged particles, then in order to penetrate as far as they do through the atmosphere and water, many of them must have energies much greater than 60 MeV. Consequently, they could also have penetrated 4.1 cm of gold and thereby have caused the observed coincidences.

It is true that the proponents of the photon hypothesis thought cosmic rays were a mixture of photons of different energies, some greater than 60 MeV. A small fraction of the recoil electrons, therefore, would have passed through the gold block used in the experiments. Although this circumstance makes the interpretation of the experiments a little less direct, it does not change the conclusion. The crucial point is this: An absorber that produces only a minor change in the radiation intensity when placed above an electroscope or a single G-M counter produces completely different effects — depending on whether primary cosmic rays are photons or charged particles — when placed between two counters. If the rays are photons, the absorber drastically reduces the coincidence rate (even though some of the Compton electrons may have enough energy to traverse the absorber). If the rays are charged particles, the absorber affects the coincidence rate only slightly.

The reader can satisfy himself on this point by going back to Fig. 3–5. Suppose first that two thin-walled counters lie one above the other at sea level with no absorber between them. In Fig. 3–5*a* and *b* one finds at sea level six ionizing particles capable of traversing both counters and thus producing coincidences. Now consider what happens when an absorber (equivalent, say, to 25 g/cm² of water) is placed between the counters. Suppose first that primary cosmic rays are charged particles. Five of the six particles present at sea level reach level *A*, 25 g/cm² below sea level (Fig. 3–5*b*). This means the number of coincidences has decreased by one-sixth.

Suppose next that primary cosmic rays are photons. Only one of the six recoil electrons present at sea level reaches level A (Fig. 3–5a). In other words, only one electron traverses the absorber. Since neither the electrons stopped by the absorber nor the Compton electrons generated in it can produce coincidences, the absorber must cut down the number of coincidences by five-sixths.

Although this discussion is based on oversimplified assumptions and on a very small statistical sample, it is certainly true that 25 g/cm² of water placed between the counters should produce a large decrease in the coincidence rate if primary cosmic rays are photons and hardly any decrease at all if primary cosmic rays are charged particles.

There was one serious objection to the conclusions reached by Bothe and Kohlhörster. The interpretation of their experiments was based on an arbitrary extrapolation of the known properties of photons and electrons at low energies. Bothe and Kohlhörster themselves were well aware of the potential pitfalls involved. It was conceivable, for example, that the energies of cosmic-ray photons might be much greater than those computed from their mean free path according to the equation of Klein and Nishina, which was known to be valid for energies of the order of 1 MeV. If such were the case, the secondary electrons would have had a greater range, more of them would have penetrated the gold block between the counters, and they might have produced much the same coincidence effects as a primary corpuscular radiation.

For this reason it would be misleading to claim that the experiment of Bothe and Kohlhörster had proved the corpuscular nature of cosmic rays. In fact, the two hypothetical pictures of cosmic rays I have sketched here turned out to be almost equally far from reality. Cosmic rays are indeed charged particles; but they behave very differently than charged particles were thought to behave at the time.

Nevertheless, the work of Bothe and Kohlhörster was a milestone in the history of cosmic rays. The particular interpretation they gave to the experimental results was not the important thing. What mattered most was that for the first time physicists had attempted to determine the nature of cosmic rays experimentally. The results of the experiments had failed to provide any support for the accepted view of cosmic rays as high-energy photons and had thus thrown the question wide open.

Puzzling clues

4

The history of cosmic rays in the following years is so closely inter-twined with my own life as a scientist that I can hardly escape the temptation to insert some personal notes in this account.

When I happened to read the paper by Bothe and Kohlhörster, I was 24 years old and had just completed a year as an assistant to Prof. Antonio Garbasso, director of the physics laboratory of the University of Florence, in Arcetri, Italy. Among my colleagues were Gilberto Bernardini and Giuseppe Occhialini, of whom more will be heard later in this story. None of us was yet committed to any long-range research program. The paper of Bothe and Kohl-hörster came like a flash of light revealing the existence of an unsus-pected world, full of mysteries, which no one had yet begun to explore. It soon became my overwhelming ambition to participate in the exploration.

Within a few months I had built my first G-M counters, had devised a new method for recording coincidences (based on the use of vacuum tubes; see Fig. 4–1), and had begun some experiments. The summer of 1930 took me to Charlottenburg, Germany, for several months of work in Bothe's laboratory at the Physikalische-Technische Reichsanstalt. There I repeated, with greater precision and some improvements, Bothe and Kohlhörster's original experiment. The improvement consisted essentially in making a direct comparison of the coincidence rates recorded when an absorber

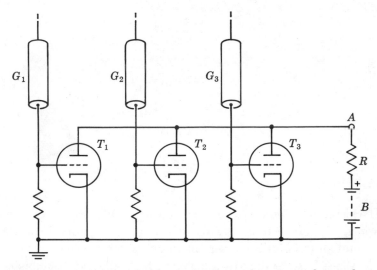

Fig. 4-1 Vacuum-tube coincidence circuit greatly reduces the number of chance coincidences recorded by G-M counters (see text). Under operating conditions, current flows from the positive terminal of the battery B through the resistor R and three tubes T_1, T_2, T_3 to a ground. This current produces a large voltage drop across the resistor, and at point A the potential is nearly that of the ground. When one of the G-M counters, G_1, say, is discharged, the grid of the corresponding tube T_1 becomes temporarily negative and the tube no longer conducts current, which, however, continues to flow through T_2 and T_3. If the resistor is sufficiently large, the current changes only slightly as a result. The simultaneous discharge of two G-M counters also fails to produce a significant change in the current. But if *all three counters* discharge simultaneously, then all three tubes become nonconducting, the current through R stops altogether, and the potential at A suddenly becomes equal to that of the positive battery terminal. This voltage jump at A thus signals the occurrence of a threefold coincidence; it can be detected by a voltmeter, or it can be made to operate a mechanical recording device. The circuit can be adapted to record coincidences involving any number of counters.

was above the counters with those recorded when the same absorber was between the counters.

Upon returning to Arcetri, I continued to experiment along similar lines. About these early experiments I shall say only that they strengthened my feeling of wonder, almost of awe, before the dimly perceived new facts that were beginning to emerge. I was convinced that cosmic rays would turn out to be something fundamentally different from the other known radiations, unless the properties of photons and charged particles changed drastically as their energies increased. This conviction was the motivation for two experiments I should like to describe here.

Cosmic-ray penetration of lead

Bothe and Kohlhörster had shown that a large fraction of the cosmic-ray particles found near sea level were capable of traversing 4.1 cm of gold, and my own work in Bothe's laboratory had confirmed their results. Curious to find out whether, perchance, a few of these particles might have enough energy to traverse much larger thicknesses of matter, say, 1 meter of lead, I arranged three G-M counters along a vertical line (Fig. 4–2). The total thickness of lead between the counters was initially 25 cm. By piling up a number of lead bricks, I could increase the absorber thickness to a total of 1 meter, and I found that 60 per cent of the cosmic-ray particles capable of traversing 25 cm of lead also traversed 1 meter of lead. Since 25 cm of lead absorbed less than half the radiation, not only a few (as I had thought) but a very sizable fraction of the cosmic-ray particles found near sea level had a range greater than 1 meter of lead.

Considering that the maximum range in lead of β rays from radioactive substances is only a fraction of a millimeter, one can easily appreciate the surprise caused by this result. In the first place, cosmic-ray particles, whatever their nature, had to be many orders of magnitude more energetic than β rays. In fact, they had to possess energies in the range of *billions* of electron volts. These energies were greater than any that could possibly be released in the synthesis of elements. And for many physicists it was a great disappointment when, in the face of the experimental evidence, they were forced to abandon Millikan's fascinating theory about the origin of cosmic rays. Moreover, the γ-ray hypothesis, already shaken by the work of Bothe and Kohlhörster, had received an even more serious blow.

Incidentally, some readers may wonder why three counters rather than two were employed in the experiment I have just described. The purpose of the third counter was to reduce the number of unwanted, chance coincidences, that is, coincidences caused by different particles crossing the counters almost simultaneously. An electronic coincidence device, Fig. 4–1, made it possible to cut down the number of chance coincidences considerably. Even so, with two counters more than 1 meter apart, the number of such events would have been greater than the number of true coincidences resulting from the passage of single cosmic-ray

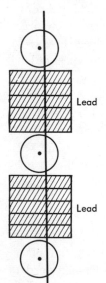

Lead

Lead

Fig. 4-2 Experimental arrangement used to demonstrate penetrating power of cosmic-ray particles. The number of lead bricks between counters can be varied to form an absorber as much as 1 meter thick. Only charged particles capable of traversing the absorber produce coincidences.

particles through both counters. With a third counter in between, the number of true coincidences remained unchanged, but the number of chance coincidences was drastically reduced.

Secondary effects of cosmic rays

The second experiment followed from observations that seemed to suggest that high-energy cosmic-ray particles occasionally produced secondary ionizing particles in matter. Perhaps the most significant observations were those made in 1929 by the Russian physicist D. Skobeltzyn. Working with a cloud chamber placed in a magnetic field, Skobeltzyn had photographed the tracks of unusually energetic negative particles passing through the chamber. The curvatures of the tracks (Chap. 5) indicated particle energies much greater than those of ordinary β rays. Skobeltzyn suggested that the tracks were probably left by electrons recoiling from Compton collisions with the hypothetical cosmic-ray photons.

Skobeltzyn also pointed out the occasional appearance, in his pictures of high-energy particles, of two and in one case, three tracks in the same picture. It was possible to explain the multiple tracks by assuming that a recoil electron had undergone one or more collisions somewhere near the cloud chamber and in these collisions had ejected secondary particles of sufficient energy to penetrate the chamber wall.

To investigate the suspected production of secondary particles by cosmic rays in matter, I placed three G-M counters in a triangular array (Fig. 4–3). The three counters could not be discharged by a single particle traveling in a straight line, and yet, when completely surrounded by lead, the array recorded a large number of coincidences (some thirty-five per hour). With the upper part of the lead shielding removed, the coincidence rate fell almost to zero. The coincidences could only have been the result of two or more ionizing particles emerging simultaneously from the lead, a direct proof that cosmic radiation did give rise to secondary ionizing rays. But even with the top lead removed, there was a small residual effect of roughly two coincidences per hour, which at the time I could not fully explain. It later turned out that this effect was due to the production of secondary rays in the atmosphere (see Chap. 12).

The unexpected finding was the great abundance of secondary rays, as evidenced by the high coincidence rate. In order to appreciate why this was a cause for surprise, one must recall the novelty of the result. The only known interaction of high-energy photons was the Compton effect. A Compton collision produces a single recoil electron, and therefore it could not account for the groups of particles found coming out of the lead absorber. The occurrence of two Compton collisions one next to the other and involving the same photon is such a rare phenomenon that it can be ignored altogether. Charged particles do knock electrons out of atoms — this, in fact, is the common ionization process; but these electrons ordinarily have a very small energy. Only on rare occasions is an electron ejected with sufficient energy to escape from the absorber.

Thus, nothing of what was known at the time could explain the abundant production of secondary particles revealed by the experiment. Actually, the results of this experiment appeared so incredible to the editors of the scientific journal to which I had

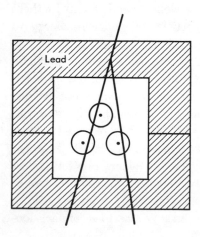

Fig. 4-3 Triangular array of G-M counters used in the first experiment demonstrating the production of secondary particles by cosmic rays. At least two charged particles emerging simultaneously from the lead are needed to produce a coincidence. One of them may be a primary particle, but the other must have been produced in the lead. (If the upper section of the lead shielding is removed, the coincidence rate falls nearly to zero.)

first submitted my paper that they refused to publish it. The paper was later accepted by another journal.

Cosmic-ray showers

But this was just the beginning, for it soon became clear that the interactions of cosmic radiation with matter give rise to effects far more complex and unusual than anyone had the right to infer from my counter experiments. The discovery of these complexities was the first result of a new experimental device that was to play a most important role in the history of cosmic rays: the counter-controlled cloud chamber.

The cloud chamber (see page 18), because it shows the tracks of charged particles, is really the ideal tool for finding out in detail what occurs in high-energy interactions. When applied to cosmic-ray phenomena, however, it has a serious drawback. The chamber must expand in order to become sensitive to the passage of an ionizing particle.[1] As I mentioned earlier, at each expansion the chamber is sensitive for approximately only 0.01 second. Cosmic-ray particles, on the other hand, arrive at the comparatively slow rate of about one per minute per square centimeter at sea level. Consequently, the probability of catching a cosmic-ray particle during the expansion phase (see page 19) is very small. Even smaller is the probability that this particle will do something of interest where the cloud chamber can "see" the results of the interaction.

Obviously, the yield of useful pictures would be increased enormously if the chamber expanded at the right time — immediately after a particle had passed through. It turns out that this timely expansion can be brought about by means of the coincidence technique. One can, for example, place single G-M counters above

[1] Some years after, in the late 1930s, cloud chambers capable of continuous operation (diffusion chambers) were developed. They had, however, a very limited application to cosmic-ray research.

and below the chamber, connect both counters to a coincidence circuit, and use the output signal of the circuit to operate a fast release mechanism (Fig. 4–4). More easily said than done, of course! The first counter-controlled chamber represented a major technical achievement. It was constructed in 1932 and 1933 at the Cavendish Laboratory of Cambridge University by P. M. S. Blackett and Giuseppe Occhialini. Blackett was already well known for his cloud-chamber studies of radioactivity. Occhialini, who had become familiar with the technique of G-M counters while working in Arcetri, was just beginning his scientific career.

The 1933 paper in which Blackett and Occhialini described their first observations with the counter-controlled chamber marked another milestone in the history of cosmic-ray research. I shall come back to it in a later chapter. Here I wish to mention only one result. A number of pictures showed the tracks of many particles that clearly resulted from the interaction of a single high-energy cosmic ray somewhere in the vicinity of the chamber (Fig. 4–5). These groups of particles, or *showers*, were unquestionably the cause of the coincidences between counters out of line that I had observed previously.

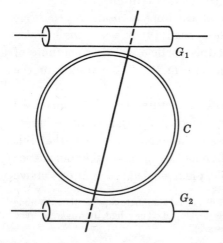

Fig. 4-4   Counter-controlled cloud chamber. A cosmic-ray particle passing through the two G-M counters G_1 and G_2 and through the cloud chamber C produces a coincidence. The signal pulse from the coincidence circuit promptly triggers the expansion of the chamber, before the ion pairs left by the particle have time to diffuse away. Vapor condensation around the ions produces a visible trail of droplets along the track of the particle.

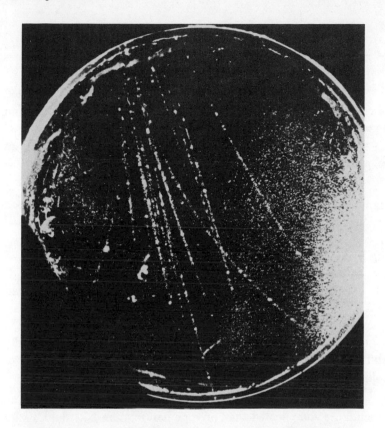

Fig. 4-5 Photograph obtained by Blackett and Occhialini with their counter-controlled cloud chamber. The chamber is situated between the poles of an electromagnet. Sixteen separate tracks of secondary particles enter the chamber simultaneously; they originate above the chamber, being produced, apparently, in the copper coils of the magnet (not shown in the picture). The curvature of the tracks is caused by the magnetic field; the tracks of positive particles curve to the right, the tracks of negative particles to the left. [From P. M. S. Blackett and Giuseppe Occhialini, *Proceedings of the Royal Society (London)*, vol. A139, p. 699, 1933.]

A summary

Let me summarize briefly what had been learned thus far:

    1. The γ-ray hypothesis had no experimental foundation.

    2. Much of the cosmic radiation found near sea level consisted of charged particles that possessed energies of 1 BeV or more and were capable of traversing very large thicknesses of matter.

    3. Cosmic rays frequently gave rise to very complex processes in which large numbers of secondary particles were generated.

The abundant production of secondary rays meant that a significant fraction of the particles observed near sea level had been produced in the atmosphere. At the time, many of us were inclined to consider the most penetrating particles (those capable of traveling large distances in lead) to be the real primary cosmic rays and the "softer" particles (those absorbed by a few centimeters of lead) to be secondary in origin. However, we clearly realized the possibility that only a few — and perhaps none — of the primary particles might be able to penetrate any great distance through the atmosphere without undergoing collisions. In that case practically all the particles found near sea level would be secondary products of collisions.

The problem of the nature of cosmic rays, which was becoming much more complicated than anyone had imagined it could, really involved two different questions:

    1. What was the nature of the *primary radiation* falling on the atmosphere from outer space?

    2. What was the composition of the *local radiation* observed in the atmosphere?

Even if all primary rays were of the same kind, it was clear that the local radiation, much of which was secondary in origin, was likely to be quite complex. Indeed, in the next two decades it was to be found that the local radiation contained not only all the radiations previously known, and several kinds of rays that theorists were to dream about, but many others as well.

Using the earth as a magnet to analyze cosmic rays

5

Cosmic-ray research had begun with the balloon flights of Hess and Kohlhörster. As the years went by, physicists studied cosmic rays at higher and higher altitudes. Sounding balloons, as we have seen, replaced manned balloons; later, sounding rockets were used. In recent years, artificial satellites and space probes have taken counters and other recording devices clear of the atmosphere and sometimes millions of miles into interplanetary space. But by the time physicists had arrived at the stage where their instruments were making direct observations of primary cosmic rays, they already knew a great deal about these rays. They had obtained much of their information by means of the earth's magnetic field.

The magnetic field surrounding the earth resembles the field of a magnetic dipole — the field that would be produced by a bar magnet short in comparison with the radius of the earth — located

near the earth's center and with its north pole toward the geographic south and its south pole toward the geographic north.
More precisely, the center of the terrestrial magnetic dipole is displaced about 200 miles from the center of the earth, and its axis
lies at an angle of about 11° from the geographic axis (Fig. 5–1.)
The field itself extends far beyond the reaches of the atmosphere.
At an altitude of 1,000 miles its strength is still about one-half the
field strength at the earth's surface. By contrast, the remaining air
mass above 20 miles constitutes less than 1 per cent of the total
atmosphere.

Thus, the primary cosmic rays encounter the magnetic field
well before they have a chance to collide with the molecules of the

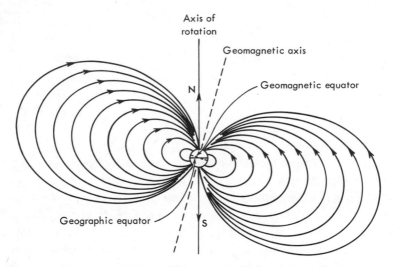

Fig. 5-1 The magnetic field of the earth resembles the field that would be
produced by a relatively short bar magnet (or dipole) located near the center
of the earth. Such a field is nonuniform, that is, the magnetic lines of force are
curved and the field strength varies from point to point, decreasing with increasing distance from the center of the dipole. For a given distance the field
strength is greatest at the poles and weakest at the geomagnetic equator. The
axis of the earth's dipole (geomagnetic axis) lies at an angle of 11° from the
earth's axis of rotation. The midpoint of the dipole does not coincide exactly
with the center of the earth.

atmosphere. If the primary rays are electrically charged particles, they will be deflected by the earth's field in one direction or the other depending on whether their charge is positive or negative. If they are neutral particles or photons, they will pass through the field undeflected. And although the earth's magnetic field is much weaker than the fields produced by laboratory electromagnets, its enormous extent more than makes up for its weakness. Hence, large deflections are to be expected even for charged primary particles of very great energy.

Magnetic rigidity

To make the discussion in this chapter more precise, it will be useful to review very briefly some of the basic facts concerning the motion of charged particles in magnetic fields. A moving charged particle in a magnetic field experiences a deflecting force that acts at right angles to both the magnetic field and the direction of motion. If the field is uniform and perpendicular to the direction of motion, this continuous sideways thrust[1] causes the particle to move in a circle (Fig. 5–2). Now for particles of a given charge, the radius R of this circle is inversely proportional to the magnetic field strength B and directly proportional to the momentum of the particle.[2]

In other words, the product BR (magnetic field times radius) is directly proportional to the momentum. For particles of the same momentum but with different amounts of charge, on the other hand, the product BR is inversely proportional to the charge. A multicharged particle experiences a stronger side thrust than a singly charged particle, and its trajectory is therefore deflected into a circle of smaller radius.

The product BR is known as the *magnetic rigidity* of the particle. The usual unit for measuring magnetic fields is the *gauss;*

[1] Generally called the *Lorentz force* in physics, after the Dutch physicist Hendrik Lorentz.
[2] See Appendix F.

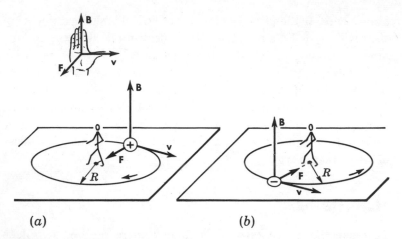

(a)   (b)

Fig. 5-2 The deflecting force experienced by a positively charged particle moving through a uniform magnetic field causes the particle to travel in a circle. The direction of the force is given by the following right-hand rule: If the fingers of the right hand point in the direction of the field **B** and the thumb points in the direction of particle motion **v**, the force **F** points out of the palm. Since the deflecting force must be directed toward the center of the circle to counteract the centrifugal force, a positively charged particle must move *clockwise* with respect to an observer lined up with the magnetic field (*a*). For the same directions of **B**, the deflecting force experienced by a negatively charged particle is directed toward the center when the particle moves *counterclockwise* (*b*). For any given set of conditions, reversal of the field, charge, or direction of motion reverses the direction of the force. Also, the radius of the circle describing the motion of the particle decreases as the momentum of the particle decreases and as the strength of the magnetic field increases.

the earth's magnetic field is a few tenths of a gauss at sea level; strong electromagnets produce fields of the order of 10^4 gauss. If B is measured in gauss and R in centimeters, the magnetic rigidity BR is measured in gauss·cm. The plot in Fig. 5–3 shows the magnetic rigidity of electrons and protons as a function of their kinetic energy. Note that for sufficiently large values the kinetic energy, in electron volts, is simply 300 times the rigidity:

E (eV) = 300 BR (gauss·cm)

This equation holds, in fact, for all singly charged particles whose kinetic energy is large compared to their rest energy; the factor 300 depends on the particular choice of units.[1] For a high-energy particle with Z elementary charges, however, the magnetic rigidity is Z times smaller than for a singly charged particle of the same energy. In this case the relation between energy and magnetic rigidity is

$$E/Z = 300 \, BR$$

Returning to the question of how the earth's magnetic field affects the motion of charged particles, consider a particle that,

[1] See Appendix F.

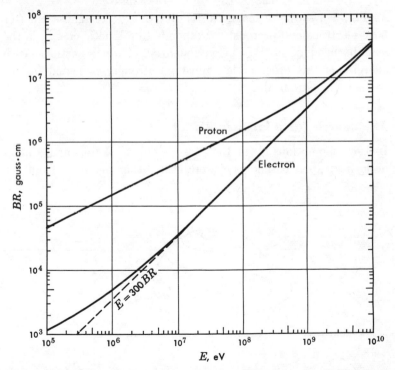

Fig. 5-3   Magnetic rigidity BR as a function of kinetic energy E for protons and electrons. Both E and BR are plotted on a logarithmic scale. For sufficiently large energies both curves approach the straight line representing the equation $E = 300 \, BR$.

under the action of this field, circles the earth at the geomagnetic equator. (Here we disregard energy losses in the atmosphere.) In the first place, to keep the particle in this particular orbit, the force exerted by the magnetic field must point toward the center of the earth. From the rule for determining the direction of the force (Fig. 5–2) it is clear that the particle must move from east to west if it is positive and from west to east if it is negative (Fig. 5–4). In the second place, the magnetic rigidity of the particle must equal the product of the radius of the earth ($R = 6.38 \times 10^8$ cm) and the field strength at the equator ($B = 0.32$ gauss):

$$BR = 0.32 \times 6.38 \times 10^8 = 2 \times 10^8 \text{ gauss} \cdot \text{cm}$$

As Fig. 5–3 shows, a magnetic rigidity of 2×10^8 gauss·cm (for both electrons and protons) corresponds to a kinetic energy in the neighborhood of 60 BeV. Consequently, charged particles with energies of this order or less must be strongly deflected by the earth's magnetic field.

The search for a latitude effect

In 1930 the notions about the possible effects of the earth's magnetic field upon cosmic rays were still rather nebulous from the

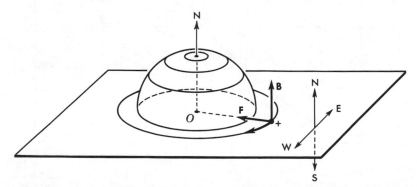

Fig. 5-4 A positively charged particle circling the earth under the influence of the earth's magnetic field moves from east to west. The magnetic field **B** points toward the geomagnetic north pole, and the deflecting force **F** toward the center O of the earth.

point of view of both theory and experiment. It was thought that if primary cosmic rays were electrically charged, they would somehow be channeled toward the poles along the magnetic lines of force. At high latitudes, then, the cosmic-ray intensity should be greater than in the equatorial regions. In 1927 the Dutch physicist J. Clay had measured the cosmic-ray intensity, by using an ionization chamber, on a trip from Leiden to Java and had found a decrease of several per cent in the vicinity of the Suez Canal. On the other hand, Millikan and his associates in 1928 had not discovered any significant change between Bolivia (19° S latitude) and Pasadena, California (34° N latitude). In 1930 Millikan again found practically no change between Pasadena and Churchill, Canada (59° N latitude). That same year, Bothe and Kohlhörster failed to detect any variation with latitude in the North Sea and the Swedish physicist Axel Corlin thought he had detected a slight latitude effect in the Baltic Sea.

Needless to say, the existence of a latitude effect seemed very doubtful. In any case the effect, if present at all, was small and could not be ascribed with any confidence to the earth's magnetic field. It was argued, with good reason, that the different conditions of the earth's atmosphere at different geographic locations could of themselves produce significant changes in the cosmic-ray intensity at sea level. To Millikan and his collaborators, the absence of a large latitude effect was proof that primary cosmic rays were *not* electrically charged.

Theory of geomagnetic effects

Much of the theoretical background for the correct treatment of the effects I have been discussing was already available at the time. The Norwegian geophysicist Carl Störmer, in an effort to explain those striking luminous displays of the upper atmosphere known as northern lights or aurorae, had made a detailed study of the motion of charged particles in the magnetic field of a dipole, to which, as I

mentioned above, the magnetic field of the earth bears a close
resemblance. Störmer believed aurorae were caused by charged
particles coming from the sun at times of increased solar activity.
From painstaking numerical calculations over a period of years, he
had derived a large number of possible trajectories for these particles. More importantly, he had also established some of the
general characteristics of the trajectories.

Although Störmer's basic assumption was correct, his theory
proved inadequate. One of the reasons is that auroral particles have
comparatively small energies and are therefore strongly influenced
by the weak magnetic and electric fields present in interplanetary
space, fields that were still unknown when Störmer was developing
his theory. (Present understanding of conditions prevailing in
interplanetary space indicates that aurorae are much more complex
phenomena than Störmer had any ground to suppose, phenomena
so complex in fact, that they have resisted all attempts at detailed
explanation; see Chap. 14.)

Cosmic-ray particles, on the other hand, have far greater
energies than auroral particles. No valid reason exists today — any
more than one existed some thirty years ago — for doubting that
their trajectories closely resemble those computed by Störmer.
Thus Störmer's theory, developed originally for a different purpose,
found its most useful application in cosmic-ray studies. This application was not immediate, however, because the step from the
problem of aurorae to the problem of cosmic rays was not an
obvious one.

Störmer, as I said, had computed the trajectories of particles
with different magnetic rigidities approaching the earth from a
definite direction, that of the sun. His aim was to discover over
which areas of the earth, and in which directions, these particles
entered the atmosphere. But cosmic rays were known to come from
all directions. A study of their geomagnetic effects by a similar
method would have required the computation of a far greater
number of trajectories. This was nearly impossible, especially before the invention of electronic computers.

I became personally interested in geomagnetic effects in 1930. While studying the papers of Störmer, I realized that if one would only ask the right questions, one could readily obtain from Störmer's work answers that went a long way toward a solution of the problems of concern to cosmic-ray physicists. Let me explain.

To formulate the questions correctly one ought, in the first place, to look backward rather than forward in time. Instead of following a hypothetical charged particle of given rigidity in its motion from outer space toward the earth, it was easier to consider a hypothetical particle arriving at a given point P near the earth's surface in a given direction (Fig. 5-5) and then to follow its trajectory in reverse through the earth's magnetic field.

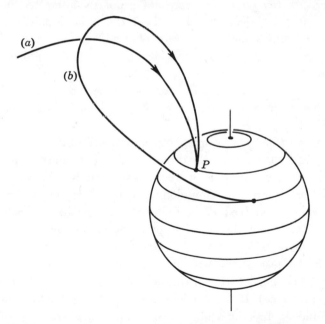

Fig. 5-5 Trajectories of two hypothetical particles of different magnetic rigidity arriving at the same point P from the same direction (schematic). Trajectory a, when traced backward, escapes to infinity; it is an *allowed* trajectory. Trajectory b, when traced backward, returns to the earth; it is a *forbidden* trajectory.

Two possibilities existed. Either the trajectory, when traced backward, would escape from the neighborhood of the earth without ever crossing the earth's surface or it would come back to the earth. In the first instance, the hypothetical particle could have come from outer space and thus might have been a cosmic-ray particle. In other words, the given direction at P was an *allowed* direction of arrival for cosmic-ray particles of the specified magnetic rigidity. In the second case, the hypothetical particle could not have come from outer space, and thus was certainly not a cosmic-ray particle. In other words, the given direction at P was a *forbidden* direction of arrival for cosmic-ray particles of the specified magnetic rigidity.

Cosmic-ray physicists were not primarily interested in computing actual trajectories. For them the basic problem was to determine which directions were allowed and which forbidden. And here Störmer's theory provided a major break. Störmer had shown that there exists a special class of trajectories (*bounded* trajectories) that remain forever in the vicinity of the dipole. Bounded trajectories are certainly not possible trajectories of cosmic-ray particles.

Störmer had also worked out a simple formula by means of which, from the position, the direction of motion, and the magnetic rigidity of a given particle, it was possible to determine whether or not the particle was moving along a bounded trajectory. By using this formula, I arrived at the following conclusion: For each point on the earth and for positive particles of any given magnetic rigidity there exists a cone (*Störmer cone*), with the axis pointing toward the east, such that all directions within the cone correspond to bounded trajectories and are therefore forbidden directions (Fig. 5–6a). If the particles are negative instead of positive, the forbidden directions fill a Störmer cone that is the mirror image of the first with respect to the meridian plane (that is, the vertical plane on the "north-south line"; see Fig. 5–6b).

The graphs in Fig. 5–7 show how the half angle of the Störmer cone (angle α in Fig. 5–6a and b) varies with magnetic rigidity at different geomagnetic latitudes. For example, at $\lambda = 20°$, α becomes 180° for $BR = 2.8 \times 10^7$ gauss·cm, which means that all directions are forbidden for particles with rigidity equal to or less than 2.8×10^7 gauss·cm. The half angle becomes 0° for $BR = 7.8 \times 10^7$ gauss·cm, which means that, for particles with a rigidity greater than this value, the Störmer cone *disappears* (in other words, there

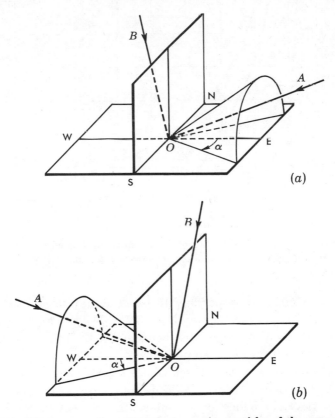

(a)

(b)

Fig 5-6 Störmer cones for positive and negative particles of the same magnetic rigidity. The plane shown in (a) and (b) is the horizontal plane at the point of observation O. For positive particles (a), all directions east of the cone (such as AO) are forbidden; directions west of the cone (such as BO) may be allowed. For negative particles (b), AO is a forbidden direction; BO may be an allowed direction. Angle α is the half angle of aperture of the cones.

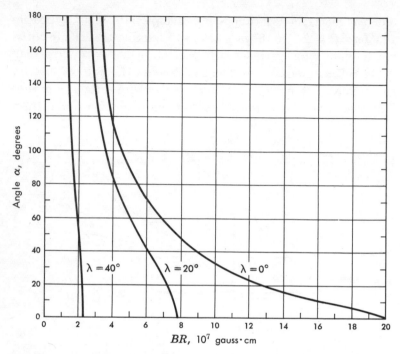

Fig. 5-7   Semiaperture of the Störmer cone (angle α in Fig. 5-6) as a function of magnetic rigidity BR, in units of 10^7 gauss·cm, for different geomagnetic latitudes λ.

are no directions corresponding to bounded trajectories). At the same latitude, $\alpha = 90°$ for $BR = 3.9 \times 10^7$ gauss·cm, which means that for this rigidity the boundary of the Störmer cone is coincident with the meridian plane.

These results were not yet complete. Although they stated that all directions within the Störmer cone correspond to bounded trajectories and are therefore forbidden, they did not specify which directions outside the cone are allowed. For, although directions outside the cone correspond to "unbounded" trajectories, some of these trajectories, when traced backward, may still cross the earth before escaping into space. Nor was it clear how the cosmic-ray intensities in the allowed directions varied with respect to one another.

Nevertheless, it was already possible to draw some interesting conclusions. By far the most important one was the prediction of an asymmetry in the intensity distribution of cosmic rays. Indeed, since in the case of positive particles the forbidden Störmer cones point toward the east, positively charged primary cosmic rays should arrive in smaller numbers from the eastern than from the western regions of the sky. But if primary cosmic rays are negatively charged, the Störmer cones point to the west, and the situation is reversed. This predicted asymmetry became known as the *east-west effect*.

It may be useful, as an illustration of these general results, to consider in detail the special case of trajectories in the plane of the geomagnetic equator. These are particularly simple trajectories, since they are the only ones that remain forever in one plane. Several equatorial trajectories, all corresponding to particles with a magnetic rigidity of 7×10^7 gauss·cm, are shown in Fig. 5–8a and b [positive in (a), negative in (b)]. They are drawn through the same point on the geomagnetic equator of the earth. In Fig. 5–8a all trajectories striking the earth from directions east of the dotted line cross the earth's surface over and over again; they are forbidden trajectories, and in fact they are *bounded* trajectories. On the other hand, all trajectories striking the earth from directions west of the dotted line, when traced backward, go directly to infinity and are therefore allowed directions. The dotted line itself is the intersection of the Störmer cone with the equatorial plane. Figure 5–8b is the mirror image of Fig. 5–8a.

The questions left open by this analysis still concerned me. I discussed the problem with Enrico Fermi, who pointed out that at least one of the gaps could be easily filled. By using a general theorem of mechanics known as the Liouville theorem, he proved to me that, since cosmic rays were supposed to be distributed uniformly in all directions at large distances from the earth, their intensity near the earth should be the same in all allowed directions. Thus the only remaining problem was to find out which of the directions outside the Störmer cone were allowed and which forbidden.

This problem was attacked with great vigor in the following years, particularly by Georges E. Lemaitre of Belgium, Manuel S. Vallarta of Mexico, and their students. In their work these scientists used a mechanical computer, known as the differential analyzer, that was developed by Vannevar Bush at the Massachusetts Institute of Technology. They did find that some of the directions outside the Störmer cone were forbidden. In most cases, the corresponding trajectories were not bounded but, when traced backward, crossed the earth before going to infinity.

To relate in detail the results of these studies would take the discussion too far afield, but one of the most significant findings

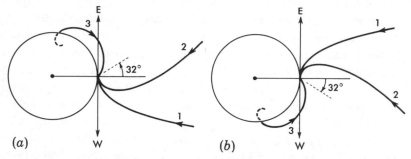

Fig. 5-8 Trajectories of positively charged particles (*a*) and of negatively charged particles (*b*) in the plane of the geomagnetic equator. [The magnetic field points out of the drawing. According to the right-hand rule (Fig. 5-2), the trajectories must curve in the directions shown.] In both cases the magnetic rigidity is 7×10^7 gauss·cm. For this magnetic rigidity there are positive particles coming from infinity and striking the earth from all directions between 32° E and 90° W of the vertical (examples 1 and 2 in illustration). However, in order to strike the earth from a direction at more than 32° E of the vertical, a particle would have to come from some point on the earth's surface [example 3 in (*a*)]. Thus, 1 and 2 are examples of allowed trajectories, 3 is an example of forbidden trajectory, and it follows that positive particles arrive more abundantly from the western than from the eastern regions of the sky. Another way of clarifying the east-west effect is to consider particles, such as 2, that approach the earth from the east but are then deflected by the magnetic field so that when they actually strike the earth, they appear to come from the west. (The same considerations, with the directions east and west interchanged, apply to negative particles.)

appears in Fig. 5–9. Each curve in the figure describes the effect of the magnetic field on the total flux at the top of the atmosphere of primary particles of specified rigidity. These curves afford quantitative predictions about the latitude effect of cosmic-ray particles with different magnetic rigidities. They show, for example, that particles with a magnetic rigidity of 3.2×10^7 gauss·cm are

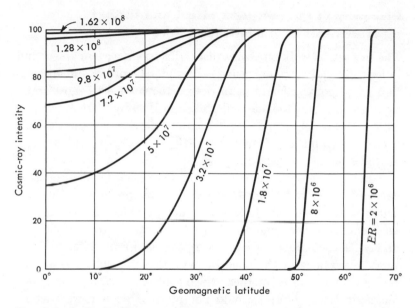

Fig. 5-9 Latitude effect on cosmic-ray intensity, according to the theoretical studies of Lemaitre and Vallarta. Each curve refers to particles of a particular magnetic rigidity, and gives the total number of such particles reaching the top of the atmosphere as a function of geomagnetic latitude. The particles are assumed to approach the earth in equal numbers from all directions. The number of particles of each magnetic rigidity that would strike the atmosphere if there were no magnetic field is arbitrarily taken to be 100. Cosmic-ray particles with a magnetic rigidity of 3.2×10^7 gauss·cm are completely excluded from an equatorial belt extending from about 12° N to 12° S geomagnetic latitude. The maximum number (100) arrive at latitudes greater than about 43° N and S. At a latitude of 32° N and S the magnetic field reduces the intensity by approximately one-half. (From a paper in *The Physical Review*, vol. 43, p. 87, 1933.)

completely excluded from an equatorial belt extending from about 12° N to 12° S geomagnetic latitude; that the flux of these particles increases gradually between 12° and 43°, north and south; and that above 43° it reaches a constant value equal to the flux that would be observed in the absence of any magnetic field.

Discovery of the east-west effect and further measurements of the latitude effect

The theoretical work on geomagnetic effects was accompanied, and indeed stimulated, by extensive experimental work in which scientists from many different countries participated. The most ambitious program was the one undertaken in 1930 by A. H. Compton, who, with the help of many collaborators, carried out a world-wide survey of cosmic-ray intensities both at sea level and at high altitudes on mountains.

For my own part, I concentrated my efforts on the east-west effect. There were two main reasons for this preference. One was that the east-west effect, to my mind, provided a surer test of magnetic influence than the latitude effect, because it did not involve a comparison of cosmic-ray intensities at different locations. Variations in the conditions of the atmosphere from one region of the earth to another, which could conceivably simulate a magnetic latitude effect, could not produce an east-west asymmetry. The second reason, of course, was that if cosmic rays were electrically charged, the east-west effect would also reveal the sign of the charge.

In 1931, at the Arcetri laboratory, I made my first attempt to detect an east-west effect. The type of instrument I used for this purpose later became known as the *cosmic-ray telescope*. This instrument consists simply of two or more G-M counters in coincidence arranged with their centers on a straight line called the *axis* (Fig. 5–10). Only particles coming from directions near the axis can traverse all counters and thereby produce simultaneous discharges, or coincidences. By changing the orientation of the telescope, it then becomes possible to compare the numbers of cosmic-ray particles arriving from different directions. The *field of view* of the telescope depends, of course, on the size and separation of the counters. Figure 5–10*a* shows a telescope with a wide field of view; Fig. 5–10*b*, a telescope with a narrow field of view. In the experiment, I pointed the G-M telescope alternately to the east and to the west of the geomagnetic meridian (Fig. 5–11), but I was unable to detect any significant difference between the counting rates recorded in the two directions. Then in 1933, as the first concrete evidence for the existence of a latitude effect was beginning to appear, with some indication that the effect might be caused by the earth's magnetic field rather than by meteorological factors, the east-west effect was discovered in three separate experiments. Thomas H. Johnson, working in Mexico City (29° N geomagnetic latitude, 2,250 meters above sea level), and Luis W. Alvarez in collaboration with Compton, working at the same location, found the intensity of cosmic rays to be greater from the west than from the east. The difference was approximately 10 per cent with the

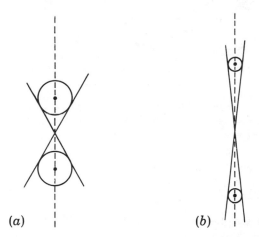

(*a*)   (*b*)

Fig. 5-10 Geiger-Müller telescopes consisting of two G-M counters in coincidence. (*a*) A telescope with a wide field of view; (*b*) a telescope with a narrow field of view. The dotted line through the centers is the *axis* of the telescope.

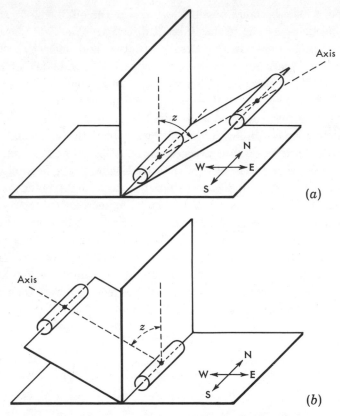

Fig. 5-11 Experimental study of the east-west effect: a cosmic-ray telescope pointing (a) to the east and (b) to the west of the geomagnetic meridian. In both cases, the telescope is inclined at the same angle z from the vertical.

cosmic-ray telescope set at an angle of 45° to the vertical. A few months later Sergio De Benedetti and I, working in Asmara, Eritrea (11° N geomagnetic latitude, 2,370 meters above sea level), found an excess of 26 per cent in the west direction, again with the telescope set at 45° to the vertical.

It was thus clear that a portion, possibly all, of the primary cosmic radiation consisted of positively charged particles. This was a most unexpected result, for the common belief among proponents of the corpuscular hypothesis had been that the primary cosmic radiation consisted of electrons. Had the east-west effect been discovered one year earlier, we would have concluded that cosmic rays must be protons or heavier nuclei, since these were the only positively charged particles known at that time. And it so happens we would have been right. But in 1932 a new positive particle had been discovered — the *positive electron* or *positron* (Chap. 6). Thus we had to leave the question of the nature of primary cosmic rays in abeyance until new evidence developed.

In the following years a wealth of experimental data on the east-west effect, and particularly on the latitude effect, became available. In 1936 Compton summarized the existing information in the form of a graph, which is reproduced in Fig. 5–12. The curves in the graph are lines of equal cosmic-ray intensity, or *isocosms*, as Compton called them. The same graph also shows the geomagnetic equator and the geomagnetic parallels at 50° N and 50° S. As the figure makes evident, the isocosms follow geomagnetic parallels more closely than they do geographic parallels. This fact supported the view that the intensity variations of cosmic radiation over the earth's surface were due primarily to the terrestrial magnetic field rather than to atmospheric factors.

The possibility of some atmospheric influence, however, could not be ruled out. Indeed, in 1937 Compton and his collaborators obtained positive evidence of a slight decrease in the intensity of cosmic rays at sea level as the temperature of the atmosphere increased. Since the average temperature of the atmosphere is greater near the equator than near the poles, this temperature variation tended to produce an apparent latitude effect. Precise measurements showed that about one-third of the latitude effect found at sea level was actually due to the temperature variation; the earth's magnetic field accounted for about two-thirds of the total effect.

But the intensity of cosmic radiation varies not only with latitude but also with longitude, as Compton's graph shows (Fig. 5–12). For example, the intensity along the geomagnetic equator

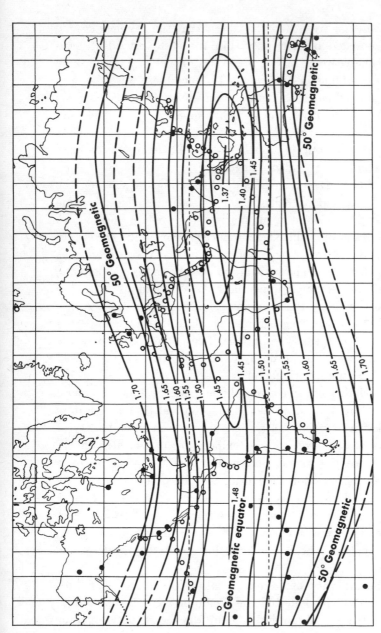

Fig. 5-12 Isocosms, or curves of equal cosmic-ray intensity, according to A. H. Compton. The numbers on the curves give the intensity of the cosmic radiation level, as measured by the number of ion pairs they produce in 1 cm³ of air at standard temperature and pressure. Dots show locations where measurements were made. The graph also shows the geomagnetic equator and two geomagnetic parallels (50° N and S). (From a paper in *Review of Scientific Instruments*, vol. 7, p. 70, 1936.)

falls to a minimum in the Indian Ocean. This observation, too, fits the picture. As I mentioned at the beginning of this chapter, the center of the earth's magnetic dipole does not coincide exactly with the geographic center. It is displaced toward the Indian Ocean, so that the magnetic field there is stronger and produces a more pronounced decrease in the cosmic-ray intensity.

The effect of the atmosphere

Thus far, I have ignored the atmosphere, and the time has come to inquire how its presence might affect our discussion. As I pointed out in the preceding chapter, at the time when the investigations related here were made, there were already good reasons for believing that the local radiation observed in the atmosphere consisted largely of secondary particles. What, then, was our justification for interpreting the observations on the basis of a theory that actually applied to the primary radiation arriving at the top of the atmosphere from outer space?

With regard to the latitude effect the answer was clear. Since the number of secondary particles observed under the atmospheric blanket would increase or decrease as the number of primary rays falling upon the atmosphere increased or decreased, secondary rays would exhibit a latitude effect similar to that of the primary rays. The effect would not, however, be quite as pronounced, because the primary particles that show the largest latitude variations are those of lowest energy, and these are likely to produce fewer secondary particles in the atmosphere.

In this connection, it is interesting to consider the measurements at high altitudes on mountains and by means of balloon that were made in the early 1930s by the teams working with Compton and with Millikan. These measurements showed that the latitude effect became more pronounced as the altitude increased (Fig. 5–13). This result was easy to account for. Under a smaller atmospheric thickness (that is, at high altitudes) the electroscopes or the G-M counters could detect (either directly or through their secondary rays) primary particles of lower energy, which were more strongly influenced by the earth's magnetic field.

The interpretation of the east-west effect, on the other hand, involved different considerations. If the particles produced in the collisions of primary rays with atoms and molecules went off at wide angles to the primary direction, the secondary radiation in the atmosphere would be distributed more or less uniformly in all directions, irrespective of the direction from which the primary radiation came. In that case, we could hope to observe an east-west effect only by sending our instruments clear of the atmosphere, where the primary cosmic radiation arrived undisturbed. Nonetheless, we had detected an east-west effect under a considerable atmospheric thickness, where presumably most of the observed rays were secondary. Thus we concluded that the secondary rays produced in the atmosphere must be strongly "lined up" in the direction of the primary radiation.

This conclusion received support from another experimental observation. Measurements with the cosmic-ray telescope revealed a sharp maximum of intensity in the local radiation when the telescope was pointed straight up. The maximum could be explained as an effect of atmospheric absorption, because the radiation traversing the atmosphere vertically passed through a smaller amount of matter than the radiation traversing the atmosphere in any other direction. Such an explanation, however, would hold true only if the secondary rays traveled in more or less the same direction as the primary rays that produced them.

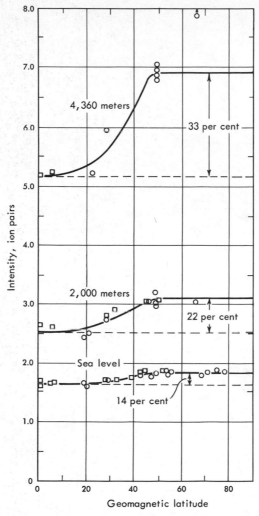

Fig. 5-13 Cosmic-ray intensity as a function of geomagnetic latitude at three different altitudes. The intensity is measured by the number of ion pairs produced by cosmic rays in 1 cm³ of air at normal temperature and pressure. (From A. H. Compton, *The Physical Review*, vol. 43, p. 387, 1933.)

Positrons and the materialization of energy

6

Through the years cosmic-ray physicists have been faced with two distinct but closely related problems. The first, of course, concerns the nature of cosmic rays. The second is: What kinds of particles exist in nature, and how do particles of very high energy behave? It would have been comparatively easy for the physicists to solve the first problem if they had known the answer to the second, and vice versa. What made life difficult was the unavoidable necessity of having to deal with both problems simultaneously. The story to be told in this and the next several chapters is a fine example of an enterprise in which skillful experimentation, bold and critical reasoning in the interpretation of experimental results, and imaginative theoretical thinking were brought to bear upon a most intricate scientific task. The successful conclusion of these efforts brought not only an answer to the cosmic-ray puzzle but also a dramatic advance over a wide front of physics.

The story begins with the local cosmic radiation. In the experiments of Bothe and Kohlhörster the coincidence rate had dropped 24 per cent when 4.1 cm of gold was placed between the counters. On the other hand, my own experiments had shown that, after passing through some thicknesses of lead, cosmic-ray particles became much "harder" and that a large proportion of them were capable of traversing lead thicknesses of the order of meters. Other measurements confirmed these results (Fig. 6–1). Therefore, the local cosmic radiation contained two distinct groups of particles: a "soft" group, responsible for the initial fast drop in the absorption curve of Fig. 6–1, and a "penetrating" group, responsible for the flat "tail" of the curve.

Moreover, as we had learned, at least some of the cosmic-ray particles produced the complex secondary processes called showers. However, we had not yet found out what the various kinds of secondary particles were. As for the showers, they were thought to result from the disintegration of atomic nuclei, but this assumption remained to be tested.

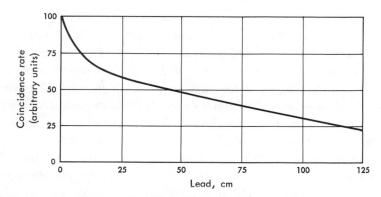

Fig. 6-1 Soft and penetrating groups of cosmic-ray particles (at sea level) account respectively for the sharp initial drop and the flatter tail of the absorption curve (see text). The horizontal scale gives the total thickness of the lead absorber between counters. The vertical scale gives the coincidence rate, in arbitrary units. The curve represents data obtained from experiments performed by the author in 1932.

The discovery of the positron

Even before the discovery of showers, Carl D. Anderson, in Millikan's laboratory at the California Institute of Technology, had started an experimental program that, together with the one begun a little later by Blackett and Occhialini, was to provide a partial answer to our questions. The major result of this work was the discovery of the *positive electron*, or *positron*, and of the strange circumstances attending its birth and its disappearance.

In his experiments Anderson used a cloud chamber placed in the field of a powerful electromagnet. At a maximum field strength of 24,000 gauss he was able to measure the magnetic deflection of tracks whose radius of curvature was as great as 7 meters and whose magnetic rigidity was therefore roughly 1.7×10^7 gauss·cm (that is, 24,000 gauss $\times$ 700 cm). The corresponding kinetic energies — about 5 BeV for particles with the mass of an electron and about 4 BeV for particles with the mass of a proton (Fig. 5–3) — were several hundred times greater than any energy that previous instruments had been capable of measuring. It soon became apparent that the particles of the local cosmic radiation had a wide range of energies extending well beyond 1 BeV. In addition, about half their trajectories bent to the right and half to the left. Assuming the direction of travel to be downward in every case, Anderson concluded that positively and negatively charged particles were about equally abundant in the local cosmic radiation.

At first Anderson thought the negative particles were electrons and the positive particles protons. As the experimental data became more precise, however, he was obliged to abandon this interpretation; for the cloud chamber also made it possible to estimate the ionizing power of the particles from the number of droplets along their tracks. Now, the ionizing power decreases with increasing velocity (Chap. 2). For a given magnetic rigidity, the velocity of a lighter particle is greater than that of a heavier particle. Therefore, the lighter particle has a smaller ionizing effect.

To illustrate this point, the graph in Fig. 6–2 gives the ion density as a function of rigidity for electrons and protons. The curves (similar to the ones in Fig. 2–2, which give ion density as a function of kinetic energy) show that electrons and protons with sufficiently small magnetic rigidities produce very different densities of ionization. Consequently, if Anderson's positive particles were protons, their tracks should have been denser than the tracks of the negative particles.

Contrary to expectation, the ionization densities were practically the same, even for magnetic rigidities in the range below 10^6 gauss·cm, where protons would have ionized at least six times more heavily than electrons. It was tempting to accept these results as evidence for the existence of a hitherto unknown particle with a positive elementary charge and a mass close to that of the electron. But that was such a daring conclusion that all possible sources of error had to be critically examined. Hence, Anderson gave serious consideration to the possibility that the particles he thought were positive particles moving downward might, in reality, be negative electrons moving upward. To test this alternative explanation, Anderson partitioned his cloud chamber into an upper and lower section by means of a lead plate. A particle traversing the plate would suffer an energy loss and thus emerge with a correspondingly reduced rigidity, thereby disclosing its direction of motion.

The results obtained with the new arrangement revealed particles moving upward as well as downward, fully justifying Anderson's misgivings. However, as the cloud chamber photographs also proved beyond any doubt, some of the positive particles had nearly the same mass as the electron.[1] Curiously enough, the most convincing evidence came from the picture of a positive particle moving *upward;* in the absence of the lead plate, it would undoubtedly have been mistaken for an ordinary negative electron

---

[1] Accurate measurements of the radii of curvature and the ion densities of a number of tracks enabled Anderson to make a fairly precise estimate of the mass. According to his results, this mass did not differ by more than 20 per cent from that of the ordinary negative electron.

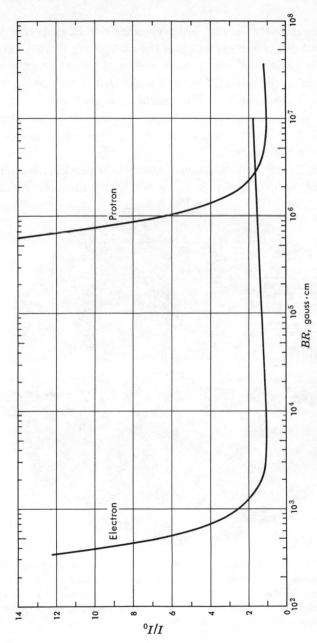

Fig. 6-2 Ion density as a function of magnetic rigidity BR for electrons and protons. The ion density I is given in multiples of the density produced by a minimum-ionizing particle I_0.

moving downward! (See Fig. 6–3.) The direction of motion of the particle is obvious from the fact that the portion of the track above the plate has a considerably smaller radius of curvature than the portion below the plate. The magnetic deflection indicates a positively charged particle. The magnetic rigidity changes from 2.1×10^5 gauss·cm to 7.6×10^4 gauss·cm as the particle traverses the plate, and the ionization density appears to be about minimum on either side.

All these results are easily understood if the particle has a mass close to that of an electron. But a proton with a magnetic rigidity

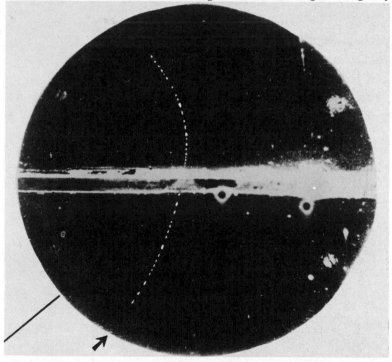

Fig. 6-3   The positron, or positive electron, was identified as the particle that entered the cloud chamber from below and produced the track curving sharply to the left after traversing the lead plate. The photograph, taken by Anderson in 1932, definitely established the existence of positrons. (From a paper in *The Physical Review*, vol. 43, p. 491, 1933.)

of 7.6 × 10⁴ gauss·cm would produce a density of ionization much greater than the density observed. Moreover, it would have a range of only 5 mm in the gas of the chamber, whereas the observed length of the track is more than 50 cm.

Dirac's theory and the origin of positrons

At the time of Anderson's work in the United States, Blackett and Occhialini, in England, were carrying out their experiments with the counter-controlled cloud chamber. These experiments, besides revealing the great complexity of cosmic-ray interactions, produced other results of crucial importance. In the first place, Blackett and Occhialini were able to confirm Anderson's discovery of the positron, announced a few months earlier. In the second place, they found that all shower particles deflected by the comparatively weak magnetic fields used in their experiments (usually from 2,000 to 3,000 gauss) were either negative or positive electrons. And, in some showers at least, the numbers of positive and negative particles were comparable.

Blackett and Occhialini had also taken many pictures with the cloud chamber partitioned by a lead plate. The pictures often showed two or more showers originating simultaneously from the plate and the chamber walls. The frequent occurrence of *multiple showers* was quite surprising. It looked as if particles generated in showers were more likely to produce secondary showers than were the average cosmic-ray particles found in the atmosphere. Last of all, in a number of pictures Blackett and Occhialini found showers that appeared to originate in the plate without any ionizing track entering the plate from above.

Such showers, therefore, were *not* produced by electrons or by any other charged particles. It became necessary to postulate the existence of neutral rays capable of producing showers. In Blackett and Occhialini's view, the neutral rays were probably high-energy photons. The experimenters went on to point out that apparently these photons were often to be found among the secondary products of showers; for it was not unusual to detect multiple showers with a "nonionizing link" (Fig. 6–4).

One of the members of the Cavendish Laboratory, where Blackett and Occhialini did their experiments, was P.A.M. Dirac, a young theorist who a few years earlier had developed a new theory of the electron. In his theory Dirac sought to combine the basic principles of quantum mechanics with the postulates of Einstein's relativity theory. To most people Dirac's theory did not make much sense: it predicted such obviously absurd things as particles with negative mass and negative energy.

Dirac showed, however, by a rather fanciful argument, that his theory could be salvaged if one assumed the existence of positive as well as negative electrons. Although he tried to identify the positive electron with the proton, his theory stubbornly refused to assign to the hypothetical particle a mass different from that of the

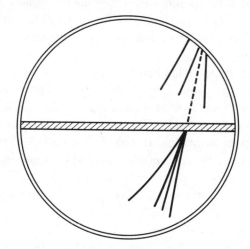

Fig. 6-4 A shower originating in the material above a cloud chamber contains a nonionizing link or photon (dashed line), which produces a secondary shower in the horizontal metal plate across the chamber. [Traced from a photograph published by Blackett and Occhialini, *Proceedings of the Royal Society (London)*, vol. A139, p. 699, 1933.]

negative electron. The two particles had to be exactly identical, except for the different sign of their charges. According to an expression that was to become fashionable later, each was the "antiparticle" of the other. Blackett and Occhialini saw in the light positive particles of their experiments nothing other than the positive electrons required by Dirac's theory. Immediately the pieces of the puzzle began to fall into place.

Why were positrons so rare that they had previously eluded observation? The answer, according to Dirac's theory, was that a positive electron in matter had a very short life, because, when it met a negative electron, the two particles annihilated each other. Their mass was changed into energy in agreement with Einstein's equation $E = mc^2$, and this energy was radiated in the form of photons.

Why did showers appear to contain equal numbers of positive and negative electrons? The answer, again according to Dirac's theory, was that a positive electron was always produced together with a negative electron. The mass of the two electrons resulted from a *materialization* process (known as *pair production*) in which part or all of the energy of the primary particle was transformed into mass.

What were the nonionizing links found by Blackett and Occhialini in their cloud-chamber photographs? They were in all likelihood photons, because Dirac's theory predicted that high-energy photons were capable of producing pairs of positive and negative electrons through the materialization of energy.

Finally, some physicists had noticed that high-energy γ rays from radioactive sources were absorbed in matter more rapidly than the theory of Klein and Nishina predicted (Chap. 2). The "excess" absorption could now be explained by pair production. At sufficiently high energy, photons were absorbed not only in Compton collisions (to which the theory of Klein and Nishina applies), but also in the materialization of photon energy into positive and negative electrons. James Chadwick, Blackett, and Occhialini in England, as well as Irène and Frédéric Joliot-Curie in

France, tested the pair-production hypothesis experimentally. They found that positrons were also produced by γ rays from terrestrial sources, specifically from beryllium bombarded with α particles.

Electrons, photons, and showers

7

The discovery of the positron, the experimental test of Dirac's theory, and the direct observation of events in which energy is transformed into matter and matter into energy are among the most striking accomplishments of physics in the twentieth century. Nevertheless, these achievements left unanswered many questions about cosmic-ray showers. Blackett and Occhialini had found, certainly, that showers were often the result of two or more successive collisions. But was this always the case, and how many particles (or, rather, how many pairs of positive and negative electrons) were produced in each collision? What was the nature of these interactions? Did they involve atomic nuclei? If so, were the nuclei disrupted? And which particles in the local cosmic radiation were capable of initiating showers? The need for new experimental data and new theoretical work was greater than ever.

Experimental properties of showers

Although the cloud chamber was unsurpassed as an instrument for discovering the nature of complex interactions and for analyzing

individual events, some of the most significant data on showers and
the radiation that produced them came from the simpler, cruder
apparatus of G-M counters out of line (Fig. 4–3). The years following the discovery of showers saw numerous coincidence experiments performed with G-M counter arrays in many different
laboratories. I shall not even attempt to give a comprehensive
account of the new information thus gathered; instead, I shall
merely mention two early results that were particularly significant
for the understanding of showers.

The first result was the so-called *shower curve*, which describes
how the coincidence rate varies as the thickness of the absorber
above the counters increases. The typical shower curve shown in
Fig. 7–1 was derived from data obtained with the experimental
arrangement shown in the inset. The material above the counters
was lead. As the curve shows, when the lead thickness was increased, the rate of coincidences due to showers coming out of the
lead increased rapidly at first, reached a maximum between 1 and 2
cm, and then — quite unexpectedly — decreased rapidly again.

At the time, many of us had thought the penetrating particles
found in the atmosphere were the primary cosmic rays themselves.
Supposedly these particles initiated showers by interacting with
atomic nuclei. The shape of the shower curve told us we were on
the wrong track. The penetrating cosmic-ray particles had a known
mean range of the order of meters in lead; their numbers and their
energies would not change appreciably in the penetration of a few
centimeters of the metal. And yet the number of showers coming
from a layer of lead decreased by roughly one-half when the lead-
layer thickness was increased from 2 to 5 cm. Clearly, the radiation
responsible for showers was much more easily absorbed by lead
than the penetrating corpuscular radiation was.

The second result had to do with the rate at which showers
occurred in different substances. In placing above the counters
layers of lead, iron, and aluminum all having the same mass per
unit area (several grams per square centimeter), I found an
approximate shower ratio of 4:2:1 for the three metals. Thus

showers were produced much more abundantly in a given mass of a heavy element (for example, lead) than in the same mass of a light element (for example, aluminum). Other experiments showed that heavier elements were also more effective absorbers of the radiation responsible for the showers. This peculiar difference in behavior between heavy and light elements was a novel feature in high-energy physics. The ionization losses of charged particles, as well as the occurrence of Compton collisions, were approximately the same in different materials when thicknesses were measured in grams per square centimeter rather than in centimeters.

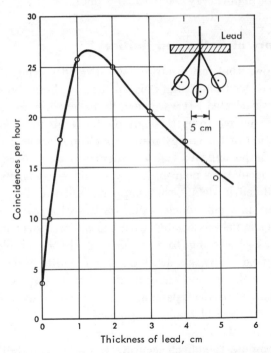

Fig. 7-1 Shower curve. The number of coincidences per hour is plotted as a function of the thickness of lead above the counters. The experimental arrangement is shown schematically in the inset. The circles are experimental points. (This figure is based on one appearing in a paper by the author in *Zeitschrift für Physik*, vol. 82, p. 151, 1933.)

These experimental observations, in addition to others I have omitted, suggested a number of interesting conclusions concerning the "shower-producing radiation" and its place in the general framework of cosmic-ray phenomena. A concrete and precise picture began very gradually to emerge. Fortunately, an important theoretical development made it unnecessary to construct the complete picture piece by piece from purely empirical data. This development came about not because physicists had discovered any essentially new principle, but rather because, from existing theories, they had succeeded in making accurate predictions of the behavior of high-energy electrons and photons.

The theory of Bethe and Heitler

It was known that fast electrons, when rapidly brought to rest in matter, produced photons. (This, in fact, is the manner in which X-rays are generated.) It was generally believed, however, that the energy lost by electrons through photon emission constituted a small fraction of the energy lost through ionization. But in 1934, Hans A. Bethe and W. Heitler, then in England, reported the results of calculations pointing to a very different conclusion. They had considered in detail what happend when a charged particle passed near an atomic nucleus and its trajectory was bent by the strong electric field associated with the positive electric charge of the nucleus. According to the classical theory of electric and magnetic fields, any accelerated charge emits electromagnetic waves. Since the motion along a curved trajectory is accelerated motion, charged particles passing near a nucleus must radiate; that is, in the language of quantum physics, the particles must emit photons.

To compute the effect accurately, Bethe and Heitler had to use quantum theory (because they were dealing with individual subatomic particles) and relativistic equations (because they were dealing with particles moving at almost the speed of light). Their main results were as follows:

1. *Radiation losses are enormously greater for light particles* (such as electrons) *than for heavy particles* (such as protons). This is easily understandable because particles radiate as a result of accelerated motion, and for a given force the acceleration is inversely proportional to the mass. The greater the mass, the smaller the acceleration.

2. *For a given mass per unit area, radiation losses are much greater in elements of high atomic number than in elements of low atomic number.* Rather than go into details, I shall only mention that this result is related to the fact that the deflecting force experienced by a particle passing near a nucleus is proportional to the electric charge on the nucleus. The atomic number Z is the number of positive charges (protons) in a nucleus.[1] Thus nuclei with higher atomic numbers, that is, with greater electric charges, cause a greater acceleration and a correspondingly larger radiation loss.

3. *Radiation losses increase rapidly with energy.* Radiation losses differ in this respect from ionization losses, which first decrease with increasing energy and then become more or less constant (Fig. 2–2). As the energy increases, therefore, radiation losses will eventually overtake ionization losses. For electrons this happens at about 10 MeV in lead and at about 100 MeV in air (Fig. 7–2). (The relation of radiation loss to energy cannot be explained by any simple argument based on classical physics, because it involves relativistic considerations.)

Bethe and Heitler also reported the rather startling results of their calculations on the process of pair production. To repeat one of the points in the preceding chapter, Dirac's theory predicted the production of pairs of positive and negative electrons by photons. Oppenheimer and one of his students had looked somewhat more closely into the nature of the actual process. Apparently the most likely event was one in which a photon passing through the strong electric field of an atomic nucleus suddenly disappeared, giving

[1] See Appendix G.

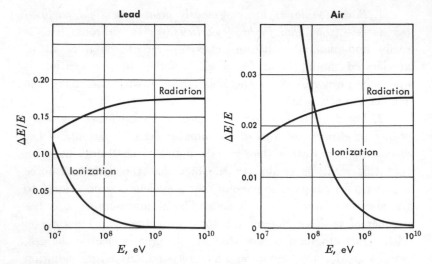

Fig. 7-2 Energy losses of electrons through ionization or radiation processes (in lead and in air) as a function of their kinetic energy. The vertical scale represents the energy loss ΔE in 1 g/cm^2 divided by the initial kinetic energy E of the electron. The graphs show, for example, that a 100-MeV electron ($E = 10^8$ eV) traversing 1 g/cm^2 of lead loses about 1.7 per cent of its energy by ionization ($\Delta E/E = 0.017$) and, on the average, 16 per cent by radiation ($\Delta E/E = 0.16$).

birth to a *single pair* of positive and negative electrons. Bethe and Heitler made an accurate computation of this process and found the following:

1. For a given photon energy *the probability of pair production in layers of different elements with the same mass per unit area increases rapidly with the atomic number Z of the element.* In this case, as in the case of radiation losses of electrons, the dependence on atomic number is an effect of the electric charge of nuclei. Photons, although they carry no charge, are a form of electromagnetic radiation and will therefore interact with an electric field: the stronger the field the more probable the interaction. Thus a photon of given energy is more likely to give rise to an electron pair when passing through the strong field of a high-Z

nucleus than it is when passing through the comparatively weak field of a low-Z nucleus.

2. Starting from an energy of 1 MeV, at which pair production first becomes possible, *the probability of pair production in a given thickness of matter first increases rapidly with increasing photon energy and then levels off at a nearly constant value.* Since the probability of Compton collisions decreases steadily with increasing energy, it follows that at low energies photons are absorbed mainly through the Compton effect and at high energies mainly through pair production. The energy at which pair production overtakes the Compton effect is about 5 MeV in lead and about 20 MeV in air (Fig. 7–3).

At the time Bethe and Heitler developed their theory it was the common belief that all charged particles in the local cosmic radiation were either positive or negative electrons. But then the fact that many of these particles penetrated as much as 1 meter of

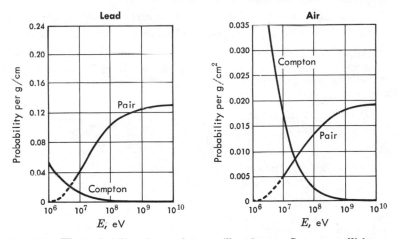

Fig. 7-3 The probability that a photon will undergo a Compton collision or a materialization event while traversing 1 g/cm² of lead or air is plotted as a function of photon energy E. The graphs show, for example, that a 10-MeV photon ($E = 10^7$ eV) has a 1.3 per cent probability of undergoing a Compton collision and a 4 per cent probability of disappearing by pair production in 1 g/cm² of lead.

lead appeared to contradict the theory. For if the theory were correct, only electrons of absurdly high energies should have been capable of traversing such a thick absorber. Moreover, Anderson had observed in his cloud chamber charged particles of about 300 MeV that did not lose nearly as much energy in matter as theory predicted. Indeed, Bethe and Heitler, on the basis of the available experimental evidence, concluded that "the quantum theory is definitely wrong for electrons of such high energy."

The shower theory

A short time later, however, there was evidence from a different quarter that the theory of Bethe and Heitler, contrary to the belief of the authors themselves, was unquestionably correct for electrons and photons of very high energy. In fact, the theory provided the key to the explanation of cosmic-ray showers.

The idea on which the explanation rests is really quite simple (Fig. 7–4). For example, suppose a high-energy photon — with an energy of several BeV, say — enters a block of lead. After traveling a short distance (approximately 7 mm according to the theory) it

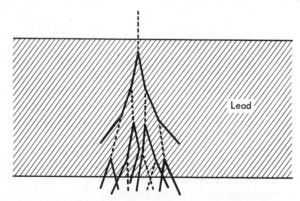

Fig. 7-4 Development of a shower in matter through successive events of pair production and radiation. Dotted lines represent photons, solid lines electrons.

disappears, giving rise to two electrons (one positive, one negative), which between them share the energy of the incident photon. The two electrons do not travel far before each of them radiates a photon, thereby losing a large fraction of its energy.

The newly created photons soon materialize into electron pairs and the process continues. With each new interaction, two particles come from one. Two electrons arise from a single photon; one electron and one photon, from a single electron. Correspondingly, the individual particle energy is, on the average, cut in half. As a result, the particles increase in number at first while their energy decreases.

Eventually, as the original energy is shared among more and more of the newly created particles, most of the electrons have so little energy that they no longer radiate efficiently and are quickly brought to rest by ionization losses. Similarly, more and more of the newly radiated photons lack sufficient energy to produce electron pairs and are soon absorbed in Compton collisions. The shower, grown old, gradually dies out. The photograph in Fig. 7–5 shows an actual shower as it develops through a number of brass plates in a large cloud chamber.

This interpretation of cosmic-ray showers was developed almost simultaneously by Homi J. Bhabha and Heitler in England and by J. F. Carlson and Oppenheimer in the United States. The detailed theory of the *cascade process*, as the gradual building up of showers through pair production and radiative collisions came to be known, presented a difficult mathematical problem. Among the many scientists who contributed to its solution I should like to mention here Lev D. Landau, Igor E. Tamm, and S. Z. Belenky of Russia; Hartland S. Snyder, Robert Serber, and Wendell H. Furry of the United States; and Bhabha and S. K. Chakrabarty of India.

The problem was of a statistical nature. The exact point at which a given photon materializes or a given electron radiates is a matter of chance. How the energy of the photon or the electron is shared between the two particles produced in a single event is also

Fig. 7-5 A shower developing through a number of brass plates 1.25 cm thick placed across a cloud chamber. The shower was initiated in the top plate by an incident high-energy electron or photon. The photograph was taken by the MIT cosmic-ray group.

largely a matter of chance. Consequently, showers initiated by photons (or by electrons) of a specified energy do not all look alike.

One may, however, inquire into the *average* behavior of showers. To take an example, Fig. 7–6 shows the average number

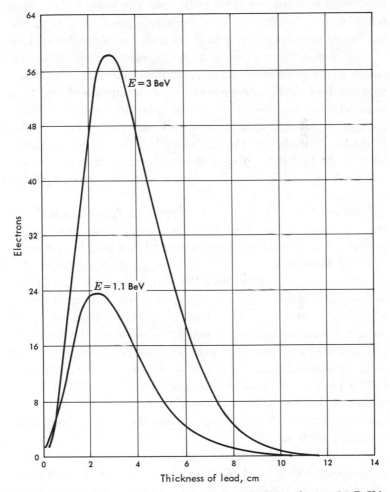

Fig. 7-6 Development of showers produced by electrons of 1.1 and 3 BeV in lead, according to the theory of Snyder. The number of shower electrons is plotted against the lead thickness.

of shower electrons to be found under various thicknesses of lead when electrons of 1.1 BeV and 3.0 BeV energy have initiated the showers. These curves bear a striking similarity to the experimental shower curve in Fig. 7–1. In both the experimental and theoretical curves there is an initial fast rise toward a maximum followed by a fast drop beyond the maximum; and in both cases the maximum appears at a lead thickness of the order of 1 cm.

Of course, the two curves do not represent precisely the same thing. The experimental curve gives the number of coincidences, recorded by G-M counters out of line, as a function of lead thickness, whereas the theoretical curves give the number of shower particles emerging from a layer of lead, again as a function of lead thickness. Nonetheless, the similarity is certainly not accidental, because the probability that a shower emerging from the absorber will produce a coincidence increases with the number of particles in the shower.

Detailed analysis of many experimental data showed that on the whole the cascade theory satisfactorily explains the observed features of showers. Quite illuminating in this regard is the development of showers in materials of different atomic number. As I pointed out a little earlier, both the initial rise of the experimental shower curve and its subsequent drop are steeper for an element of high atomic number such as lead ($Z = 82$) than for one of low atomic number such as aluminum ($Z = 13$) when the thicknesses are measured in grams per square centimeter. Precisely the same behavior is found in the theoretical shower curves, the reason being that a photon will traverse a smaller thickness of lead than of aluminum before undergoing materialization and an electron will also traverse a smaller thickness of lead than of aluminum before it emits a photon.

The successful explanation of showers proved the essential correctness of Bethe and Heitler's theory and established several other important facts:

1. The local cosmic radiation contains electrons and photons with energies of billions of electron volts.

2. The observed showers result from cascade processes initiated by these electrons and photons.

3. The individual interactions responsible for the cascades are radiative collisions of electrons and pair production by photons. These processes occur in the vicinity of atomic nuclei. However, they do not involve any change in the structure of nuclei (contrary to the earlier belief that showers are the result of nuclear disintegrations). Each interaction gives rise to only two particles (two electrons or one photon and one electron). The groups of many particles that occasionally appear to diverge from a single point arise from several individual interactions occurring next to one another in matter.

4. The ionizing particles that constitute the soft component of the local cosmic radiation are the electrons of showers originating in the atmosphere or in the roof of the building where the experiments are performed.

These results, of course, were very gratifying. However, it was still necessary to account for the apparent contradiction between the experimental data on showers, which seemed to confirm the theory of Bethe and Heitler, and the data on penetrating particles, which seemed to disprove it.

Mu mesons

8

The theory of radiation losses and pair production, along with the consequent explanation of showers, shifted the mystery from one component of the local cosmic radiation to another. To recapitulate, before the theory had made possible any precise predictions of the behavior of high-energy electrons and photons, physicists had thought the penetrating group of particles (Fig. 6–1) were electrons, which in traversing matter lost energy mainly by ionization. Since they were unaware of the overwhelming predominance of radiation processes at high energies, they had only to postulate electron energies of a few BeV in order to explain the tremendous penetrating power of these particles.

The great puzzle, then, was the nature of the so-called shower-producing radiation. Obviously, the production of showers involved something more than ionization losses by electrons and Compton collisions by photons. After learning about pair production and radiation processes, physicists realized that the shower-producing radiation consisted of high-energy electrons and photons behaving exactly as they ought to behave. But, at the same time, it was equally evident that the penetrating particles could not possibly be electrons behaving in accordance with theoretical predictions.

What, then, were these particles? Two obvious possibilities suggested themselves, and each had its proponents among cosmic-ray physicists. Either the particles are not electrons or, if they are electrons, the theory breaks down at energies in the range of several BeV. Beyond a certain critical energy, in other words, electrons must lose their ability to radiate photons if they are to behave as penetrating particles.

Eventually the second assumption became untenable. On the one hand, the British physicist E. J. Williams in 1933 and the German physicist C. von Weiszäcker in 1935 had shown, on theoretical grounds, that Bethe and Heitler's predictions concerning radiation by electrons were bound to be essentially correct up to energies well beyond a few BeV. On the other hand, even disregarding these theoretical arguments, it was difficult to choose a critical energy that would explain all the experimental findings. Some of the observed showers were so large as to require primary-particle energies of many BeV, whereas a large number of the penetrating particles appeared to have energies of 1 BeV or less. Thus, physicists began to speculate in earnest about the first possibility.

According to theory, if a particle does not radiate as much as an electron, it must have a greater mass (Chap. 7). Since the only known particle heavier than the electron was the proton, Williams suggested in 1934 that the penetrating cosmic-ray particles were protons. Williams was also forced to include *negative* as well as positive protons in his hypothesis, for cloud-chamber experiments had already shown the penetrating particles to carry electric charges of both signs.[1]

A new particle of intermediate mass

The proton hypothesis immediately ran into considerable difficulties. Indeed, Williams had hardly made his proposal before

[1] Negative protons had been predicted by Dirac's theory as the antiparticles of ordinary protons (Chap. 10).

extensive cloud-chamber studies by Anderson and Seth H. Neddermeyer at the California Institute of Technology began to uncover evidence directly contradicting it.

Across their cloud chamber Anderson and Neddermeyer had placed a lead plate, 3.5 mm thick, for the purpose of studying the energy lost by cosmic rays in matter. Many of their pictures revealed particles with magnetic rigidities between 10^5 and 10^6 gauss·cm that did not seem to ionize as heavily as protons of the same rigidities should have (Fig. 6–2), but which on traversing the plate lost less energy than the radiation theory predicted for electrons.

However, energy loss by radiation is a statistical effect. While the theory predicts, *on the average*, a large energy loss in 3.5 mm of lead, it would have been quite possible for some electrons to traverse the absorber without passing near an atomic nucleus at sufficiently close range to undergo an appreciable energy loss. Thus Anderson and Neddermeyer's experiments were very suggestive but not entirely conclusive. To obtain more definite evidence, they replaced the lead plate with a platinum plate 1 cm thick, which was equivalent to nearly 2 cm of lead as far as radiation losses were concerned. The probability that an electron would pass through such a thick plate without suffering a radiative collision was negligible. The results of their new experiments, which they published in the spring of 1937, established the following facts:

1. There exist two sharply separated groups of particles. The first group consists of penetrating particles, which lose a small fraction of their energy in traversing a lead plate. The second group consists of absorbable particles, which lose a large fraction of their energy. The energy loss of the absorbable particles is in agreement with the values computed for electrons that radiate and ionize according to theory. Hence, the absorbable particles are probably electrons. The energy loss of the penetrating particles, however, is accounted for entirely by ionization; therefore, *the penetrating particles do not radiate appreciably.*

2. Absorbable particles, because they often occur in groups, are presumably secondary particles of showers originating above the chamber. The particles themselves frequently produce showers, confirming the view that they are electrons. Penetrating particles, however, usually appear as single tracks in cloud-chamber pictures.

3. Of the particles whose cloud-chamber tracks show the same curvature, some lose large amounts of energy and others lose small amounts of energy in traversing the plate. Consequently, electrons cannot behave as absorbable particles below a certain critical energy and as penetrating particles above that energy. For if they did so behave, the energy loss would always be the same for particles of the same magnetic rigidity (that is, curvature of trajectory). This confirms the conclusion that the behavior of penetrating particles cannot be explained by a breakdown of Bethe and Heitler's theory, and it proves that the penetrating particles are not electrons.

4. Many of the penetrating particles have magnetic rigidities of less than 1.5×10^6 gauss·cm. Below this value protons ionize at least three times more heavily than fast electrons (Fig. 6–2). The ionization density along the tracks of these particles, however, is about the same as that of electrons. Since the penetrating particles ionize less than protons, their mass must be *smaller* than the proton mass; since they do not radiate as much as electrons, their mass must be *larger* than the electron mass.

From these results, Neddermeyer and Anderson concluded that, in all likelihood, "there exist particles of unit charge, but with a mass (which may not have a unique value) larger than that of the normal free electron and much smaller than that of a proton."

The mu meson and its mass

Neddermeyer and Anderson were unable to determine the mass of the new particles with any reasonable accuracy. Nor, for that matter, could they rule out the possibility that penetrating particles had the same mass as electrons but possessed some unknown property that prevented them from radiating as normal electrons radiate. The reason for this uncertainty is clear from the curves in Fig. 8–1, where ionization density is plotted as a function of magnetic rigidity for singly charged particles with masses intermediate between those of the electron and the proton. At magnetic rigidities of about 10^6 gauss·cm, no charged particle with a mass up to several hundred times that of the electron can be distinguished from an electron on the basis of the ion trails the two particles leave. Only particles whose mass approximates or exceeds the proton mass ionize heavily enough to announce their separate identity.[1]

From Fig. 8–1 it is also evident that in order to measure their mass, it was necessary to observe penetrating particles of fairly low energy. This is what J. C. Street and E. C. Stevenson, working at Harvard University, had set out to do while Neddermeyer and Anderson were carrying out their own experiments.

Like the latter, Street and Stevenson used a cloud chamber in a magnetic field. Since low-energy particles were rare in the penetrating group, they tried to increase the yield of useful pictures by observing only particles that stopped in the chamber. To this end, they triggered the chamber with an arrangement of G-M counters that signaled when a particle entering the chamber failed to come out of its walls (Fig. 8–2). They also took pains to operate the chamber in such a way as to facilitate the counting of droplets and therefore the measurement of the ionization. With this device, Street and Stevenson obtained a number of pictures, among which was one of particular importance that was published in the fall of 1937 (Fig. 8–3). The concentration of droplets along the track indicates an ionization density of about six times the minimum, and the curvature of the track indicates a magnetic rigidity of

---

[1] Cloud-chamber measurements of ionization densities, which involve counting the droplets along a track, are by their nature imprecise. Small changes in the adjustment of the chamber cause the vapor to condense on ions of one sign alone or, in varying degrees, on ions of both signs.

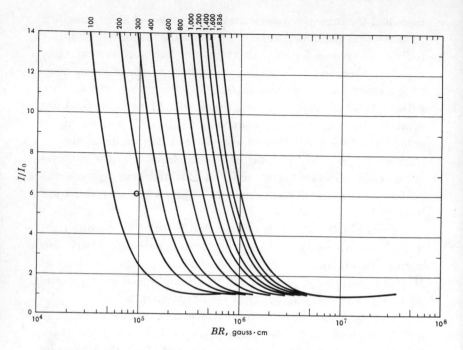

Fig. 8-1 Ionization density as a function of magnetic rigidity for singly charged particles of different masses. The circle represents the result of density and rigidity measurements of the particle track in Fig. 8–3.

Determining the mass of a particle from ionization density and magnetic rigidity

The density of droplets along the cloud-chamber track of a particle gives the ionization density. If a magnetic field is applied to the chamber, the resulting curvature of the track gives the magnetic rigidity. With these two quantities, one can determine the mass of a charged particle from the graphs in Fig. 8-1. Here the magnetic rigidity BR is plotted along the horizontal axis on a logarithmic scale; the observed ionization density I divided by that of a minimum-ionizing particle I_0 is plotted on the vertical axis. The various curves represent particles of unit charge and different masses; the latter are indicated as multiples of the electron mass along the top of the graph. (The particle of mass 1,836 is the proton; the corresponding curve is identical with that appearing in Fig. 6-2.)

The values of the magnetic rigidity and ionization density of a given track define a point on the graph. The curve passing through this point indicates the mass of the particle. To take a specific example, for the particle track in Fig. 8-3, $BR = 9.6 \times 10^4$ gauss·cm and $I/I_0 = 6$. The corresponding point lies close to the curve of 200 electron masses.

As the graph shows, the curves are widely separated when the magnetic rigidity is not too great but are close together when the rigidity increases. At $BR = 10^5$ gauss·cm, for example, $I/I_0 = 7$ for a particle of mass 200; and for a particle of mass 300, $I/I_0 = 13$. A crude estimate of the ionization is therefore sufficient to distinguish the two particles. At $BR = 10^6$ gauss·cm, however, both particles have nearly the same (minimum) ionization and cannot be distinguished.

9.6×10^4 gauss·cm. The point corresponding to these two values of ionization and rigidity falls close to the "200" curve in Fig. 8-1. The particle in question, then, had a mass of approximately 200 electron masses.

Thus the work of Street and Stevenson, in addition to establishing beyond any doubt the existence of a new particle, also provided a fairly accurate estimate of its mass. This new particle was variously called *baryon, yukon, mesotron,* and *meson.* The last name eventually won general acceptance. Later, when investigations revealed the existence of other mesons, physicists gave the original meson the identifying prefix mu (μ).

Over the years many physicists endeavored to make precise measurements of the mass of μ mesons. Some of the most accurate determinations were those of Robert B. Brode and his collaborators

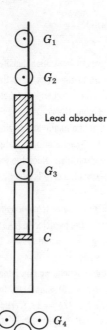

G_1

G_2

Lead absorber

G_3

C

G_4

Fig. 8-2 Experimental arrangement used by Street and Stevenson to obtain cloud-chamber pictures of low-energy penetrating particles. The cloud chamber C is triggered by particles that discharge the G-M counters G_1 to G_3 without discharging any of the counters G_4. These particles have sufficient energy to traverse the three upper counters and the lead absorber but not enough to traverse the walls of the cloud chamber and the plate across the chamber.

at the University of California in Berkeley. Instead of measuring magnetic rigidity and ionization, Brode's group measured magnetic rigidity and range. The curves in Fig. 8–4 show the relationship between these two quantities for particles of different masses and illustrate the principle of the method. The arrangement of one of the experiments is shown in Fig. 8–5. It consisted of two cloud chambers placed one above the other. The upper chamber measured the magnetic rigidity; the lower chamber contained a number of lead plates and measured the range.

The final value of the μ-meson mass announced by Brode's group in 1950 was 206 ± 2 electron masses. By 1950, μ mesons were also being produced artificially in the laboratory by means of high-energy particle accelerators. Today the accepted value of the μ-meson mass, which comes from a variety of experiments on artificially produced mesons, is 206.8 electron masses.

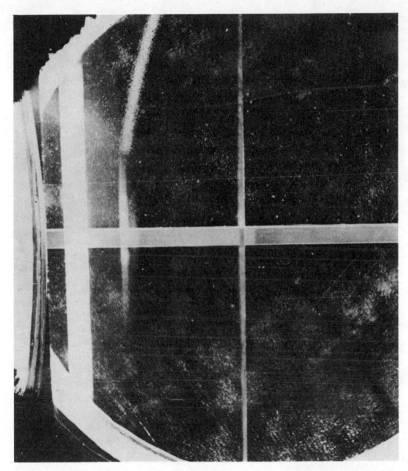

Fig. 8-3 Mass of the μ meson was first determined by Street and Stevenson from this cloud-chamber photograph of a μ-meson track (see text). (From a paper in *The Physical Review*, vol. 52, p. 1003, 1937.)

The discovery of μ mesons in 1937 brought to a close the second chapter in the history of cosmic rays, which had opened with the experiments of Bothe and Kohlhörster. The nature of the *local* cosmic radiation observed in the atmosphere was now clear: The penetrating particles were μ mesons; the absorbable particles

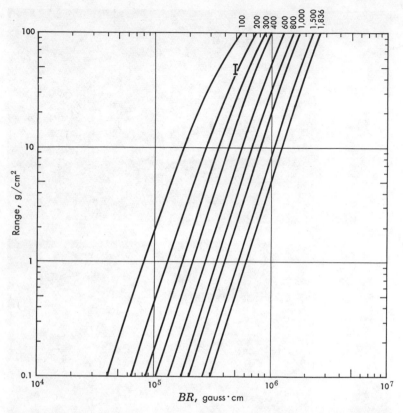

Fig. 8-4 Range in lead as a function of magnetic rigidity for singly charged particles of different masses. The vertical bar represents one of the results obtained with the experimental arrangement shown in Fig. 8-5.

were electrons. The nonionizing particles were photons. Mu mesons, electrons, and photons accounted for practically all of the radiation found near sea level.

Yukawa's theory

The discovery of the μ meson, like that of the positive electron, had been preceded by a theoretical prediction. In 1935 the Japanese

Determining the mass of a particle from magnetic rigidity and range

The graphs in Fig. 8–4 can be used to determine the mass of a particle whose magnetic rigidity and range have been measured experimentally. The magnetic rigidity BR is plotted along the horizontal axis on a logarithmic scale; the range, in grams per square centimeter, is plotted along the vertical axis, also on a logarithmic scale. The various curves represent particles of unit charge and different masses (in multiples of the electron mass). The magnetic rigidity and the range of a single particle define a point on the graph. The curve passing through this point determines the mass of the particle.

In the experiments of Brode (see Fig. 8–5) the measurements of range in lead contained an uncertainty of 0.63 cm, or about 7 g/cm². The vertical bar in Fig. 8–4 represents a typical case, in which the range of the particle falls somewhere between 44 and 51 g/cm² and the magnetic curvature is 5×10^5 gauss·cm. From the graph one can see that the mass of the particle lies between 170 and 200 electron masses. The uncertainty in the measurement of magnetic rigidity makes this mass determination consistent with the assumption that the particle is a μ meson. The over-all accuracy obtained by averaging a large number of measurements is, of course, considerably greater than that of any individual measurement.

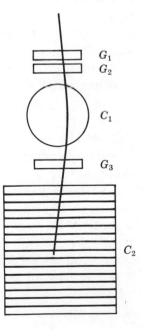

Fig. 8-5 Schematic diagram of the arrangement used by Brode and his collaborators to measure the mass of μ mesons. Both cloud chambers C_1 and C_2 are triggered by particles that discharge the three G-M counters G_1 to G_3. Chamber C_1 is placed in a magnetic field; the curvature of the tracks seen in this chamber gives the magnetic rigidity. Chamber C_2 contains 15 lead plates, each 0.63 cm thick. When a particle stops in this chamber, its range can be determined with an uncertainty equal to the thickness of a single plate.

physicist Hideki Yukawa had postulated the existence of a subatomic particle several hundred times heavier than the electron. I cannot do justice to Yukawa's theoretical reasoning within the bounds of this book, and what follows is hardly more than a crude attempt to lend some small degree of plausibility to his conclusions.

As I mentioned briefly in Chap. 2, nature has obliged us to accept the fact that all radiations behave in certain respects as waves, in other respects as particles. The waves associated with photons are electromagnetic waves. As such they are related to the electric forces between charged particles. In fact, quantum theory reveals a close relationship between the properties of photons and the nature of electric forces.

Electric forces of attraction between the positive nucleus and the negative electrons of an atom are the forces that hold the atom together. By 1935 the nucleus itself was known to contain both protons and neutrons.[1] Now, protons repel each other because of their electric charges, whereas neutrons do not interact electrically with one another or with protons. Yet atomic nuclei are remarkably stable structures. This fact had made it necessary to assume forces of attraction of a nonelectric nature between protons and neutrons. Over the small distances characteristic of atomic nuclei these nuclear forces are much stronger than electric forces; over greater distances they are much weaker. In other words, nuclear forces decrease with distance far more rapidly than they would if they behaved according to the inverse-square law, which governs electric forces.

Yukawa argued that, just as electric forces are associated with the photon, so nuclear forces should be associated with some kind of particle. He then proceeded to study the properties of this hypothetical particle and found that the short range of nuclear forces required a particle of finite mass; in fact, a mass of the order of several hundred electron masses. Yukawa also predicted that the particles associated with the nuclear field would be *unstable;*

[1] See Appendix G.

that is, would decay much as the nuclei of radioactive substances do. Furthermore, the mean life[1] of the μ meson, before it decays, should be of the order of 1 microsecond (10^{-6} second), and the disintegration products of each particle should be one electron and one *neutrino*. The latter was a particle with zero mass and no electric charge whose existence had been postulated by Wolfgang Pauli and Enrico Fermi in order to explain why the electrons emitted in the β decay of a given radioactive element have a variety of energies.[2]

After the discovery of mesons, some physicists, recalling Yukawa's theory, concluded that the penetrating particles in cosmic radiation were the "quanta of the nuclear force field" predicted by the theory — hence the name *yukon*. As will be seen in Chap. 9, this identification proved incorrect. Moreover, when the quantum of the nuclear force field was found, its properties differed somewhat from those envisaged by Yukawa. Nevertheless, the idea that cosmic-ray mesons might be Yukawa particles led to a very important discovery.

The discovery of mu-meson decay

Between 1936 and 1937, scientific teams in England, France, Germany, and Italy had made accurate measurements of the numbers of cosmic-ray particles found at various altitudes in the atmosphere. And the results had been rather puzzling. Contrary to the

---

[1] The concept of *mean life* is taken over from the theory of radioactivity, according to which it represents the average life span of all nuclei in a given radioactive sample. The mean life happens to coincide with the period in which the total number of nuclei is reduced, by decay, to $1/2.7$ of its original value. (The number 2.7 is the base of natural logarithms; the definition of mean life is, from a mathematical point of view, similar to the definition of *mean free path;* See page 24 and Fig. 2–4.) The reader is perhaps more familiar with the concept of *half-life*, the period in which the total number of nuclei is reduced to one-half its original value. The mean life of a radioactive nucleus is 1.4 times its half-life.

[2] See Appendix H.

earlier findings of Millikan's group (Chap. 1), it looked as if air absorbed cosmic rays more effectively than solid or liquid matter did when layers of the same mass per unit area were compared. Moreover, the thinner air at very high altitudes appeared to be a better absorber than the denser air in the lower atmosphere.

Now, Yukawa particles were supposed to be unstable. If cosmic-ray mesons were identical with Yukawa particles, they should decay spontaneously. In 1938 the German physicist H. Kuhlenkampff pointed out that this property offered a natural explanation for the anomalous absorption of cosmic-ray particles in air. The argument is very simple (Fig. 8–6). Consider, for example, a layer of water 10 cm thick. Near sea level a layer of air of the same mass per unit area is 8,000 cm thick, since air is 800 times less dense than water. At an altitude of about 5,100 meters, where the air density is one-half that at sea level, the equivalent air layer is 16,000 cm thick. A particle moving at nearly the speed of light will travel 10 cm in 3.3×10^{-10} second, or 0.00033 microsecond. The same particle will need 0.265 microsecond to travel 8,000 cm and 0.53 microsecond to travel 16,000 cm.

Suppose now that mesons have a mean life of the order of microseconds. Then practically none of them will decay while traversing 10 cm of water. Only mesons with a range less than 10 cm of water will be stopped by this absorber. Many mesons, however, will undergo spontaneous decay while traversing 8,000 cm of air, and even more will do so while traversing 16,000 cm of air. Consequently, to the normal absorption of mesons is added the effect of spontaneous decay. As a result, air will appear to be a better absorber than condensed matter, the more so the thinner it is, which is exactly what the experiments had indicated.

Kuhlenkampff's idea was taken up by a number of investigators, including Werner Heisenberg and H. Euler in Germany and Blackett in England, who worked out its various consequences. Indeed, from late in 1938 to the end of 1939 the question of the radioactive decay of mesons was one of the most hotly debated subjects in cosmic-ray physics. The experimental evidence from

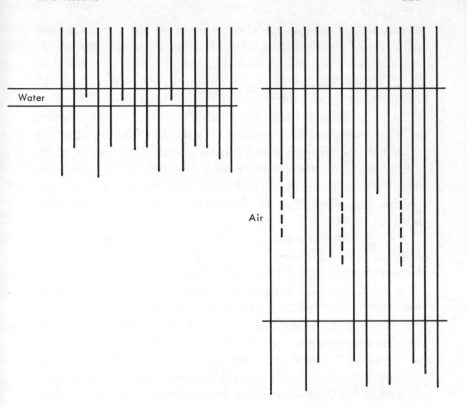

Fig. 8-6 Comparison of meson absorption in layers of water and air of the same mass per unit area. Equal numbers of mesons come to rest in the two layers. However, some mesons undergo spontaneous decay in traveling the greater distance through the air layer. Thus, fewer mesons are found under the layer of air than under the equivalent layer of water.

atmospheric absorption was highly suggestive, but not compelling. In addition, attempts to detect the decay of mesons directly in cloud-chamber experiments had all failed.

I became interested in this problem myself while visiting the Institute for Theoretical Physics in Copenhagen, directed by Niels Bohr, in the fall of 1938 and Blackett's laboratory at the University of Manchester during the following winter. In the spring of 1939 I moved to the University of Chicago at the invitation of A. H. Compton. At the time, I was toying with the idea of testing the hypothesis of the instability of mesons by making a direct and precise comparison of meson absorption in air and in some dense material.

Compton most generously put at my disposal the means for carrying out this experiment. Two members of his group, Norman Hilberry and J. Barton Hoag, offered their assistance. We set up, in a truck, a meson detector consisting of three G-M tubes in coincidence, with enough lead between and around the counters to cut off the electron component (Fig. 8–7). With this equipment we took measurements in Chicago (180 meters above sea level); then we drove to Colorado and took measurements at Denver (1,600 meters), Echo Lake (3,240 meters), and Mt. Evans (4,300 meters). At each of the Colorado stations we counted mesons both with and without a layer of graphite (about 87 g/cm²) above the counters.

The results are presented in Fig. 8–8. They showed the absorption in graphite to be much less than that in air. For example, starting from an atmospheric depth of 699 g/cm² (Echo Lake), the addition of 87 g/cm² of graphite cut down the number of mesons by 10 per cent, while the addition of 87 g/cm² of air reduced this number by 20 per cent. The additional apparent absorption was due to the decay of mesons "in flight" through the atmosphere.

From the measurement of the additional absorption we were able to estimate roughly the mean life of mesons. In making this estimate, we had to take into account the fact that, according to the theory of relativity, the determination of a time interval depends on the frame of reference in which the measurement is made. If, for example, a clock is moving with a velocity v with respect to some observer, it will appear to tick at a slower rate to that observer than to another observer moving with the clock. The time intervals between ticks, as measured by the first and second observer, respectively, are in the ratio of $1/\sqrt{1 - v^2/c^2}$, where c is the velocity of light.

When different values are substituted for v, it is clear that the effect becomes appreciable only when the velocity of the clock is very close to c (that is, when the value of the denominator $\sqrt{1 - v^2/c^2}$ approaches zero). Now, unstable cosmic-ray mesons are subatomic "clocks" moving at very great speeds. The measured mean life τ' of these mesons is therefore markedly greater than the mean life τ of mesons at rest. For example, it is found that for mesons with a kinetic energy of 500 MeV, $\tau'/\tau = 4.7$. In other words, the measured mean life of these mesons is 4.7 times longer than their

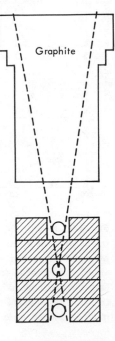

Fig. 8-7 Experimental arrangement for the comparison of the meson absorption in air and graphite.

mean life at rest.[1] Therefore, to determine the mean life of mesons at rest from measurements involving mesons in motion, it was essential to know their energy. By making suitable estimates of the energy (or, more precisely, of the average energy of the mesons we were observing) we found a mean life for mesons at rest of the order of 2 microseconds (2×10^{-6} second).

[1] From the relativistic expression of kinetic energy E [see Appendix D, Eq. (D-2)], it follows that $1/\sqrt{1 - v^2/c^2} = (E/107) + 1$. In this equation E is measured in MeV and 107 represents the "rest energy" of the μ meson, mc^2, also in MeV.

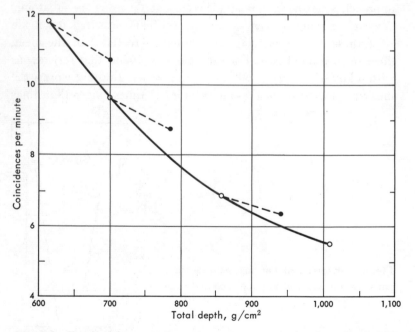

Fig. 8-8 Results of meson-absorption measurements in air and graphite (made with the arrangement shown in Fig. 8-7). Open dots are counting rates per minute observed at Chicago, Denver, Echo Lake, and Mt. Evans with no absorber above the counters. Solid dots are counting rates observed at the three higher stations under 87 g/cm² of graphite. The horizontal scale gives the total thickness of matter (air plus graphite) above the counters, measured in grams per square centimeter.

Similar experiments were performed in the following years by many physicists, including W. M. Nielsen, H. Victor Neher, Martin A. Pomerantz, and their collaborators in the United States and Gilberto Bernardini, Giuseppe Cocconi, Oreste Piccioni, and others in Italy. On the whole, their results were in agreement with ours. In passing, I should like to recall one such experiment, performed by David B. Hall and myself, in which we measured the apparent mean lives of mesons of different energies and found that they changed with energy just as the theory of relativity predicted. The effect was quite large — about a factor of 3 from the fastest to the slowest mesons detected in the experiment.

Electrons from the decay of mu mesons

In the meantime, Williams and G. E. Roberts in England had succeeded in obtaining the first cloud-chamber picture of meson decay. The meson in question, positively charged, had stopped in the gas of the chamber (a very rare event indeed), and out of the end of its track had appeared the track of a positive electron. This picture, besides providing final, crucial proof of meson decay, also showed that (as anticipated) when a μ meson disappears, an electron is born. (Many pictures of this kind were obtained in later years. Figure 8–9 shows a particularly clear example from experiments performed in 1948 by Robert W. Thompson, then a graduate student at the Massachusetts Institute of Technology.)

Direct measurements of the mean life of mu mesons

The next major step was taken by Franco Rasetti. Williams and Roberts' photograph had shown pictorially the decay of a meson brought to rest by ionization losses in matter. Mesons stopping in matter should not decay immediately, but should "wait around" for a period equal, on the average, to their mean life. Since the

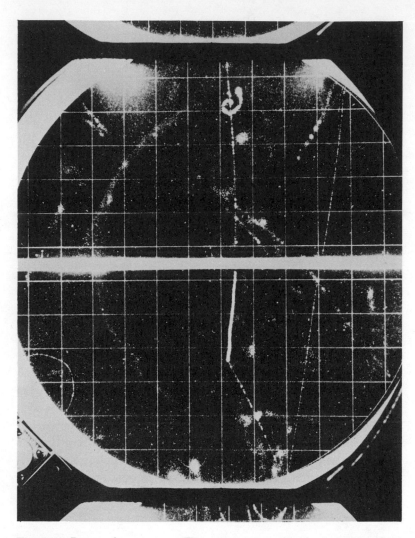

Fig. 8-9 Decay of a μ meson. The meson enters the cloud chamber from
above. It traverses an aluminum plate 0.63 cm thick, where it loses most of
its energy. The meson, which leaves the plate as a slow and therefore heavily
ionizing particle, comes to rest in the gas. The track of an electron originates
from the end of the μ-meson track. The electron, traveling at nearly the speed
of light, produces a track approximating that of a minimum-ionizing particle.
The tracks of the meson and the electron are slightly bent by a magnetic field,
and the direction of the deflection shows that both particles are positively
charged. (From R. W. Thompson, *The Physical Review*, vol. 74, p. 490, 1948.)

mean life had already been estimated to be several microseconds, it was expected that electrons arising from the decay of μ mesons would come out of an absorber after an average delay of a few microseconds.

In an attempt to demonstrate directly the delayed emission of electrons by mesons brought to rest in matter, Rasetti in 1941 performed the experiment illustrated schematically in Fig. 8–10.

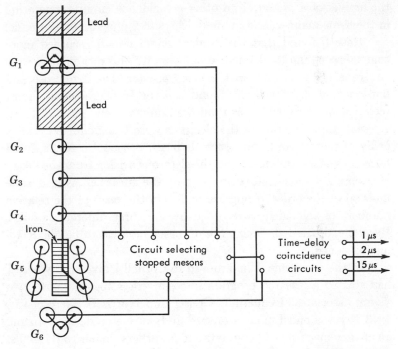

Fig. 8-10 Decay of μ mesons at rest was observed in 1941 by Rasetti, using the experimental apparatus shown here. A μ meson discharges counters G_1 to G_4 and then stops in the iron absorber. (A particle passing through the absorber would discharge one of the counters, G_6.) A short time later, its decay electron (if it comes out of the absorber in the right direction) discharges one of the side counters G_5. Three different electronic circuits select events in which the discharge of counters G_5 occurs within 1, 2, or 15 microseconds (μs), respectively, after the discharge of counters G_1 to G_4.

The G-M counters G_1 to G_4 and G_6 and the associated electronic circuit selected mesons that stopped in the iron-block absorber. These mesons discharged one of the three G_1 counters as well as the single counters G_2, G_3, and G_4, but they did not discharge any of the G_6 counters. Along each side of the absorber were six counters G_5 whose function was to detect the electrons arising from the decay of stopped mesons. A coincidence circuit gave a signal whenever one of the G_5 counters was discharged less than 1 microsecond after the arrival of a meson. Two other coincidence circuits, operating in the same manner, had allowed delays of 2 and 15 microseconds.

Rasetti found that the 2-microsecond circuit recorded more coincidences than the 1-microsecond circuit. This meant there were electrons being emitted with a delay greater than 1 microsecond but less than 2. Rasetti also found that the 15-microsecond circuit recorded more coincidences than the 2-microsecond circuit. Thus, a considerable fraction of the electrons were being emitted after a delay of more than 2 microseconds but less than 15. As expected from previous estimates, then, the electrons arising from the decay of stopped mesons had come out of the absorber over a time interval of the order of microseconds. On the basis of the relative numbers of coincidences recorded by the three different circuits, Rasetti estimated the mean life of mesons at rest to be about 1.5 microseconds.

In the meantime, I had moved to Cornell University, where I had started a research program in cosmic rays together with two young associates, Kenneth I. Greiser and Norris G. Nereson. In 1943 Nereson and I made a precise study of meson decay by using an arrangement of G-M counters and absorbers similar to Rasetti's. The novel feature of our experiment was an "electronic clock" that we built for the purpose and that enabled us to measure the individual delays between the arrival of mesons and the emission of electrons. We found that the decay of mesons, like the decay of radioactive atoms, is exponential (Fig. 8–11). This means that, out of any large group of mesons present at a given time, a fixed fraction will decay during the next microsecond regardless of how long

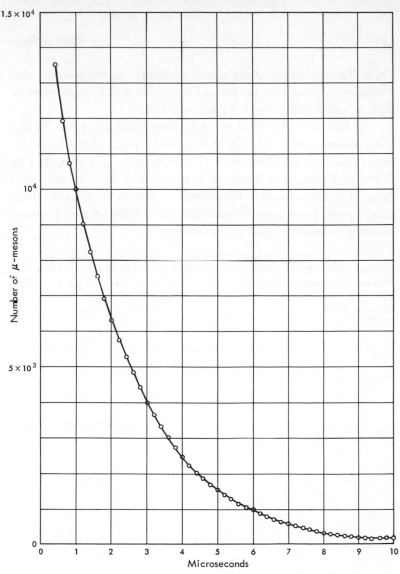

Fig. 8-11 Decay curve of μ mesons brought to rest in lead, as measured by Nereson and the author. Shown on the horizontal axis is the time interval following the arrival of a meson in the absorber; on the vertical axis is shown the number of observed μ mesons whose decay occurred after the corresponding interval indicated on the horizontal axis. For example, 10,000 mesons survived more than 1 microsecond, 6,300 mesons survived more than 2 microseconds, and so on.

the individual mesons have already "lived." From our measurements, we obtained for the mean life a value of 2.15 microseconds, with an estimated error of 0.1 microsecond.

In the next few years several other physicists made similar measurements on cosmic-ray mesons and confirmed the value we had found. Among them were R. Chaminade, A. Freon, and R. Maze in France and Marcello Conversi and Piccioni in Italy.[1] After it became possible to produce μ mesons with high-energy accelerators, their mean life was measured with greater accuracy and turned out to be 2.212 microseconds.

[1] To appreciate the contributions of the European scientists, one must consider the severe handicaps under which they worked in the war years. The Italians, for example, did most of their experiments while hiding in a cellar, where they had smuggled their equipment when the Germans descended on Rome in 1943.

Pi mesons

9

The history of scientific exploration, like the history of geographical exploration, is full of instances in which an unexpected discovery overshadows the original goal. Columbus, searching for a new route to India in the last decade of the fifteenth century, discovered America. Physicists, searching for a solution to the cosmic-ray puzzle in the fourth decade of the twentieth century, came across two previously unknown particles, the positron and the μ meson. The discovery of these particles, which arise from the interactions of high-energy rays with matter but are not among the building blocks of ordinary matter, opened an entirely new field of research. Here cosmic-ray physicists found such a wealth of novel and unexpected phenomena that for many years the exploration of this field was their main concern.

Eventually the development of accelerators in the multi-billion eV range, by providing controlled and much stronger sources of high-energy particles, brought a decline in cosmic-ray research as a means for studying elementary particles. Before that happened, however, cosmic-ray physicists had succeeded in drawing a fairly comprehensive, though not entirely complete or very detailed, map of the entire field of elementary-particle physics.

The puzzling behavior of negative mu mesons

For physicists interested in the atomic nucleus, as well as for those interested in cosmic rays, the most important development in the exploration of the new world of particle physics came with the discovery of the pi meson (π) in 1947. The investigations leading to this discovery began in 1940, when the Japanese physicists Sin-itiro Tomonaga and Gentaro Araki pointed out that positive and negative μ mesons should behave in a characteristically different manner after coming to rest in matter.

A positive meson, they argued, can never approach very near an atomic nucleus because of the electric forces of repulsion exerted by the positive nuclear charge. Therefore, it will "wait around" until it disappears by spontaneous decay. A negative meson, however, is attracted by the nuclear charge and thus might be captured by a nucleus before it has a chance to decay. If the interaction between μ mesons and the nuclei of an absorber is sufficiently strong, almost all the negative μ mesons will be swallowed up by nuclei; few of them will decay into electrons. If the interaction is weaker, some will be absorbed and some will decay.

In any case, the life expectancy of negative mesons must be less than that of positive mesons, for the latter die a "natural" death, while the former are exposed to the additional risk of "accidental" death by nuclear capture. Once captured, negative mesons presumably disappear, and their mass turns into energy according to Einstein's equation. Like a tiny bomb, such a release of energy should cause the nucleus to explode.

Shortly after Tomonaga and Araki published their paper, Rasetti performed the experiment on μ-meson decay described in the preceding chapter. By comparing the number of mesons stopping in his iron block with the number of decay electrons coming out of it, Rasetti was able to show that only half the mesons decayed into electrons. He concluded that the decay electrons came from positive mesons and that the negative mesons disappeared by nuclear capture, as Tomonaga and Araki had predicted.

A more direct experimental proof developed from the investigations of Conversi, Pancini, and Piccioni. The experiment they performed was similar to the earlier experiments by Rasetti and by Nereson and myself, except for the addition of a device capable of concentrating upon the absorber either positive or negative mesons. This device, whose design goes back to my own early work on cosmic rays in 1931,[1] is known as a *magnetic lens*. It takes advantage of the strong magnetic fields that can be generated in iron and also of the fact that cosmic-ray mesons can traverse fairly large thicknesses of iron without suffering much energy loss or scattering (which is not true of particles of lower energy, such as α or β rays from radioactive sources). Thus one can use magnetized iron to deflect cosmic-ray mesons. Since it is much easier to magnetize a piece of iron than to produce an equivalent field in air, the device also has great practical advantages.

The principle of the magnetic lens is illustrated in Fig. 9–1. Two bars of iron placed side by side are magnetized in opposite directions. Two G-M counters, one above and one below the bars, are connected in coincidence. Suppose the magnetic field of the bar on the right points toward the observer and the field of the bar on the left away from the observer. Positive mesons traveling downward through the first counter will be deflected toward the second counter, thereby increasing the number that passes through both. Negative mesons (except for the very few that travel straight down between the bars) will be deflected away from the second counter.

[1] At that time, of course, I did not know about mesons. I had developed the lens in an attempt to find out whether the cosmic-ray particles capable of traversing large thicknesses of matter were positively or negatively charged. The result of the experiment was ambiguous; I could only conclude either that the particles had too much energy to undergo appreciable magnetic deflection in the magnetized iron of the lens or that positive and negative particles were about equally abundant.

If the magnetization is reversed in both bars, the lens will concentrate negative mesons and reject positive mesons.

With an iron absorber below their lens, Conversi and his two colleagues found only positive mesons giving rise to the delayed electrons characteristic of spontaneous decay. Thus they concluded that practically all negative mesons stopping in iron were captured by iron nuclei before they had a chance to disintegrate spontaneously.

Between 1947 and 1948, the Italian group, as well as research teams at the University of Chicago and the Massachusetts Institute of Technology, extended the decay experiments to a number of different substances. The most important result, first announced by the Italians, revealed that capture by the atomic nuclei of light elements (for example, carbon) did not compete significantly with the spontaneous decay of negative mesons. The probability of

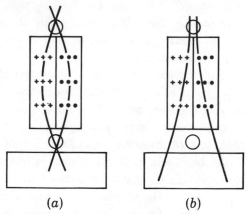

(a)   (b)

Fig. 9-1 Magnetic lens consisting of two iron bars magnetized in opposite directions. (*a*) The magnetic field points away from the observer (that is, into the page) in the bar at left and toward the observer (that is, out of the page) in the bar to the right. *Positive* particles passing through the upper G-M counter are deflected by the magnetic field toward the lower counter. (*b*) The magnetization of the bars is reversed. Positive particles passing through the upper G-M counter are deflected away from the lower counter. The lens in (*a*) will deflect *negative* particles away from the lower counter; the lens in (*b*) will deflect them toward the counter.

nuclear capture appeared to increase gradually with increasing atomic number. In magnesium ($Z = 12$) about one-half of the negative μ mesons disappeared by decay, one-half by nuclear capture. In elements heavier than magnesium, nuclear capture exceeded spontaneous decay; in elements lighter than magnesium, the reverse was true.

The fact that nuclear capture became increasingly effective with increasing atomic number was not in itself surprising. Heavy nuclei have a greater positive charge and therefore must provide a more effective trap for negative mesons to fall into. Physicists, however, found it extremely difficult to understand how, even in elements as light as carbon ($Z = 6$), negative mesons could possibly escape nuclear capture. Their argument ran as follows. Mu mesons were known to have a mean life of about 2 microseconds. Now, 2 microseconds may seem a very short interval, but on the atomic scale of time it was very long. In fact, it was at least 20 million times longer that the most generous theoretical estimate of the interval required for nuclear capture.

In other words, one could be sure on theoretical grounds that all negative μ mesons, once they were stopped in carbon, would fall into carbon nuclei before they had a chance to decay. If, nevertheless, most mesons did undergo spontaneous decay, they must retain their identity *within* the nuclei for a time interval so great that they had a chance to come out again. In the language of modern physics, this meant an exceedingly *weak interaction* between the μ mesons and the protons and neutrons of carbon nuclei.

Such a weak interaction was puzzling, to say the least. In the first place, if μ mesons were the "quanta of the nuclear force field" predicted by Yukawa (see Chap. 8), they had to interact strongly with protons and neutrons. In the second place, it was thought, μ mesons were produced in the passage of high-energy particles through nuclei, an event that lasts an extremely short time, something of the order of 10^{-22} second. If this were the case, why did the opposite process, namely, the absorption of μ mesons by nuclei, require periods of several microseconds? The answer, when it came,

was another instance of the close interplay between technical
developments and scientific advances, of which the history of
science offers so many examples.

Nuclear emulsions

The cloud chamber is a truly wonderful tool. It has enabled
physicists to "see" elementary particles and the results of their
collisions with atoms or nuclei. But, like any experimental device,
the cloud chamber has inherent limitations. Because of the low
density of gases, very few of the particles entering a cloud chamber
collide with nuclei or stop within the chamber.

To improve the situation, physicists, in the 1930s, began to
build larger chambers and to place slabs of solid materials (such as
carbon or various metals) across them. The technique of *multiplate
chambers* proved very useful in a number of studies, some of which I
shall relate in the next chapter. Still, it was not an entirely satisfactory solution to the problem; for when a particle interacts
within a plate (which is usually from a few millimeters to a few
centimeters thick), it is impossible to see exactly what happens at
the point where the collision occurs. Similarly, when a particle
stops in a plate and then decays, the decay products can be
observed only if they have enough energy to come out of the plate.
The direct observation of interactions and decay processes requires
some dense substance in which particles have a good chance of
undergoing collisions or of coming to rest and in which they will
somehow leave visible tracks.

In the middle 1940s physicists succeeded in perfecting a detector with the desired properties, the so-called *nuclear emulsion*.
Photographic emulsions had, of course, been widely used in radiation studies for many years. They had been responsible for Roentgen's discovery of X-rays, had played an important role in nuclear
physics, and had been used occasionally in cosmic-ray research.

The effect of high-energy radiations upon a photographic
emulsion is similar to that of light. Ionizing particles "sensitize"
the grains of silver bromide that they encounter along their path

in the emulsion. An appropriate "developer" solution will then reduce the sensitized grains to silver. Under a microscope, the trajectories of individual ionizing particles appear as rows of dark silver grains. But ordinary emulsions are sensitive only to comparatively slow particles, which leave a very dense trail of ions in their wake. Moreover, until the middle 1940s the available emulsions were exceedingly thin, and only particles traveling almost exactly parallel to the photographic plate left a track of any appreciable length. For these reasons, photographic emulsions had been almost completely abandoned as a means of detecting charged particles.

The emulsion technique was revived by a group of physicists at the University of Bristol in England under the leadership of C. F. Powell and Occhialini. Working in collaboration with scientists at the Ilford Company, they prepared new emulsions that contained a much higher concentration of silver bromide than ordinary photographic types and were thus more sensitive to ionizing particles. Soon afterward, scientists of the Kodak Company in the United States were also working in this field and making important contributions to its progress. New and ingenious methods for developing exposed plates made it possible to use emulsions almost a millimeter thick, or more than 100 times thicker than those previously available. A later technical development was the *stripped emulsion*, an emulsion without any glass backing, which could be stacked in layers to form what became known as *emulsion chambers*.

At the same time, physicists became experienced in recognizing the properties of charged particles from the appearance of their tracks in nuclear emulsions. When the emulsion is developed under carefully controlled conditions, the density of the black silver grains along a track is proportional to the density of ion pairs that the particle would produce in a gas. Thus the density decreases with increasing velocity in a known and well-defined manner.

Another measurable characteristic is *scattering*, or the "wiggliness" of a track. The scattering decreases as the kinetic energy increases, but it also depends to some extent on the mass of the

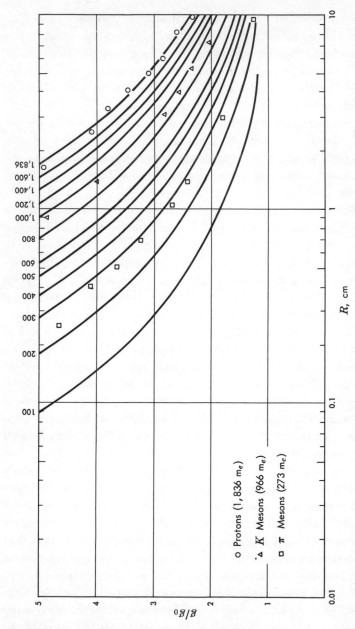

Fig. 9-2 Grain density as a function of residual range in an emulsion for singly charged particles of different masses. The experimental points belong to the proton, the K meson, and the π meson.

Measuring the mass of a particle from the grain density along its track in a nuclear emulsion

Figure 9-2 can be used to determine the mass of a particle that stops in a nuclear emulsion. Plotted on the horizontal axis is the *residual range R*, in centimeters, that is, the distance of a given point from the end of the track. Plotted on the vertical axis is the *grain density g* around this point, divided by the grain density of a minimum-ionizing particle g_0. The various curves represent particles of unit charge and different masses; the latter are indicated as multiples of the electron mass along the top of the graph. By measuring g at various points along a given track, one obtains a series of points; the curve that fits these points most closely indicates the mass of the particles. Shown in the figure are experimental points obtained by the Bristol group for protons (mass 1,836), for π mesons (mass 273), and for particles of mass 966 (the K mesons, discussed in chapter 10).

particle. Finally, if a particle stops in the emulsion, one can measure its range; the range, too, depends on the energy and the mass of the particle. Consequently, by measuring any two of the three quantities grain density, scattering, and range, it becomes possible to determine the particle mass (Fig. 9-2). In principle, this method for determining mass is similar to that used in cloud-chamber experiments (Figs. 8-1 and 8-4).

The discovery of the pi meson

In 1947 C. M. G. Lattes, Occhialini, and Powell exposed some of the newly developed nuclear plates to cosmic rays at mountain altitudes. In these plates they found several tracks of the kind shown in Fig. 9-3. The picture shows a particle (π) entering the emulsion and coming to rest. The gradual increase of grain density due to the gradual decrease in velocity leaves no doubt as to the direction in which the particle is traveling. The rate at which the grain density increases as the particle approaches the end of its range indicates a mass several hundred times that of an electron (Fig. 9-2). From the point at which this particle comes to rest, another particle (μ) emerges. The second particle, which comes to rest in the emulsion after traveling a distance of slightly more

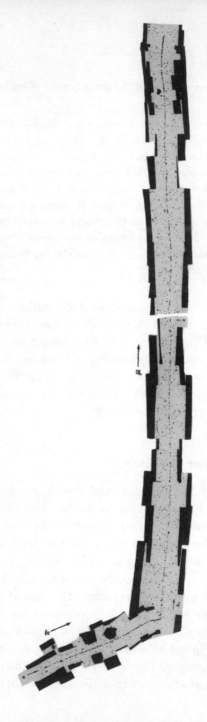

Fig. 9-3 Photomicrograph showing a π meson (π) coming to rest in a nuclear emulsion and a μ meson (μ) arising from the end of the π-meson track. (From C. M. G. Lattes, H. Muirhead, G. Occhialini, and C. F. Powell, *Nature*, vol. 160, p. 453, 1947.)

than 0.5 mm, also appears to have a mass of a few hundred electron masses. However, careful measurements of the grain densities at different distances from the end of the range show conclusively that the second particle is somewhat lighter than the first.

After discarding several interpretations, Lattes, Occhialini, and Powell came to the conclusion that the picture showed the decay of one meson into a lighter meson. But the heavier "parent" particle could not be the meson associated with the penetrating component of the local cosmic radiation, because when that meson decays, it produces an electron, not another meson. Thus, unless there were more than two kinds of mesons, it was the lighter, "daughter" particle that had to be identified with the previously known meson.

If this explanation were correct, the secondary meson, after coming to rest in the emulsion, should decay and produce an electron. The emulsions used in the 1947 experiments were not sufficiently sensitive to detect minimum-ionizing particles such as fast electrons. When emulsions sensitive to those particles became available in 1949, the decay electron duly appeared (Fig. 9–4). There was no longer any doubt about the conclusion reached by the Bristol group. The heavier, parent particle became known as the π meson. The lighter secondary particle, which until that time had been the *only* meson, was called the μ meson.

The discovery of the π meson clarified the meson puzzle considerably. The "quanta of the nuclear force" predicted by

Fig. 9-4 Photomicrograph of tracks in a nuclear emulsion, showing a π meson (π) that comes to rest and decays into a μ meson (μ). The μ meson in turn comes to rest and decays into an electron (e). (From R. H. Brown, U. Camerini, P. Fowler, H. Muirhead, C. F. Powell, and D. M. Ritson, *Nature*, vol. 163, p. 47, 1949.)

Yukawa were π mesons, not μ mesons. Pi mesons were the particles produced in high-energy nuclear interactions. The fact that μ mesons did not interact strongly with nuclei was no longer surprising, because μ mesons were not produced in nuclear interactions, but were born through the decay of π mesons. This picture, however, was quite different from the earlier, theoretical one. Yukawa had thought his particles would decay into electrons. Instead, they decayed into μ mesons, and μ mesons in turn decayed into electrons.

But what about negative π mesons, the original source of the meson puzzle? If π mesons were actually the particles of Yukawa's theory, and if they were abundantly produced in nuclear interactions, then negative π mesons that stopped in matter were also captured promptly by nuclei. As I have already pointed out, the energy suddenly released by the disappearance of a captured meson should produce a nuclear explosion. That is exactly what happens. Negative π mesons coming to rest in a nuclear emulsion are never seen to decay into μ mesons. Rather, a "star" appears at the end of their track, as was first shown by D. H. Perkins and by Occhialini and Powell in 1947 (Fig. 9–5). The star is produced by the particles into which the nucleus disintegrates as a result of the explosion. Thus, unlike a negative μ meson, a negative π meson that stops in matter has no chance to decay before a nucleus commits the "suicidal" act of trapping and "killing" it.[1]

Since the mesons found in the cosmic radiation near sea level were almost entirely of the μ variety, π mesons had to decay so fast that practically none of them survived the journey through the atmosphere. The earliest calculations indicated a mean life considerably shorter than 1 microsecond. This surmise proved to be

[1] It is interesting to note that when π mesons stop in an emulsion, they leave an unmistakable signature: a π-μ decay in the case of a positive π meson (Figs. 9–3 and 9–4) and a nuclear star in the case of a negative π meson (see Fig. 9–5). Thus the nuclear emulsion technique is ideally suited for the study of low-energy π mesons, which is the main reason why it has been so widely applied in studies of cosmic radiation and in experiments with high-energy accelerators.

correct even though the argument on which it rested was not entirely foolproof (π mesons fail to travel as far as μ mesons because, besides decaying more readily, they interact more frequently with atomic nuclei). Experiments carried out between 1948 and 1950 with high-energy accelerators gave a value of 2.55×10^{-8} second for the mean life of π mesons, or about 100 times shorter than the mean life of μ mesons. High-energy accelerators also made possible a precise measurement of the π-meson mass, which was found to be 273 electron masses.

When the mean life and mass of both π and μ mesons had been determined, there still remained the question of what disintegration products arose in the decay of these particles. Yukawa had pre-

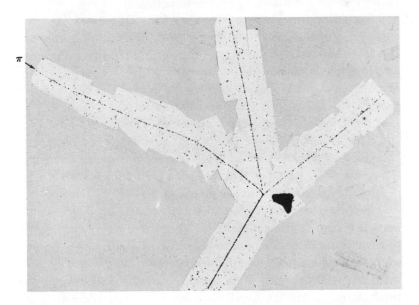

Fig. 9-5 Nuclear capture of negative π meson. The meson comes to rest in a nuclear emulsion and is promptly captured by a nucleus. The mass of the meson is immediately changed into energy, causing the nucleus to explode. The star in the picture is composed of the tracks left in the emulsion by the charged fragments of the nucleus. (From a paper by C. F. Powell in *Colston Papers*, Butterworth & Co. (Publishers), Ltd., London, 1949, p. 83.)

dicted that his quantum of the nuclear force field would decay into
an electron and a neutrino. But the charged particles appearing in
the decay of π mesons were μ mesons rather than electrons. And the
μ mesons, which did give rise to electrons, had nothing to do with
Yukawa's theory. Consequently, there was no reliable theory on
which to base any prediction concerning the decay of either meson.
Only experiment could provide the answer.

In the decay of a meson (as in the decay of a radioactive atom)
a certain amount of mass is transformed into energy in accordance
with Einstein's equation $E = mc^2$. The mass that disappears is the
difference between the mass of the parent meson and the combined
mass of the particles arising from its decay. The energy released
appears as the kinetic energy of these particles.

Considering the decay of π mesons first, the only visible track
coming out of the end of a π meson track was that of a μ meson.
But there had to be at least one other particle born in the process.
The principle involved here is *conservation of momentum;* the same
principle is at work when a gun recoils in the opposite direction
from that in which the shot is fired. The π meson, when it decays,
is at rest and therefore has no momentum. The decay μ meson, on
the other hand, does have a momentum, which must be exactly
canceled by an equal and opposite momentum carried by one or
more "invisible" particles. This invisible particle carries no charge,
or it would leave a track in the emulsion.

Suppose that in addition to the μ meson only one invisible
particle is born in a π-meson decay. Then there is only one way for
this particle and the μ meson to share the available kinetic energy
so as to acquire equal and opposite momenta. But if two or more
invisible particles arise from each π-meson decay, the decay
products can share the available energy in many different ways
without violating the conservation of momentum or the conservation of energy (Fig. 9–6). Now according to the experimental data,
whenever a decay μ meson stopped in an emulsion, it always
traveled the same distance from the point of origin (0.63 mm).
Since the μ meson always acquired the same energy (4.17 MeV),

the total energy was shared in only one way and therefore there was only one invisible particle.

What was this neutral particle? The property most easily determined was its mass. According to Einstein's law, when the π meson decays, it releases an amount of energy equal to $m_\pi c^2$

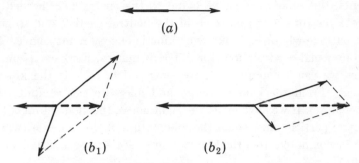

(a)

(b_1) (b_2)

Fig. 9-6 (a) A charged particle that decays into another charged particle (heavy arrow) and a neutral particle (light arrow). The parent particle was at rest and therefore had zero momentum. Conservation of momentum requires that the momenta of the two "daughter" particles be equal and opposite, so that they add up (vectorially) to zero. The kinetic energies of the two particles must add up to a fixed value equal to the velocity of light squared times the mass difference between the parent and the daughter particles. These two conditions determine in a unique manner the energies acquired by each of the two daughter particles. Thus, the charged daughter particle has the same energy in all decay events. The mass of the unknown neutral particle can be calculated from this energy. (b_1) and (b_2) A charged particle that decays into another charged particle and two neutral particles. The momentum of the charged daughter particle must be equal and opposite to the vector sum of the momenta of the two neutral particles. The kinetic energies of all three must add up to a fixed value equal, as before, to the energy released by the disappearance of mass in the decay process. These two conditions, however, do not uniquely determine the energies acquired by each of three daughter particles. Consequently, charged particles arising from various decay events will have a variety of energies. The energy will be small if the two neutral particles are emitted in nearly opposite directions (b_1) and large if they are emitted in nearly the same direction (b_2). The energy of the charged daughter particle is maximum when the two neutral particles are emitted in exactly the same direction. From this maximum energy it is possible to calculate the combined mass of the two neutral particles.

(m_π is the π-meson mass). Of this energy an amount equal to $m_\mu c^2$ appears as the mass m_μ of the μ meson. Another known amount (4.17 MeV) is accounted for by the kinetic energy of the μ meson. It is a simple matter to determine the amount of energy left over (about 30 MeV, to be specific). Because of conservation requirements, this amount must be equal to the energy $m_0 c^2$ needed to create the (unknown) mass m_0 of the neutral particle and to give the particle whatever (unknown) kinetic energy it may have. We can now make calculations for different masses. For each assumed mass we can compute $m_0 c^2$; the energy left over is the kinetic energy. From the kinetic energy and mass we can compute the momentum. If we have made the right guess, the momentum of the neutral particle must equal the momentum of the μ meson (which can be computed from the known values of its mass and its kinetic energy).

An analysis of the kind outlined above showed that the mass of the neutral particle is much smaller than the mass of the electron, and most likely is zero. There are two neutral particles with zero mass, the photon and the neutrino. Because of their very weak interaction with matter,[1] neutrinos are exceedingly difficult to detect, but photons can be detected without too much trouble through the secondary electrons they generate in matter by pair production or the Compton effect. Failing to find photons among the decay products of π mesons, physicists concluded that the neutral, massless particle arising from the decay of a π meson was a neutrino. The decay of positive and negative π mesons can be described symbolically by the formulas:

$$\pi^+ \rightarrow \mu^+ + \nu$$
$$\pi^- \rightarrow \mu^- + \bar{\nu}$$

where ν represents a neutrino and $\bar{\nu}$ an antineutrino.[2]

In the case of μ mesons, many experimenters undertook to measure the energies of the electrons arising from the decay of

[1] See Appendix H.
[2] See Appendix I.

"natural" μ mesons in cosmic radiation and of "artificial" μ mesons produced in high-energy accelerators. In 1949 Robert B. Leighton, Carl D. Anderson, and A. J. Seriff at the California Institute of Technology proved conclusively that the energies of the decay electrons were distributed over a wide range extending all the way from zero up to about 50 MeV. This meant there were at least *two* invisible particles among the decay products.

By that time physicists had gathered evidence that no photons were produced in the decay of μ mesons. In addition, some of the decay electrons had such a large energy as to require a combined mass for the "invisible" particles of practically zero. (Figure 9–6 clarifies this argument.) Therefore the neutral particles must again be neutrinos, and theoretical arguments showed that there were just two neutral particles. The decay schemes of positive and negative μ mesons then can be described symbolically by the formulas

$$\mu^+ \rightarrow e^+ + \nu + \bar{\nu}$$
$$\mu^- \rightarrow e^- + \nu + \bar{\nu}$$

where c represents an electron.

The discovery of the neutral pi meson

To complete the π-meson story, I should mention one other important discovery, a discovery that resulted from the combined efforts of cosmic-ray physicists and physicists working with high-energy accelerators.

Ever since the discovery of positive and negative mesons, physicists had speculated about the existence of neutral mesons. They had rather foggy ideas about what the properties of these particles might be until, in 1947, the problem was brought into sharper focus by Oppenheimer. He suggested that neutral mesons might decay very rapidly into photons and that the photons thus produced might be responsible for most of the cosmic-ray photons and electrons found in the atmosphere.

Oppenheimer's suggestion proved correct. The first experimental indication of the existence of neutral mesons came from cosmic-ray observations. Cloud-chamber photographs obtained in 1950 by the cosmic-ray group at the Massachusetts Institute of Technology provided strong evidence that high-energy nuclear interactions frequently gave rise not only to penetrating particles (charged π mesons) but also to neutral particles capable of initiating cascades. These neutral particles could well be photons arising from the decay of neutral mesons. Observations with nuclear emulsions exposed to cosmic rays confirmed these results. The final and crucial evidence for the existence of neutral mesons, however, came from experiments with a high-energy accelerator performed in 1950 at the University of California in Berkeley.

Subsequent experimental studies assigned a mass of 264 electron masses to the neutral meson, a value very close to the mass of the positive or negative π meson. Hence, the neutral meson was a π meson rather than a μ meson. Supporting this view was the fact that neutral mesons, like charged π mesons, were abundantly produced in high-energy nuclear interactions. The mean life of the neutral meson was estimated to be of the order of 2×10^{-16} second. It was also found that the meson produces two photons when it decays. Its decay scheme, therefore, is:

$$\pi^0 \rightarrow \gamma + \gamma$$

where π^0 represents a neutral π meson and γ a photon (γ ray).[1] The mean life of π^0 mesons is about 100 million times shorter than the mean life of charged π mesons. Consequently, π^0 mesons decay so near the point at which they originate that the two photons arising from their decay usually appear to come exactly from that point. (The photon paths, though invisible, can be derived from the observed tracks of the electron pairs produced in the emulsion when the photons undergo materialization of energy.) Only π^0 mesons of exceedingly high energy live long enough (because of the

[1] There are other possible modes of decay for π^0 mesons, but they are exceedingly rare.

relativistic effect discussed on page 117) to travel a distance of several microns before decaying (one micron is one-millionth of a meter). It was through accurate measurements of this distance in nuclear emulsions that it became possible to estimate the mean life of π^0 mesons.[1]

[1] Within the bounds of this book it is impossible to give proper credit to the many scientists who made important contributions to the discoveries related above. However, it is of historical interest to note that Japanese physicists, working in almost complete isolation during World War II, reached a number of conclusions that later proved to be correct. Even before the magnetic-lens experiment of Conversi, Pancini, and Piccioni (see page 127), Japanese physicists had become convinced that cosmic-ray mesons did not interact with atomic nuclei as strongly as those postulated by Yukawa. They argued that, if the interaction were strong, cosmic-ray mesons would not have been capable of traversing very large thicknesses of matter. As a way out of this difficulty, Tomonaga and his associates, in 1943, suggested that the cosmic-ray mesons and the Yukawa mesons might be different particles. (This two-meson hypothesis was formulated again by Robert E. Marshack and Hans A. Bethe, who did not know of Tomonaga's work, shortly before the experimental discovery of π mesons.) Also, in 1942, H. Tamaki postulated the existence of neutral mesons and presented the hypothesis that they decayed into photons, thereby giving rise to the bulk of the soft component of cosmic radiation.

Nuclear interactions of cosmic rays

10

On several occasions I have referred to the *nuclear interactions* of cosmic-ray particles. The time has come to look into this matter more closely. What evidence is there to show that such interactions actually occur? What are they like? Which among the various kinds of particles found in the cosmic radiation are actually capable of producing them? The present understanding of these inter-actions, which is still incomplete, has come from more than a quarter century of experimental and theoretical investigation.

Early evidence

As I mentioned in Chap. 6, when showers were first discovered in the early 1930s, many of us thought they resulted from the colli-sions of cosmic-ray particles with atomic nuclei. In such collisions, supposedly, nuclei were broken up and many positive and negative electrons were produced simultaneously. Theories of such *multiple-production processes* were developed by a number of physicists, notably Werner Heisenberg in Germany and Gleb Wataghin in Italy. However, it soon became clear that showers required a very different explanation.

Positive and negative electrons appeared in single pairs, not in groups of many pairs at a time. The large numbers of particles in the observed showers were the result of many separate events involving pair production by photons and radiation by electrons. These processes occurred *in the vicinity* of atomic nuclei, which provided the electric field necessary for pair production and radiation but were themselves left intact.

Nonetheless, there were also reasons for believing that cosmic-ray particles did sometimes break up atomic nuclei and, in so doing, gave rise to groups of secondary particles entirely different from those of ordinary showers.

The earliest evidence for such nuclear disintegrations came from the so-called *cosmic-ray stars* discovered by Marietta Blau and H. Wambacher of Austria in 1932. These stars, which appeared in photographic emulsions that had been lying about for a long time before development, consisted of groups of particle tracks diverging from a single point. Because they were working with emulsions in which only heavily ionizing particles would leave observable tracks, Blau and Wambacher attributed the tracks to comparatively slow protons and α particles with energies of the order of 10 MeV. They then attempted to determine whether the "stars" were produced by radioactive contamination of the plates. (A tiny speck of a radioactive substance, such as polonium, can produce a star of α particles appearing to come from a single point, even though the decay of each polonium nucleus gives rise to only one α particle.) However, Blau and Wambacher had to discard this interpretation, because the energy of the particles was too high, and they concluded that the stars were the result of nuclear disintegrations caused by cosmic rays. Later, in confirmation of their conclusion, the stars were found to occur more frequently in photographic plates kept at high elevations, where the cosmic-ray intensity is greater.

New experimental methods

For several years cosmic-ray stars remained the only *direct* evidence for interactions between cosmic rays and atomic nuclei. The energy required to produce these stars was modest on the cosmic-ray scale (of the order of 100 MeV). Moreover, the stars were quite rare. Hence, it appeared that nuclear interactions did not play any significant role in the general picture of cosmic-ray phenomena. But the discovery of mesons changed the picture completely. Mesons had a short life, and therefore they could not come from any great distance. In other words, they were not part of the primary cosmic radiation but were born in the atmosphere. The question that then arose was how they were produced.

Some physicists considered the possibility that photons might produce meson pairs by a materialization process similar to the production of electron pairs. However, it was generally believed to be more likely that the observed mesons were the result of nuclear interactions. (Pair production of mesons by photons does occur, as experiments performed many years later demonstrated, but the event is extremely rare.) The theoretical ideas about multiple production of particles in nuclear collisions, originally proposed to explain ordinary showers, were now revived and applied to mesons, and experimental physicists set out to search for these processes.

Wataghin, then in Brazil, and Jánossy, in England, were the first to begin this new line of research, in about 1940. One of the experimental arrangements used by Jánossy and his collaborators is illustrated in Fig. 10–1. It consisted of a number of G-M counters with the appropriate electronic circuits to detect coincidences between counters out of line. In principle the method was very much like the one used for the detection of ordinary showers (Chap. 4). However, Jánossy's counters were so arranged that thick layers of lead could be placed between them. Although the presence of lead between the counters cut down the number of coincidences markedly, a significant number was still observed with as much as 50 cm of lead between the counters. These coincidences could not have been due to ordinary showers, since ordinary showers could not have traversed 50 cm of lead. They were therefore ascribed to groups of penetrating particles, presumably mesons, produced by nuclear interactions of cosmic rays in the material above the counters.

Counter arrangements similar to the one shown in Fig. 10–1 (known as *penetrating-shower detectors*) proved to be very convenient in the study of nuclear interactions of cosmic rays. Notice

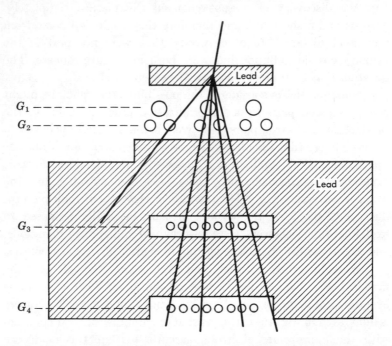

Fig. 10-1 Penetrating-shower detector used by Jánossy in his early experiments. Electronic circuits select simultaneous discharges of at least one counter in group G_1 and two counters each in groups G_2 to G_4. Such coincidences can be produced only by showers containing penetrating particles capable of traversing large thicknesses of lead.

that they will respond only to interactions initiated by particles of very high energies — many BeV at least — for it takes a large amount of energy to produce several particles capable of traversing 50 cm of lead.

At about the same time another very useful instrument, the multiplate cloud chamber to which I made incidental reference in Chaps. 7 and 9, was being developed. The multiplate cloud chamber, often rectangular in shape, contains a number of horizontal plates, usually metal. The purpose of the plates is to increase the probability that a cosmic-ray particle will interact with matter while traversing the chamber. In most cases, the chamber is triggered by an array of G-M counters so arranged as to favor the detection of such interactions. A multiplate chamber can be thought of as an absorber cut into slices; the particle tracks are visible in the space between slices and thus provide a fairly detailed picture of what actually happens when the particles traverse the absorber.

In about 1939, J. C. Street (who had collaborated with E. C. Stevenson in making the first measurement of the μ-meson mass; see Chap. 8) constructed a multiplate chamber for the purpose of studying ordinary photon-electron showers. Among large numbers of showers he observed a few events of a different type in which, apparently, cosmic-ray particles had collided with atomic nuclei. The distinguishing feature of these events was the production of secondary particles that passed through the metal plates without initiating electron showers; the particles were not electrons, then, but probably mesons. A typical shower containing mesons is shown in Fig. 10–2.

A third instrumental development of very great importance in the detailed study of the nuclear interactions of cosmic rays was the revival in the middle 1940s of the nuclear-emulsion technique discussed in the preceding chapter. Nuclear emulsions sensitive to minimum-ionizing particles made it possible to detect the production of high-energy mesons in cosmic-ray stars. It was found, indeed, that when a particle of sufficiently high energy collides

with a nucleus, it often produces groups of many mesons, as some theorists had predicted (Fig. 10–3).

It would have been difficult to establish this important fact by any technique that did not allow experimenters to "see" the nuclear interaction at its origin, as the emulsion technique did. In a multiplate chamber, for example, the interactions occur within the plates and the particles arising from them must travel a certain distance before they appear in the space between plates. When many particles emerge from a plate, one can never be completely certain that they were all produced in a single event and not in several successive collisions occuring next to one another.

Nuclear-active particles

The reader, at this point, may wonder which of the various kinds of particles found in cosmic radiation are responsible for nuclear interactions. Are all or only some of the particles capable of producing these interactions? Or are the interactions caused by particles of a still different kind that the experiments described thus far had failed to discover?

These very questions began to worry physicists after they realized the importance of nuclear interactions in cosmic-ray phenomena. Some interesting clues came to light when they began to study the rate of occurrence of nuclear interactions under various absorbers and at different altitudes. For example, in 1947 D. H. Perkins reported that the number of cosmic-ray stars found in plates kept under a thick lead shield was not much smaller than that found in unshielded plates. Since the shield was sufficiently

---

Fig. 10-2 Mesons in a penetrating shower traverse several metal plates of a cloud chamber without producing secondary showers. In plate 4, however, a secondary interaction gives rise to a high-energy photon or electron, which initiates an ordinary shower. The brass plates across the chamber are 1.25 cm thick. The photograph was made by the MIT cosmic-ray group in 1950.

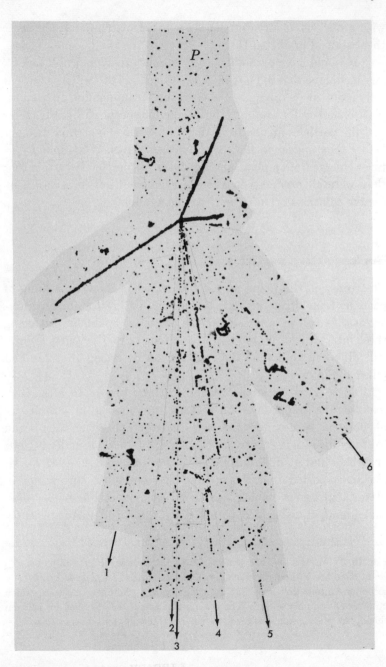

thick to absorb practically all electrons and photons, some other particle or particles produced stars.

In 1946 I had moved to the Massachusetts Institute of Technology and there resumed my research on cosmic rays, which the war had interrupted. At one time or another in the following years, many distinguished scientists from the United States and other countries were associated with the MIT cosmic-ray group. Even a partial list would run to several dozen names. But it should be clearly understood that whenever I refer to the contributions of the MIT group, I am speaking primarily of work done by these scientists, and not of my own.

Among the first problems to which the MIT group turned its attention was the nuclear interactions of cosmic rays. To determine whether μ mesons were responsible for these interactions, John Tinlot in 1948 made a careful survey of the altitude variations in the rate of occurrence of nuclear interactions. Using a penetrating-shower detector (Fig. 10–4), Tinlot carried out measurements at sea level, at different locations in the Rocky Mountains of Colorado, and at different elevations aboard a B-29 plane. His results showed that the number of high-energy particles responsible for the penetrating showers increased with altitude much more rapidly than the number of μ mesons. For instance, between sea level and 4,300 meters (the top of Mt. Evans), the rate of production of penetrating showers increased by a factor of 32 and the number of μ mesons by a factor of 2.5. Obviously, the particles that gave rise to penetrating showers in nuclear collisions *could not be μ mesons*. Similar results were obtained at about the same time by other physicists using instruments designed to detect cosmic-ray stars.

Fig. 10-3 Star resulting from a nuclear collision of a high-energy particle (*P*). The star contains a number of tracks, among which those numbered from 1 to 6 show minimum ionization. They belong to particles, presumably mesons, moving at nearly the speed of light. This is a typical example of multiple-meson production. (From R. H. Brown, U. Camerini, P. H. Fowler, W. Heitler, D. T. King, and C. F. Powell, *The Philosophical Magazine*, vol. 40, p. 862, 1949.)

What did these results mean? In the first place, they proved
that high-energy electrons, photons, and μ mesons, which together
form the bulk of the cosmic radiation near sea level, do not interact
appreciably with atomic nuclei. In the second place, they proved
that the cosmic radiation in the atmosphere contains not only

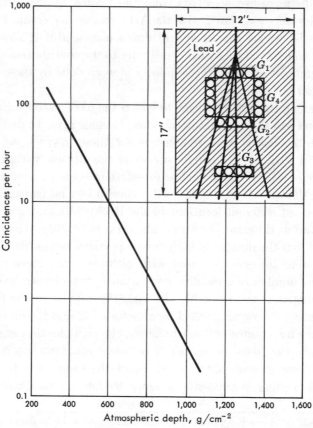

Fig. 10-4 Increase of penetrating showers with altitude as measured by
Tinlot with the detector shown in the inset. Penetrating showers were detected
by the simultaneous discharges of two or more G-M counters in each of the
rows G_1 to G_3 (counters G_4 were not used in this particular measurement).
The vertical scale gives the number of coincidences per hour; the horizontal
scale gives the air mass above the instrument, in grams per square centimeter.

electrons, photons, and μ mesons but also particles of one or more different kinds that are capable of breaking up nuclei and producing secondary mesons. These *nuclear-active* particles are very rare near sea level but they rapidly increase in number with altitude.

The dimensions of atomic nuclei were known fairly accurately. From the cross-sectional area of nuclei and from the known number of atoms per gram, one could easily compute the probability that a particle traveling in a straight line would hit a nucleus while traversing a given layer of matter. For a particle traveling a distance of 1 cm in iron, the probability was about 1 in 20. In the case of charged particles this estimate applied only if the particles had sufficiently high energy not to be deflected appreciably by the electric fields of nuclei.

Cosmic-ray particles certainly satisfied this condition. And yet thousands upon thousands of cosmic-ray electrons, photons, and μ mesons traversed 1 cm of iron without producing a single nuclear interaction. This meant that when one of these particles passed through a nucleus, nothing happened, either to the particle itself or to the nucleus. In other words, with respect to electrons, photons, and μ mesons, a nucleus seemed to behave like a cloud penetrated by a bullet. The inability of μ mesons to interact with nuclei was consistent with the fact, mentioned in the last chapter, that the mesons were not easily absorbed by nuclei when stopped in matter. The absence of nuclear interaction also explained why μ mesons were absorbed so slowly in the atmosphere. Nuclear-active particles, on the other hand, were absorbed very rapidly in the atmosphere (Fig. 10–4). In fact, the observed atmospheric absorption was more or less consistent with the view that a nuclear-active particle disappeared whenever it happened to hit a nucleus of nitrogen or oxygen.

The next problem was to determine the nature of nuclear-active particles. Various clues pointed to protons, to neutrons, and to π mesons as likely candidates. The cohesion of protons and neutrons in a nucleus, as I noted earlier, indicated that at close distances these particles exerted tremendous forces of attraction upon one another. Therefore, a proton or neutron should interact strongly with any nucleus it met. Pi mesons also should interact strongly with nuclei, since they were supposed to be produced in nuclear collisions. A number of experiments, which I cannot relate here in detail, established the correctness of these suppositions. The strongly interacting cosmic-ray particles found in the atmosphere were indeed protons, neutrons, and those π mesons that had not already decayed into μ mesons.

Hosts of new particles

The rapid increase in the number of protons, neutrons, and π mesons with altitude made it very desirable for physicists interested in the nuclear interactions of these particles to carry out experiments at the highest possible elevations. In answer to this need, the sounding balloon technique was perfected to the point where it became possible to fly fairly heavy and elaborate scientific instruments for hours or days at altitudes above 100,000 feet.

To accommodate experiments requiring ground-based instrumentation, mountain laboratories sprang up throughout the world: the Laboratory of Pic du Midi at 2,860 meters in the French Pyrenees (near a well-known solar observatory of the same name); the Laboratory of Testa Grigia, near Cervinia, at 3,500 meters in the Italian Alps; the Inter-university High-altitude Laboratory of Echo Lake, near Denver, Colorado, at 3,240 meters in the Rocky Mountains; the Laboratory of Chacaltaya, near La Paz, at 5,200 meters in the Bolivian Andes; and many others. Cosmic-ray experiments performed with balloons, in the mountain laboratories, and at sea level provided a wealth of information on high-energy nuclear interactions. Among the groups that distinguished themselves in this work were those at the University of Chicago under Marcel Schein, the École Polytechnique of Paris under Louis Leprince-Ringuet, and the University of Bristol under C. F. Powell.

Among the effects of high-energy interactions discovered by

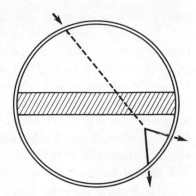

Fig. 10-5 Tracing of a cloud-chamber picture obtained by Rochester and Butler in 1947, which they interpreted as showing the decay, in flight, of a neutral particle (represented by the dashed line) into two charged particles. (From a paper in *Nature*, vol. 160, p. 855, 1947.)

cosmic-ray physicists, the most baffling was the production of an amazing variety of previously unknown, short-lived "elementary" particles. Where the π meson had filled a theoretical gap, the new particles created a totally unexpected and even staggering overflow. Indeed, the problem of finding a place for such particles, as well as for the μ meson, in the general framework of physics became one of the most pressing tasks of theoretical physics.

In 1947, just a few months after the paper announcing the discovery of the π meson appeared, George D. Rochester and C. C. Butler of the cosmic-ray group at the University of Manchester published two remarkable cloud-chamber photographs. One of them showed the tracks of two charged particles diverging down-

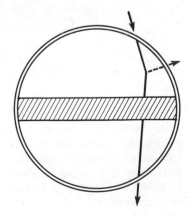

Fig. 10-6 Tracing of a cloud-chamber picture obtained by Rochester and Butler in 1947, which they interpreted as showing the decay, in flight, of a charged particle into one charged and one neutral secondary particle. (From a paper in *Nature*, vol. 160, p. 855, 1947.)

ward from a point in the gas of the cloud chamber (Fig. 10–5). After the most careful consideration of all possible interpretations, Rochester and Butler were forced to conclude that both particles had originated in the decay of a neutral particle that had come from above and, of course, had left no visible track.

In the second photograph a charged particle had, it seemed, suddenly changed direction while traversing the chamber (Fig. 10–6). Rochester and Butler were unable to explain this picture except by assuming that the charged particle had decayed in flight and had given rise to a secondary charged particle and to an invisible neutral particle. More importantly, neither the neutral particle invoked to explain the first event nor the charged particle in the second could possibly be identified as any known particle.

Powell's group at Bristol reported another unusual event in 1949. Working with nuclear emulsions, they found a particle with an apparent mass intermediate between that of the π meson and that of the proton. After coming to rest in the emulsion, the

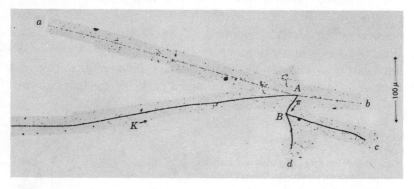

Fig. 10-7   Decay of a heavy meson into three π mesons, observed by Powell's group at the University of Bristol in 1949. The heavy meson K comes to rest at A. There it decays into two fast π mesons (tracks a and b) and a slow negative π meson, which comes to rest at B. The negative π meson is captured by a nucleus, which explodes, ejecting two heavily ionizing fragments (c and d) and, presumably, one or more neutrons, which leave no visible track. (From R. Brown, U. Camerini, P. H. Fowler, H. Muirhead, C. F. Powell, and D. M. Ritson, *Nature*, vol. 163, p. 82, 1949.)

particle appeared to decay into three mesons. One of the mesons stopped in the emulsion and left the signature characteristic of negative π mesons, a nuclear star (Fig. 10–7).

It was difficult to draw any clear conclusions from these few isolated observations. But the evidence quickly began to multiply. Anderson and his collaborators at the California Institute of Technology (working at sea level and at 3,200 meters altitude) obtained a substantial number of pictures confirming the findings of Rochester and Butler. In the following years cosmic-ray physicists throughout the world detected more and more "new" unstable particles in cloud-chamber photographs and in nuclear emulsions.

For a while there was a great deal of confusion about the number and properties of the particles required to explain all the experimental data. Finally it became clear that there were two groups of new particles, to which the Cosmic-Ray Conference held at Bagnère de Bigorre, France, in 1953, gave the names *heavy mesons* and *hyperons*. Heavy mesons and hyperons may be neutral or electrically charged. Heavy mesons are lighter than protons but heavier than π mesons. Hyperons are heavier than protons. Heavy mesons and hyperons never occur singly. Pairs of heavy mesons may be produced in nuclear collisions by a direct process of materialization of energy. A high-energy proton or neutron may turn into a hyperon when it strikes an atomic nucleus, giving rise at the same time to a heavy meson. In this case part of its energy appears in the mass of the heavy meson and in the greater mass of the hyperon.

The first of the two particles reported in 1947 by Rochester and Butler had been a neutral lambda particle (Λ) — a hyperon — which decayed into a proton and a negative π meson:

$$\Lambda \rightarrow p^+ + \pi^-$$

The second particle found by Rochester and Butler had been positive sigma particle (Σ^+) — another hyperon — which decayed into a neutron (n) and a positive π meson:

$$\Sigma^+ \rightarrow n + \pi^+$$

The particle reported in 1949 by the Bristol group had been a heavy meson, positively charged (K^+), which decayed according to the scheme

$$K^+ \rightarrow \pi^+ + \pi^+ + \pi^-$$

One of the reasons it was so difficult to disentangle the experimental findings was that many of the new particles decay in several different ways; for example, the positive K meson can also decay according to any one of the following schemes:

$$K^+ \rightarrow \pi^0 + \pi^0 + \pi^+$$
$$K^+ \rightarrow \pi^0 + \pi^+$$
$$K^+ \rightarrow \mu^+ + \nu$$
$$K^+ \rightarrow \mu^+ + \pi^0 + \nu$$
$$K^+ \rightarrow e^+ + \pi^0 + \nu$$

Some of these decay schemes were considered incompatible with one another, according to previously accepted theoretical ideas, and the difficulty was resolved only when one of these ideas was shown to be wrong. I am referring here to the discovery (due to the theoretical work by T. D. Lee and C. M. Yang and to the experimental work by C. S. Wu and her collaborators in 1956) that *conservation of parity*, unlike the conservation of energy or the conservation of momentum, is not a law of nature.[1]

The completion of this very brief and sketchy account requires some mention of the *antiproton* and the *antineutron*. The first is a negative particle having the same mass as the proton. It bears to the proton the same relation as that borne by the positive to the negative electron. As in the case of the electrons, mutual annihilation is the result of the encounter of a proton with its antiparticle. The antineutron, though neutral and having the same mass, is not identical with the ordinary neutron but is instead the counterpart of it as the antiproton is the counterpart of the proton. Thus, a

[1] The law of conservation of parity involves rather subtle concepts. Crudely speaking, it postulates that a physical system and its mirror image (exemplified by a right-handed and a left-handed screw) must obey the same physical laws.

neutron and an antineutron, when they come together, also annihilate each other.

Antiprotons and antineutrons had been predicted by Dirac's theory. In 1954, cosmic-ray observations with cloud chambers and nuclear emulsions recorded two events that looked suspiciously like annihilations involving antiprotons. However, it was only through the work done with high-energy accelerators by Emilio Segrè and Owen Chamberlain at Berkeley that, in 1956, the existence of antiprotons and antineutrons became an experimental certainty.[2]

Neutrons in cosmic rays

Nuclear collisions produce not only high-energy secondary particles but also substantial numbers of protons, neutrons, and α particles with energies of the order of millions of electron volts. Protons and α particles of such low energies are very rapidly absorbed through ionization losses. As a result, they never occur naturally in any great abundance. But neutrons, of course, do not lose energy by ionization. In successive collisions with nuclei, they gradually slow down and eventually become easy prey to nuclear absorption. The most voracious nucleus in the atmosphere happens to be that of nitrogen ($A = 14$; $Z = 7$). Consequently, most neutrons end their free lives by falling into nitrogen nuclei, each of which then emits a proton to become a nucleus of the radioactive isotope carbon 14 ($A = 14$; $Z = 6$).

The experimental study of slow neutrons in the atmosphere has proved to be of considerable interest in the general framework of cosmic-ray research. Among the physicists who made important contributions to this subject, I wish to mention here Serge Korff of New York University and John A. Simpson of the University of Chicago. Moreover, the production of carbon 14 by slow neutrons has had an important application in a field quite removed from the

[2] See Appendix I for a list of the known "elementary" particles and a description of some of their basic properties.

study of cosmic radiation: archeology. The age of a piece of wood, say, can be determined by measuring the ratio of carbon 14 to carbon 12 (the common, nonradioactive isotope) in a sample of the wood. All plants take in carbon dioxide in the process of photo-synthesis and "exhale" it in respiration. During the life of a plant or tree, then, the ratio of carbon 14 to carbon 12 will always be the same as that in the atmosphere. When the plant dies, however, the ratio decreases as carbon 14 decays. Since carbon 14 has a half-life of 5,600 years, the ratio will decrease by one-half in that time. Thus it becomes possible to make fairly reliable age determinations on a wooden object (or other once-living material) dating back twenty thousand years or more. This is the principle of *carbon dating*, which was developed in the 1940s by Willard F. Libby.

What cosmic rays are and what they do in the atmosphere

11

Between 1940 and 1950, as the nature and the properties of the various particles found in the local cosmic radiation were gradually puzzled out, a unified and self-consistent picture of all cosmic-ray phenomena began to emerge. And by the end of that decade physicists had found the answer to the original question raised by Hess's discovery in 1912: What is the primary cosmic radiation that rains upon the earth's atmosphere from outer space?

The primary radiation

In 1940, experimental studies of the effect of the earth's magnetic field on the incident radiation (Chap. 5) had already shown that most, and possibly all, primary cosmic rays are positively charged particles. A few years earlier some physicists had identified the penetrating particles observed near sea level with primary cosmic rays. By 1940, however, these penetrating particles were known to be mesons (that is, μ mesons), which did not live more than a few microseconds. The mesons, therefore, could not be part of the radiation arriving from outer space, but had to be produced in the atmosphere by primary cosmic-ray particles of a different kind.

Barring the existence of hitherto unknown, positively charged, stable particles, the primary radiation had to consist of positive electrons, or protons, or heavier nuclei, or a mixture of all three. But until 1940, experimental investigations provided no clear evidence on which to base a conclusion. Then in the early 1940s Marcel Schein and his group at the University of Chicago undertook a series of balloon experiments (up to altitudes of about 70,000 feet, where the pressure is about one-thirtieth of an atmosphere) the results of which convinced them that primary cosmic rays were not electrons. Judging from their experiments, the particles found at very high altitude passed through several centimeters of lead without producing showers as abundantly as high-energy electrons were known to produce. Moreover, they did not appear to be absorbed by lead as rapidly as electrons. On the basis of the evidence, Schein and his collaborators took the view that primary cosmic rays were probably protons.

The experiments on the nuclear interactions of cosmic rays discussed in Chap. 10 greatly strengthened this conclusion; for the number of nuclear-active particles, which constituted a small fraction of the total radiation found near sea level, increased with increasing altitude much more rapidly than the number of electrons, photons, and μ mesons. Indeed, it increased steadily up to the highest elevations attained in the experiments, whereas the intensities of other components of the cosmic radiation reached a maximum and then decreased again (see Fig. 11–7). Through careful analysis and discussion of their experimental data, physicists became convinced that practically all primary cosmic rays were nuclear-active particles.

The nuclear-active particles found in the atmosphere were protons, neutrons, and π mesons. The only stable positive particle among these was the proton. It was thus natural to conclude that primary cosmic rays were protons. This conclusion proved to be correct — in part.

Our story takes us now to the Universities of Minnesota and Rochester, where, soon after the war, strong cosmic-ray groups had been established by Edward P. Ney and by Hans L. Bradt and Bernard Peters, respectively. In 1948 the two groups, working in collaboration, sent a sounding balloon, carrying nuclear-emulsion plates, up to an altitude of 94,000 feet. When the plates were developed, they showed a number of very dense tracks, most of which passed through the entire pile of plates. From the *grain density* it was possible to estimate the rate of energy loss along the path and therefore the total energy spent by the particles in traversing the plates. The conclusion was that the particles had energies of at least many BeV.

At such large energies protons behave more or less as minimum-ionizing particles. Since the ionizing power (and hence the grain density) increases with the mass and with the electric charge of a particle of given energy, the observed particles either were heavier than protons or carried more than one elementary charge. Indeed, it soon became apparent that both the mass and electric charge were greater than the mass and charge of protons and that the particles were the nuclei of elements heavier than hydrogen stripped of their electrons. (The same balloon that carried the nuclear plates also carried a small cloud chamber. The cloud-chamber photographs, too, showed tracks of fast, multiply-charged particles.)

The heavy nuclei found in the upper atmosphere, because of their high energy, were without question related to cosmic radiation. The physicists who discovered them presented several convincing arguments that they were not secondary particles, but belonged to the primary cosmic radiation itself. Perhaps the most direct line of reasoning rested on the observation of nuclei carrying a greater charge than that of the nuclei of atmospheric gases. Obviously these nuclei could not arise from the disintegration of gas nuclei in collisions with primary cosmic-ray particles.

The emulsions used in the Minnesota-Rochester experiment were not sensitive enough to detect fast protons. When some time later more sensitive plates were flown, they showed, as expected, large numbers of proton tracks. In fact, it turned out that most of the primary radiation actually consists of protons. The relative abundance of the various nuclei is given in Table 11–1.

While there was no longer any doubt that primary cosmic rays are for the most part protons and, to a lesser extent, bare nuclei of heavier elements, experimenters continued to search for high-energy electrons and photons in the primary radiation. Experiments performed at the Massachusetts Institute of Technology in 1948 and at the University of Minnesota in 1952 gave negative results. In 1961, however, James Earl at the University of Minnesota and Peter Meyer and Rochus Vogt at the University of Chicago succeeded in detecting primary electrons with an abundance of the order of a few electrons per hundred incident particles (which makes the electron flux intermediate between that of helium nuclei and the combined flux of all other heavier nuclei). In the same year William Kraushaar and George W. Clark at the Massachusetts Institute of Technology, using a detector carried beyond the atmosphere by an artificial satellite, found some evidence (still unconfirmed as this is written) for a flux of primary photons with energy greater than about 50 MeV of the order of 1 or 2 per 1,000 incident particles.

The generation of secondary rays in the atmosphere

Out of all this there arises a natural question about what physicists call the "genetic relation" between the various components of the local cosmic radiation. In other words: Through what chain of interactions does the primary radiation produce the many different kinds of rays observed at various levels in the atmosphere?

Table 11-1 **Composition of primary cosmic radiation**
The table gives the number of different nuclei per 100,000 protons in the primary radiation. Only primary particles with energies greater than 2.5 BeV *per nucleon* are considered [i.e., protons (A = 1) with energies greater than 2.5 BeV; helium nuclei (A = 4) with more than $4 \times 2.5 = 10$ BeV; carbon nuclei (A = 12) with more than $12 \times 2.5 = 30$ BeV, and so on]. The data are taken from a paper by V. L. Ginzburg and S. I. Syrovatsky, *Journal of Theoretical Physics (Supplement)*, No. 20, p. 1, 1961.

Nuclei	Z	Relative number
Hydrogen (*p*)	1	100,000
Helium (*α*)	2	6,770
Light nuclei	3 to 5	146
Medium nuclei	6 to 9	430
Heavy nuclei	≥ 10	246

I have already mentioned the extensive and remarkable observations carried out by Erich Regener and his group at high altitudes and at great depths under water. It was one of Regener's collaborators, Georg Pfotzer, who in 1935 first flew an instrument designed to detect cosmic-ray particles traveling in a more or less vertical direction. Pfotzer's experiment was cleaner than those performed previously with electroscopes, because electroscopes record rays coming from *all* directions; and at a given altitude the effective thickness of the atmosphere is different for rays arriving at different angles to the vertical.

Pfotzer's instrument was essentially a G-M telescope pointing vertically. Figure 11-1 shows the experimental arrangement. The curve in Fig. 11-2 gives the coincidence rate as a function of atmospheric depth.[1] The most striking feature of the curve, which closely resembles the shower curves discussed earlier (Fig. 7-1), was the maximum found at an atmospheric depth of about 90 g/cm². It showed, more directly than any prior experiment had, that most charged particles found in the atmosphere are of secondary origin. Indeed, the large increase in the counting rate from the top of the atmosphere to a depth of 90 g/cm² could only be ex-

[1] See Appendix A. Atmospheric depth as a function of altitude is given in Fig. 11-8.

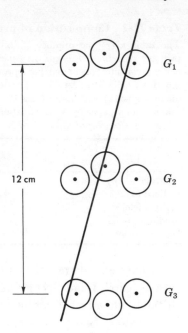

Fig. 11-1 Geiger-Müller telescope used by Georg Pfotzer in 1935 to measure the intensity of cosmic rays traveling through the atmosphere in a vertical direction. A coincidence is recorded whenever a particle discharges one G-M counter in each of the three groups G_1, G_2, and G_3.

12 cm

plained as the gradual buildup of secondary rays through the interactions of primary particles in air.

For several years in the middle 1930s, my own group at the University of Padua in Italy was actively engaged in experiments designed to study the genetic relationship between the various secondary components. We used different arrangements of G-M counters and absorbers to sort out individual groups of particles. For example, a vertical telescope of G-M counters separated by thick blocks of lead selected penetrating particles (later identified as μ mesons). A triangular array of counters under a lead plate detected high-energy electrons and photons that produced showers in the plate (Fig. 11–3). For the most part, our experiments consisted of comparing the counting rates of various detectors at different altitudes on mountains. Other investigators undertook similar experiments. Particularly valuable and illuminating results were obtained in the middle 1940s by a group of Italian physicists under Gilberto Bernardini.

It would be impossible for me to describe here in any detail the results of these experiments, just as it would be impossible to describe the subtle and often quite involved arguments used in their interpretation. I should like, however, to recall briefly how the general view of the problem gradually evolved. I shall do it by imagining the descriptions of cosmic radiation that one would have been likely to elicit, at different times, from a cosmic-ray physicist. Of course, not every physicist would have given the same answer, and I may not have been completely unbiased in my selection.

1928   The primary cosmic radiation consists of high-energy photons; the charged ionizing particles observed in the atmosphere are secondary electrons arising from Compton collisions with these photons. (*False*)

1931   The charged particles found in the atmosphere are, for the most part, primary cosmic rays. (*False*) However, among the observed particles there are also some secondary electrons produced in the atmosphere. (*True*)

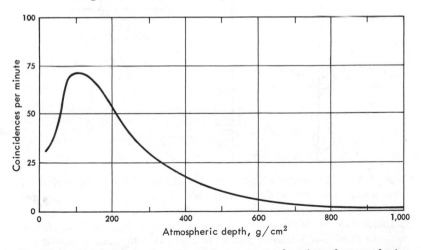

Fig. 11-2   Vertical intensity of cosmic rays as a function of atmospheric depth, according to Pfotzer. The horizontal scale gives the atmospheric depth in grams per square centimeter; the vertical scale, the number of coincidences per minute recorded with the telescope shown in Fig. 11-1.

1934 The cosmic-ray particles found in the atmosphere include high-energy electrons and photons, which can be recognized by their property of producing showers. (*True*) They also include penetrating particles, whose nature is still a puzzle. The penetrating particles are probably part of the primary radiation. (*False*) Some of the electrons and photons are produced by collisions of the penetrating particles with atoms in the atmosphere. However, not all of them originate in this way, because experiments have shown that the number of electrons and photons increases with altitude more rapidly than the number of penetrating particles. (*True*)

1939 The penetrating particles are mesons and, since mesons are unstable, they must be produced in the atmosphere. (*True*) The decay of mesons gives rise to electrons; electrons initiate showers containing photons as well as electrons.

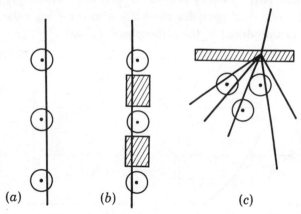

(a)   *(b)*   *(c)*

Fig. 11-3 Experimental arrangements for selecting different components of local cosmic radiation. (*a*) Coincidences between three G-M counters, placed one above the other, measure the flux of both "soft" and "penetrating" particles (that is, electrons and μ mesons, respectively). (*b*) Coincidences between three G-M counters, placed one above the other and separated by lead blocks with a total thickness of approximately 10 cm measure the flux of "penetrating particles" alone. (*c*) Coincidences between three G-M counters in a triangular array, with a lead plate about 1 cm thick above them, measure the flux of shower-producing particles (high-energy electrons and photons).

These electrons and photons increase with altitude more rapidly than mesons because the density of air decreases as the altitude increases, and the probability that a meson will decay in a layer of air of a given mass per unit area increases correspondingly. (*True*) Thus the altitude variation of electrons and photons is consistent with the assumption that these particles originate entirely from mesons, mainly through decay processes. (*False*)

1945   The recent, more accurate data on the altitude variations of electrons and photons have once more changed our views concerning the origin of these particles. We now believe that they do not arise solely from the decay of mesons or from the collisions of mesons with atoms. Probably some of them are produced in the same nuclear interactions believed to be involved in the production of mesons. (*True*)

1950   There are several types of mesons, and those constituting the penetrating component of the local radiation are of the mu variety. Mu mesons arise from the decay of charged π mesons. Although electrons and photons arise in part from the decay of μ mesons, to a large extent they arise from the decay of neutral π mesons and from the subsequent production of showers by the γ rays born in these processes. Charged and neutral π mesons are produced in the high-energy interactions of primary protons and heavier nuclei with nuclei of the atmospheric gases. (*True*)

A summary

All the pieces of the cosmic-ray puzzle have now fallen into place, and it may be useful to look at the picture they make (Fig. 11–4). Figures 11–6 and 11–7 summarize the most significant data on the primary radiation and the various components of the secondary radiation. In both figures the vertical scale measures the *directional intensity* of the various kinds of rays; Fig. 11–5 explains the exact meaning of this parameter.

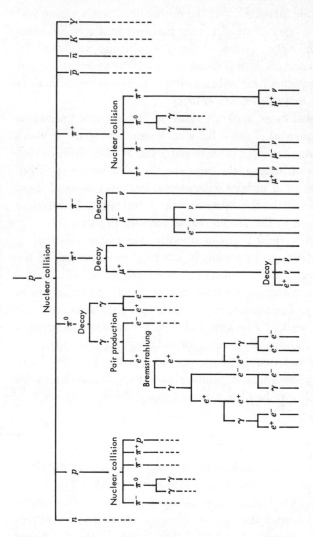

Fig. 11-4 Progeny of a cosmic-ray particle. The primary particle (usually a proton) collides with a nucleus of oxygen or nitrogen in the atmosphere. The products include neutrons (n), protons (p), neutral π mesons (π^0), charged π-mesons (π^+ and π^-), antiprotons and antineutrons ($\bar{p}$ and $\bar{n}$), heavy mesons (K), and hyperons (Y). Neutral π mesons decay into gamma rays (γ), which in turn materialize into positive and negative electrons (e^+ and e^-). Charged mesons may strike other atmospheric nuclei or decay into μ mesons (μ^+ and μ^-) and neutrinos (ν). The electrons radiate part of their energy in the form of gamma rays (bremsstrahlung). Broken lines indicate that further interactions will take place. Most charged particles arriving at the surface of the earth are electrons, positrons, and μ mesons.

Fig. 11-5 Measurement of directional intensity. Consider a G-M telescope consisting of two identical counters of length l and diameter d. The distance D between them is large compared to l and to d. The number of particles per second passing through the upper counter is proportional to the cross-sectional area $A = l \times d$. The fraction of these particles that traverse the lower counter is also proportional to A and inversely proportional to the square of the distance D. Thus the coincidence rate is proportional to A^2/D^2. The quantity that, multiplied by A^2/D^2, gives the coincidence rate is defined as the directional intensity per square centimeter per unit solid angle per second. For example, the directional intensity is 100 times the counting rate of two counters with the dimensions $d = 1$ cm and $l = 1$ cm and at a distance $D = 10$ cm. $A = 1$ cm $\times 1$ cm $= 1$ cm²; $D^2 = 100$ cm²; $A^2/D^2 = 1/100$.

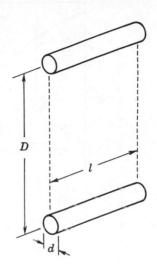

Primary cosmic rays are protons and bare nuclei of heavier elements. Their energies are distributed over a broad spectrum extending to unbelievably large values (Fig. 11-6). As these particles approach the earth, their trajectories are bent by the earth's magnetic field. Particles of all energies can enter the atmosphere at the magnetic poles. Moving from the poles to the equator, however, particles of increasingly high energy are prevented by the magnetic field from reaching the earth (*latitude effect*). At the same time, magnetic deflection creates an asymmetry in the distribution of the arrival directions of cosmic-ray particles entering the atmosphere. Being positively charged, these particles arrive with greater abundance from the west than from the east (*east-west effect*).

Upon entering the atmosphere, cosmic-ray particles soon collide with the nuclei of the atmospheric gases. The exact point at which the first collision occurs is, of course, a matter of chance. On the average, protons collide after traversing about 70 g/cm², or about one-fourteenth of the total air mass above sea level; α par-

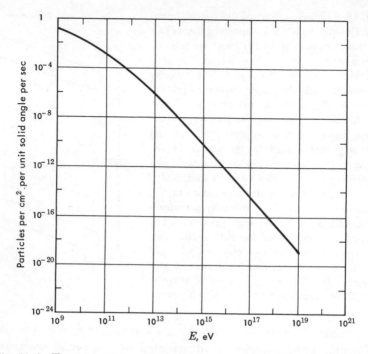

Fig. 11-6 Energy spectrum of primary cosmic rays. Plotted on the horizontal axis is the energy E of cosmic-ray particles, in electron volts. Plotted on the vertical axis is the directional intensity (see Fig. 11–5) for particles of energy *greater* than E striking the atmosphere above the geomagnetic poles (where the effect of the earth's magnetic field is negligible). The portion of the curve between 10^9 and 10^{11} eV was obtained from balloon measurements of the geomagnetic-latitude effect. Observations with nuclear emulsions exposed at balloon altitudes have provided some data in the energy region between 10^{11} and 10^{13} eV (the particle energy being estimated from the characteristics of their nuclear interactions). All data beyond 10^{15} eV come from experiments on air showers (Chap. 12). Note that the energy varies from about 1 BeV (10^9 eV) to about 10 billion BeV (10^{19} eV). Actually, the largest energy recorded, as of August, 1962, was 6×10^{19} eV (equal to the energy required to lift a mass of about one kilogram to a height of one meter). Note also the enormous range of intensity, which varies from about 0.15 particle per square centimeter per unit solid angle per second at 10^9 eV to a value about 10^{18} times smaller at 10^{19} eV. Since it can be shown that the total flux of particles from all directions above the horizon is π times the directional intensity, we find that a detector of 2 cm² at the top of the atmosphere will record about one primary particle per second and that the whole atmosphere (about 10^{18} cm² in area) will receive, every second, about two or three particles with energies above 10^{19} eV.

ticles collide after traversing, on the average, about 25 g/cm²; and heavier nuclei collide after traversing still smaller thicknesses. Consequently, the probability that a primary cosmic-ray particle will escape nuclear collision until it reaches sea level is practically nil. At the highest accessible altitudes on mountains one will find a few surviving primary protons. But primary α particles and heavier nuclei are found only near the top of the atmosphere and thus require balloon-borne experiments for their detection.

When a primary cosmic-ray particle collides against a nucleus, the target nucleus usually breaks up, as does the cosmic-ray particle itself if it is an α particle or a heavier nucleus. Among the disintegration fragments are protons and neutrons, which often acquire sufficient energy to produce violent effects when they, in turn, collide with other nuclei in the atmosphere.

But that is not all. Much of the energy of the primary particle goes into the creation of new, short-lived particles such as π mesons, heavy mesons, and hyperons. If the energy is great enough, pairs of protons and antiprotons, neutrons and antineutrons are also produced. Among all of these secondary particles, π mesons are the most abundant (at least in the range of energies typical of most primary cosmic radiation). Pi mesons (charged and neutral) are just about as effective as protons and neutrons in producing nuclear interactions, but nearly all neutral mesons decay before they have a chance to produce such interactions. On the other hand, charged π mesons, having a much longer mean life, often collide before they can decay. Also, according to the theory of relativity, the mean life of a moving meson increases considerably as the speed of the meson approaches the speed of light. Therefore, the probability that a π meson will live long enough to collide with a nucleus increases with the energy of the meson.

Secondary protons, secondary neutrons, and secondary π mesons, along with other less abundant secondary products and whatever primary particles may survive, account for the nuclear interactions observed at any given level in the atmosphere. The short average distance between nuclear collisions, the large energy degradation that every successive collision brings about, and the fast disappearance of π mesons by spontaneous decay explain why the number of nuclear-active particles decreases with increasing atmospheric depth as fast as it does (Fig. 11–7).

Neutral π mesons decay promptly into photons. Photons soon disappear in a materialization process that produces pairs of positive and negative electrons. The electrons radiate more photons.

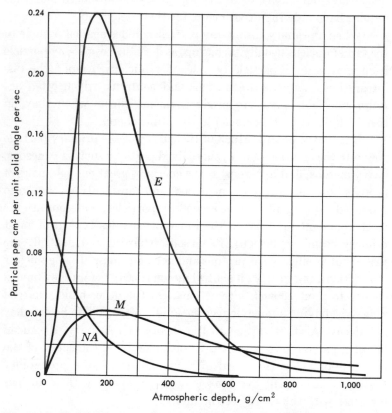

Fig. 11-7 Vertical intensity of three components of local cosmic radiation as a function of atmospheric depth, in grams per square centimeter. Curve *NA* represents nuclear-active particles with energies greater than about 1 BeV. Curve *E* represents electrons with energies greater than about 100 MeV. Curve *M* represents μ mesons with energies greater than about 200 MeV. Atmospheric depth as a function of altitude is given in Fig. 11–8.

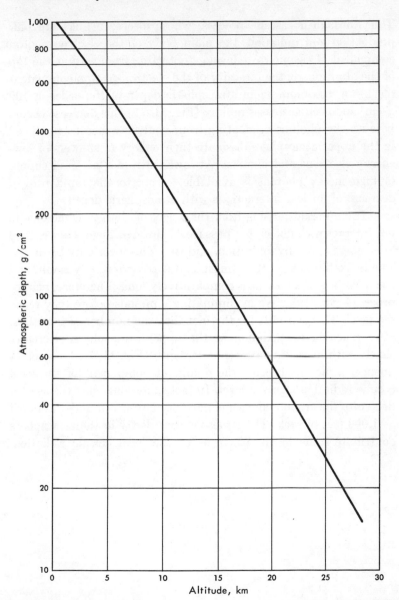

Fig. 11-8 Atmospheric depth, in grams per square centimeter, as a function of altitude above sea level, in kilometers.

Thus through a cascade process, whose alternate links are pair production and radiation, the main body of the electron-photon component of cosmic rays develops. Starting from zero at the top of the atmosphere, the intensity of the electron-photon component reaches a maximum at an atmospheric depth of the order of 100 g/cm^2 and then decreases rapidly (Fig. 11-7). This decrease occurs because the photons originating from neutral π mesons produced in the upper atmosphere dissipate their energy in showers of low-energy electrons and photons. At lower altitudes no fresh supply of high-energy photons is available, owing to the rapid rate of decrease of nuclear interactions with atmospheric depth.

The μ mesons arising from the decay of charged π mesons do not interact with nuclei, but pass freely through them. Hence, they loose energy only by ionization, and they disappear only by decay. The ionization loss in the atmosphere is comparatively small, and the mean life of μ mesons is comparatively long. Therefore, neither process is very effective in eliminating μ mesons before they reach sea level. This accounts for the fact that the number of μ mesons, after reaching a maximum in the upper atmosphere, decreases slowly with increasing atmospheric depth (Fig. 11-7). As a consequence, μ mesons become the dominant component of the local cosmic radiation near sea level. In fact, μ mesons bury themselves deep into the ground, and some have been observed under as much as 1,000 feet of rock. The μ mesons that decay in the atmosphere contribute some of the electrons of the local cosmic radiation.

Giant showers
of the atmosphere

12

The life history of a cosmic-ray particle and its progeny outlined at the end of the preceding chapter applies to primary particles of all energies. But, as Fig. 11–6 shows, the energy spectrum of primary cosmic rays covers an enormous range, and there is an important difference in quantity, if not quality, between the observable effects of low- and high-energy particles.

The family of secondary particles initiated by an "average" primary particle (with an energy, say, of 10 BeV) dies out after a few generations. Nowhere in the atmosphere does this family include any large number of members. At sea level a single particle (ordinarily a μ meson) may represent the last of the "line," or the family may have disappeared altogether. By contrast, a primary particle with an energy, say, a million times greater — 10 million BeV — gives rise to a family much better equipped to survive. Although the particles of each new generation have considerably less energy than those of the preceding one, the original "capital" is so great to begin with that it takes a large number of generations before the energy received by each new particle falls below the limit where further production of secondary particles becomes impossible. Thus the family will grow to an enormous size before it begins to die out, and at sea level its membership will still number in the millions. All of these particles, coming from a single primary cosmic ray, form what is known as an *air shower*.

The discovery of air showers

Air showers were discovered, more or less by chance, through the widespread application of coincidence-counter arrangements to the experimental study of cosmic rays. The devices used to detect coincidences will record as simultaneous the pulses of two or more counters if these pulses arrive within a certain small time interval. This interval, the *resolving time*, was of the order of 0.01 second in the early experiments of Bothe and Kohlhörster. The development of vacuum-tube circuits of increasing sophistication eventually reduced the resolving time to considerably less than 1 microsecond. But, however short the interval, there is always a possibility that unrelated particles will cross the counters in such quick succession as to produce a coincidence.

After physicists began to experiment with coincidences, it became a common practice to test the operation of the equipment by placing the counters out of line, usually on a horizontal plane. Then there could be no true coincidences caused by a single particle traversing all counters. And without any heavy material above the counters, the number of true coincidences resulting from showers produced locally was negligible. Several experimenters must have noticed that the number of coincidences recorded under these circumstances was too large to be accounted for entirely by chance. I know I did, and I also noticed that the unexplained coincidences were more abundant at high altitude than at sea level. From these observations I concluded, if I may be forgiven for quoting from one of my own papers, "It would seem that occasionally very extensive groups of particles arrive upon the equipment." That was in 1934. Gradually the idea began to emerge that these "very extensive groups of particles" were the result of cascade processes in the earth's atmosphere, just as ordinary showers were the result of cascade processes occurring in lead or other dense materials.

In 1938 the French physicist Pierre Auger and his collaborators undertook a systematic study that established beyond any doubt the occurrence of air showers and provided some preliminary information about their properties. These early experiments were carried out with relatively simple equipment that consisted of a few G-M counters and a coincidence circuit. In one of their experiments Auger and his group used the three-counter setup illustrated in Fig. 12-1. As they moved counter *C* farther and farther away from counters *A* and *B*, the coincidence rate gradually decreased (Fig. 12-2). At the maximum distance between counters (75 meters), the apparatus still recorded coincidences, which showed that the air showers covered rather large areas.

At first it was believed that air showers were initiated at the top of the atmosphere by high-energy electrons or photons and that the only processes involved in their development were radiation losses by electrons and pair production by photons. Before

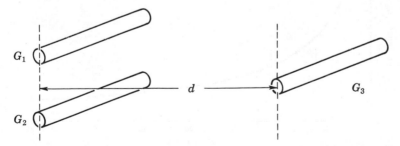

Fig. 12-1 Air-shower experiments by Auger and his collaborators in 1938 were made with the counter arrangement shown here. Counters G_1 and G_2 were placed one above the other, with their axes 22 cm apart. The third counter G_3 was moved horizontally to various distances d ranging from 15 centimeters to 75 meters.

long, however, mesons had been added to the list of air-shower particles. In the meantime, it was becoming increasingly evident that primary cosmic rays were neither electrons nor photons but, for the most part at least, protons and heavier nuclei. Obviously, an air shower was more than a simple electron-photon cascade. It was clearly a complex phenomenon in which nuclear interactions and spontaneous decay processes also played an important role.

Here, then, is the general picture of an air shower. A high-energy primary particle (proton or heavier nucleus), upon entering the atmosphere, initiates a chain of nuclear interactions. The particles born in these interactions are mainly high-energy protons, neutrons, and charged π mesons, which go on to produce other nuclear interactions (Fig. 11–4). They form the narrow "bundle" known as the *core* of the shower. At sea level the core is no more than a few meters in diameter.

In each nuclear interaction a certain fraction of the energy is spent in the production of neutral mesons, which immediately

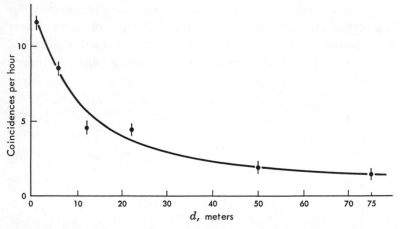

Fig. 12-2 Air-shower data obtained by Auger with the counter arrangement shown in Fig. 12–1. The horizontal scale gives the horizontal distance d between counter G_3 and the pair of counters G_1 and G_2; the vertical scale, the number of coincidences per hour. (From a paper in *Le Journal de Physique et Le Radium*, vol. 10, p. 39, 1939.)

decay into photons. These high-energy photons, which occur throughout the shower core, initiate ordinary cascade showers and thereby give rise to large numbers of positive and negative electrons. Also, some of the charged π mesons decay into μ mesons instead of colliding with nuclei. Thus, μ mesons also originate from the shower core.

Multiple scattering in the atmosphere causes shower particles to spread out laterally from the core. Such scattering represents the cumulative effect of the many small-angle deflections that occur when charged particles pass through the electric fields of atomic nuclei. By the time the shower has traveled some distance through the atmosphere, its particles are distributed over a wide area. Their density is greatest at the center — the point where the primary particle would have hit if there had been no collisions — and it decreases gradually with increasing distance from this point.

Air-shower experiments

Since the middle 1940s the study of air showers has held a prominent place in cosmic-ray research for one reason in particular. Air showers are produced by those rare primary cosmic-ray particles whose energy is enormously greater than that generated in the most powerful particle accelerators. The minimum energy necessary to produce a shower observable at sea level is about 10^{14} eV. The energy of the particles responsible for the largest showers ever observed is about 6×10^{19} eV. These are indeed extraordinarily large energies for individual subatomic particles; 6×10^{19} eV is about 10 joules, the energy required to lift a mass of 1 kilogram to a height of about 1 meter.

Physicists, of course, are keenly interested in the properties of particles with such extreme energies. They cannot expect to produce them in the laboratory in the foreseeable future. Existing accelerators reach a maximum energy of 35 BeV (3.5×10^{10} eV), and the most ambitious plans for future machines aim at energies of the order of 1,000 BeV (10^{12} eV). Consequently, physicists must turn to cosmic rays as the sole source of supply. To the astrophysicist the very existence of these particles poses formidable and fascinating problems. Indeed, what extraordinary processes are capable of accelerating particles to such enormous energies? In the hope of finding clues to the solution, they would like to know whether the most energetic particles come from all directions or only from certain regions of the sky. They would like to know what their energy distribution is; for example, how the number of particles with energies between 10^{17} and 10^{18} eV compares with the number of particles with energies between 10^{18} and 10^{19} eV.

There is no way of studying the high-energy region of the cosmic-ray spectrum other than by observing air showers. If physicists were to fly a detector with an area of 1 square meter on a satellite circling the earth above the atmosphere, they would not achieve their purpose. The detector would record only a few particles of energy greater than 10^{16} eV in a single year. In a period of about 1 million years, on the average, the detector would record only one particle with an energy greater than 10^{19} eV.

Fortunately, the occurrence of air showers reduces the problem to manageable proportions. If the number of particles in a shower is sufficiently large (that is, if the primary energy is sufficiently great), the density of particles hundreds of meters from the core is still large enough to be measured with appropriate detectors. Thus one can observe all large showers striking an extensive area by distributing over this area a comparatively small number of detectors. In this manner one can compensate for the very small number of high-energy particles by using a very large area of detection.

Over the past decade and a half, air-shower experiments have been carried out intensively at many institutions throughout the world. A partial list includes the Lebedev Institute of Physics in Moscow, U.S.S.R.; the Institute for Nuclear Studies in Tokyo, Japan; the Tata Institute of Fundamental Research in Bombay, India; the Atomic Energy Research Establishment in Harwell,

England; the University of La Paz, Bolivia; the University of Sydney, Australia; and, in this country, Cornell University and the Massachusetts Institute of Technology.

The instrumentation for the detection and study of air showers has become more and more sophisticated, and it has now reached the point where it is possible to obtain a great deal of precise information about each shower that strikes the equipment. To take a specific example, I shall describe here the experimental method developed by the cosmic-ray group at MIT.

The basic detectors are disks of fluorescent plastic, each about 1 meter square and 10 cm thick. A shower particle passing through a disk generates a brief flash of light. The flash is picked up by a *photomultiplier*, which converts it into an electric pulse. The pulse travels along a cable to a central station, where it is amplified and fed into a cathode-ray oscilloscope. The effect of the pulse is to deflect the electron beam of the oscilloscope vertically. (The beam itself appears as a point of light on the oscilloscope screen.) At the same time the beam is rapidly swept across the screen, producing the familiar oscilloscope trace. Consequently, the deflection caused by the pulse is recorded as a spike in the horizontal oscilloscope trace.

The fluorescent disks used in a given air-shower experiment feed their pulses to separate oscilloscopes, which are mounted one next to the other. Every time a shower strikes, the beams of the oscilloscopes are swept simultaneously, and a camera records the traces on all screens in a single photograph (Fig. 12–3).

At the time when the MIT program began, there was available a fair amount of information on the lateral spread of the shower particles around the core. However, no one had yet measured the *longitudinal* spread; that is, no one had taken a "snapshot" showing the distribution of the shower particles along the direction of propagation. Since particles of all successive generations travel at nearly the velocity of light along paths that diverge only slightly from the direction of the primary particles, the longitudinal spread was believed to be quite small. George Clark of MIT and Pietro

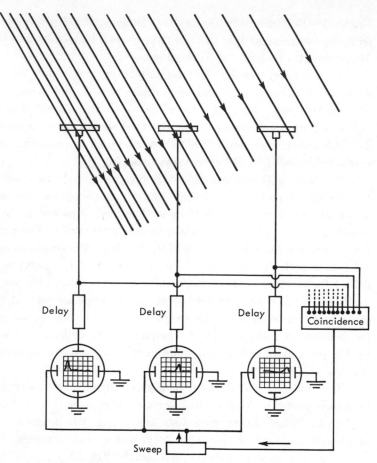

Fig. 12-3 Experimental arrangement used by the MIT cosmic-ray group to study air showers. Fluorescent plastic disks (thin rectangles at top) emit flashes of light when struck by charged particles. At the center of each disk is a photomultiplier tube that converts the light into an electrical pulse; the amplitude of the pulse is proportional to the brightness of the flash. Pulses travel to cathode-ray oscilloscopes (circles) through transmission lines containing delay circuits, which equalize the lengths of the electrical paths. Horizontal sweeps of all oscilloscope screens (grids) are triggered at the same time whenever three or more pulses pass through the coincidence circuit simultaneously. The amplitudes of the "spikes" (that is, the heights of the vertical deflections in the oscilloscope traces) indicate the numbers of particles striking the corresponding detectors. The positions of the spikes in the horizontal traces show the relative arrival times of the particles.

Bassi, a visiting scientist from Italy, proved that it is. They found that all shower particles went through each of their detectors within intervals of the order of a few times 10^{-9} second. Since the velocity of light is 3×10^8 meters per second, this meant that the longitudinal spread was of the order of a meter or so.

In other words, at a given instant, all shower particles are crowded within a flat disk about one meter thick. One can, then, visualize the propagation of a shower by thinking of this disk as traveling through the atmosphere at nearly the velocity of light while shower particles are continuously fed into it from the core and spread gradually outward.

The results of Clark and Bassi's work suggested a convenient method for determining the direction of propagation of showers. Indeed, it is clear that, if a shower travels vertically downward, it will strike all detectors at the same time. If the shower comes from an inclined direction, then it will strike some of the detectors a little sooner, others a little later. Since the horizontal sweeps of the oscilloscopes are triggered simultaneously, the relative positions of the spikes in the oscilloscope traces are a measure of the time intervals between the pulses from the corresponding detectors (Fig. 12-4). By knowing the time when the shower first hits each detector, one can then compute the direction in which it was

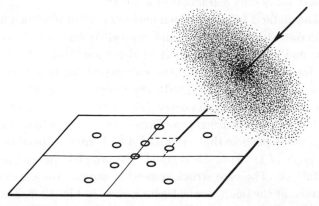

Fig. 12-4 Shower disk approaching detectors (represented by circles on a horizontal plane).

traveling. This is also the direction of the primary particle that produced the shower.

Furthermore, since the shower particles arrive almost simultaneously, their pulses combine into a single pulse whose size is a measure of the density of shower particles at the corresponding detector. This information is the basis for determining the center of the shower and the total number of shower particles. The method is one of trial and error. Inspection of the record provides a preliminary estimate of the position of the shower center, the point at which the concentration of particles is greatest. Next, the number of particles recorded by the various detectors is plotted against the distance of the detector from the presumed center. Since the density of shower particles decreases in a regular fashion with increasing distance from the center, the points should lie on a smooth curve. If they do not, one tries a second guess, using the observed deviations to figure out in which direction to move in order to obtain a better fit, and so on.

Once the center is located and the curve giving the density of particles as a function of distance from the center is found, one can calculate the total number of particles in the shower. Actually, this whole process of successive approximations is carried out automatically by an electronic computer, and the complete analysis of a shower takes only a fraction of a minute.

The method I have outlined here has been applied in a number of experiments performed at different altitudes, at different latitudes, and with different areas of detection. Between 1954 and 1957, for instance, an experiment was carried out near Cambridge, Massachusetts, at sea level, with eleven detectors arranged within a circle 460 meters in diameter (Fig. 12–5). The largest shower detected in the experiment contained about 2.5 billion particles. The primary particle that produced it had entered the atmosphere at an angle of 11° from the vertical. The primary energy was about 5×10^{18} eV. The core struck somewhat outside the outer ring of detectors, at the point marked with a cross in Fig. 12–5. The figure also shows the number of shower particles that traversed each detector in this particular event. Figure 12–6 gives the number of

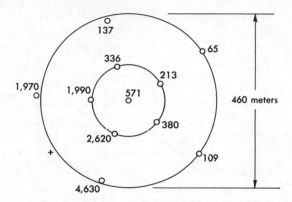

Fig. 12-5 Detector array used by the MIT group in an experiment at sea level (see text). The core of the largest shower observed struck at the point marked with a cross. The numbers of shower particles recorded by the various detectors on this occasion are indicated.

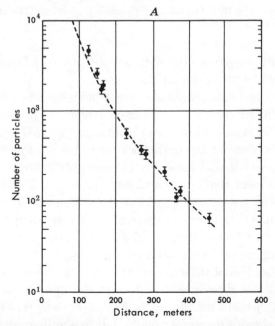

Fig. 12-6 The number of shower particles that traversed each detector shown in Fig. 12-5 is plotted (on a logarithmic scale) against the distance of the detector from the center of the shower (cross in Fig. 12-5).

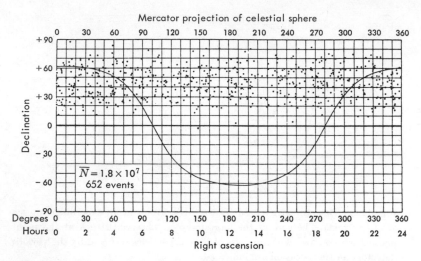

Fig. 12-7 Directional distribution of the 652 largest showers recorded by the array shown in Fig. 12–5. Dots on this Mercator projection of the sky represent arrival directions.

shower particles passing through each detector as a function of the distance of the detector from the core.

One of the main purposes of the experiment was to determine from which regions of the sky primary cosmic-ray particles of very high energies come. The dots on the maps in Fig. 12–7 represent the arrival directions of the particles responsible for the 652 largest showers observed. Absorption by the atmosphere favors the detection of showers coming from directions near the vertical. This explains why the dots in Fig. 12–7 cluster around the line at 42° declination, 42° being the latitude of Cambridge. Apart from this trivial effect, however, the data give no indication of any preferred direction of arrival for the primary particles.

Another aim of the experiment was to determine the relative arrival rates of showers with different total numbers of particles. The experimental data, plotted in Fig. 12–8, show that the rate of arrival of showers decreases rapidly, but in a quite regular fashion, as the number of shower particles increases. There is no indication of any maximum shower size. By further increasing the detection area or by continuing the observations over longer and longer periods of time, then, one should be able to detect showers with greater and greater numbers of particles.

This surmise was borne out in an experiment carried out by John Linsley of MIT and Livio Scarsi, a visitor from Italy, between 1959 and 1960 at an altitude of 1,700 meters near Albuquerque, New Mexico. Nineteen detectors, each consisting of four fluorescent disks, were arranged in a hexagonal array 1.8 kilometers in diameter, as shown in Fig. 12–9. In a 6-month period about 10,000 showers of more than 10 million particles each were observed. Among them there were two of nearly 10 billion particles each Linsley and Scarsi then expanded the array to form a hexagon 3.6

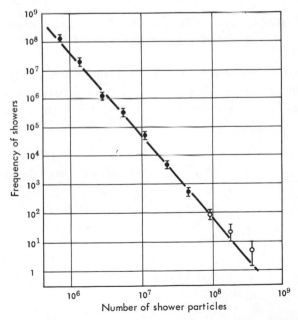

Fig. 12-8 Frequency, in arbitrary units, of air showers as a function of the number of shower particles. Notice the very rapid decrease in shower frequency with increasing shower size (10^7 showers with about 1.7×10^6 particles for every 10 showers with about 2×10^8 particles).

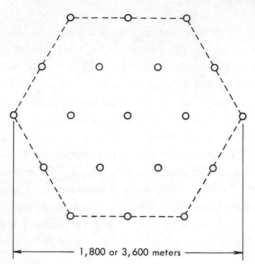

Fig. 12-9 Detector array used by the MIT group in an experiment at 1,700 meters altitude near Albuquerque, New Mexico (see text).

kilometers in diameter. In the first few months of operation, the larger array recorded a shower containing about 30 billion particles, corresponding to a primary energy of about 6×10^{19} eV.[1]

[1] The data obtained from the experiments I have described here, as well as data from similar experiments, were used in plotting the energy spectrum of cosmic rays shown in Fig. 11–6.

The Van Allen radiation belt

13

On October 4, 1957, when Soviet scientists launched the first artificial satellite into an orbit around the earth, the direct exploration of outer space became a concrete possibility. Cosmic-ray physicists were quick to seize upon this opportunity. On November 3, 1957, the U.S.S.R. launched Sputnik II; and the United States satellites Explorer I and Explorer III followed on February 1 and March 26, 1958, respectively. All three satellites carried G-M counters for the purpose of making a preliminary survey of the cosmic-ray intensity at very high altitudes. The most striking result of these observations was the discovery of a great radiation belt surrounding the earth.

Whether or not the particles in this belt are to be called cosmic rays is merely a matter of definition. In any case, the radiation belt is such an important feature of the space environment of the earth and has such close connections with cosmic rays themselves that it deserves at least a brief mention in this book.

The discovery of the Van Allen belt

The discovery of the radiation belt had its roots in scientific investigations dating from the early part of the twentieth century. In discussing the effects of the earth's magnetic field upon cosmic rays, I have already mentioned the theoretical work by Störmer on the trajectories of charged particles in the field of a magnetic dipole. Among other results, Störmer's computations had demonstrated that charged particles could be "trapped" indefinitely in this field (they are the particles traveling along the bounded trajectories mentioned in Chap. 5). This means that a particle injected with the proper momentum and in the proper direction will move forever within a limited volume of space surrounding the dipole (Fig. 13–1). The trajectories of the trapped particles are, in general, very complicated and very difficult to predict theoretically. However, they become comparatively simple when the momentum of the particles is sufficiently small.

To understand the character of these trajectories, consider first the case of a uniform magnetic field. From Chap. 5 it will be recalled that the motion of a charged particle traveling at right angles to the magnetic lines of force describes a circle whose radius

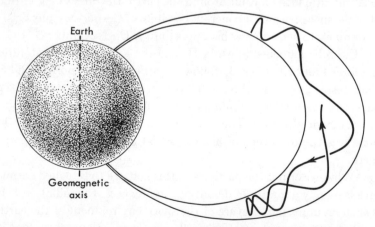

Fig. 13-1 Trajectory of a charged particle trapped in the magnetic field of a dipole, according to computations by Carl Störmer (1913).

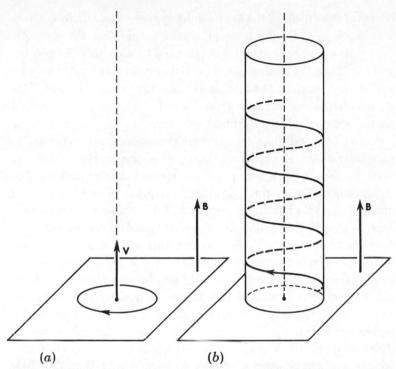

Fig. 13-2 Motion of a particle in a uniform magnetic field **B**. (*a*) The particle moves along a circle in plane perpendicular to **B** while the plane moves at a constant speed **V** in the direction of **B**. (*b*) The trajectory is a spiral winding around a cylindrical tube of force.

decreases as the momentum of the particle decreases or as the strength of the field increases (Fig. 5–2). If the particle is injected at any other angle to the field lines, it will spiral around a "tube of force" (Fig. 13–2). In simpler language, the particle rotates around a circle that lies in a plane perpendicular to the field lines while the center of the circle moves at a constant velocity along a field line.

In a dipolar magnetic field such as the earth's, the lines of force are curved and the field strength varies from point to point (Fig. 5–1). Still, within a sufficiently small volume — a volume whose dimensions are small compared to its distance from the center of the dipole — the field will be *approximately* uniform. Now consider a particle with so small a momentum that the magnetic field makes it go around and around many times within the selected volume. Then the motion of the particle within this limited volume will closely resemble the motion in a uniform magnetic field. This means that, *on a first approximation*, the trajectories of charged particles are spiral paths around field lines.

To go beyond these approximate conclusions, it is necessary to carry out a fairly sophisticated analysis of the problem. This was done by the Swedish astrophysicist Hannes Alfvén in 1942. His computations led to the following description of the behavior of charged particles in a dipole magnetic field. Each charged particle travels in a circle the center of which (*guiding center*) oscillates back and forth in latitude between two symmetrically located *mirror points* along a curved *guiding line*. The guiding line has the shape of a line of force and rotates slowly about the axis of the dipole from east to west if the particle is positively charged and from west to east if it is negatively charged. As the guiding center oscillates along the guiding line — thus passing through regions of different magnetic field strength — the radius of the circle traced by the particle changes gradually in such a way that the circle encloses a constant magnetic flux (Fig. 13–3).

Early in 1957 the American physicist Fred Singer published an article in which he called attention to the possibility that protons and electrons originating from the sun might occasionally become trapped in the earth's magnetic field. The opposite drift in longitude of the positive and negative trapped particles, Singer pointed out, would give rise to a sheath of electric current quite similar to the so-called "ring current" geophysicists had found it necessary to postulate in order to explain certain disturbances of the terrestrial magnetic field (the main phase of magnetic storms; see Chap. 14). These, then, were the notions and the ideas current when Sputniks I and II initiated the exploration of outer space.

The G-M counter aboard Sputnik II revealed nothing unusual. But the counters installed in Explorers I and Explorer III by the

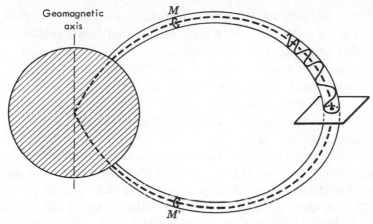

Geomagnetic axis

M

M'

Fig. 13-3 Motion of a particle of small momentum in the earth's magnetic field (schematic). The particle moves in a circle; the center of the circle oscillates back and forth along a guiding line, coincident with a line of force, between two mirror points M and M'. At the same time the guiding line slowly rotates in azimuth (that is, about the geomagnetic axis). The magnetic flux through the circle (defined as the product of the area times the magnetic field strength at right angles to the area) is constant. Since the field strength varies from point to point, this requires the area of the circle to change in accordance with the variations in the field.

cosmic-ray group under James A. Van Allen of the University of Iowa behaved in a very peculiar fashion. At every revolution, the trajectories of Explorers I and III swung from a minimum altitude of several hundred kilometers (356 and 187, respectively) to a maximum altitude of several thousand kilometers (2,546 and 2,796, respectively).

Up to altitudes of about 1,000 km the counting rates showed only a modest and fairly regular increase. Above 2,000 km, however, the counters apparently stopped working. Since the counters again transmitted pulses regularly when the satellites returned to lower altitudes, and since both satellites gave roughly the same results, it was hardly possible to suspect a malfunction in the equipment. It was equally impossible to suppose that there were no cosmic rays above 2,000 km.

The only alternative explanation possible rests on the inherent "inertia" of G-M counters: if they are exposed to a radiation of excessive strength, they become "jammed" and stop counting altogether. Van Allen came to the conclusion that this was indeed the correct explanation of his results. According to his estimates, the intensity of the radiation responsible for jamming the counters must have been at least 15,000 times greater than the intensity of ordinary cosmic radiation.

Van Allen announced his discovery at a meeting held in Washington, D.C., on May 1, 1958. In his report he stressed the fact that the radiation, though detected by G-M counters with fairly thick walls, could not penetrate within 600 km of the earth's surface. Since the total thickness of the atmosphere above 600 km is equivalent to only a minute fraction of the thickness of the counter walls, Van Allen concluded that the radiation must consist of charged particles prevented from approaching the earth's surface by the terrestrial magnetic field. He suggested that these particles originate from the sun, that they penetrate the trapping region of the earth's magnetic field by virtue of some sort of perturbation in the field, and that subsequently they remain trapped in this region.

Sputnik II had failed to discover the radiation belt because its trajectory did not take it into the high-intensity zone while it was in radio contact with a receiving station. Immediately after Van Allen's announcement, the U.S.S.R. launched Sputnik III, equipped with various radiation detectors designed to record large radiation fluxes without jamming. These detectors counted at very high rates when the satellite passed through certain regions of space, thus confirming the existence of the high-intensity radiation discovered by Van Allen.

In August of the same year, the United States launched Explorer IV, equipped with a variety of instruments specifically designed by the Iowa group to study the new radiation. At some locations these instruments revealed fluxes as high as 100,000 particles per square centimeter per second. In agreement with the previous results, the intensity proved to be strongly dependent on latitude. More important, the intensity varied with latitude measured from the *geomagnetic* equator rather than with latitude measured from the *geographic* equator. These observations confirmed the view that the intensity distribution of the radiation was governed by the earth's magnetic field.

Until that time, no observations had been carried out at altitudes of more than a few thousand kilometers. Although the intensity had been found to increase steadily with increasing altitude, it was not known whether or not at still higher altitudes the intensity reached a maximum and then decreased. In other words, it remained uncertain whether the earth was actually surrounded by a radiation belt or whether it was immersed in a region of high-intensity radiation that might extend throughout the solar system. The deep space probes launched by the U.S.S.R. and by the United States in late 1958 and early 1959 provided the answer to this important question. They showed that the high-intensity radiation was confined to a belt around the earth and that at large distances (about fifteen earth radii or greater) only the normal cosmic-ray flux remained.

These results (first announced by Van Allen — for whom the belt is named — and his collaborators and then verified by the Soviet scientists) left practically no doubt that the high-intensity radiation consists of particles trapped by the earth's magnetic field. Moreover, in the spring of 1959 a group of American scientists announced the results of an experiment, known as Project Argus, that confirmed in the most direct manner the theory of magnetic trapping. In the Argus experiment (suggested by the Greek-born scientist N. C. Christofilos prior to the discovery of the radiation belt and performed in the late summer of 1958) high-energy electrons were injected into the earth's magnetic field by means of small, rocket-borne atom bombs exploded at high altitude. The instruments aboard Explorer IV continued to detect these electrons, now trapped by the terrestrial magnetic field and spread into a thin shell around the earth, for a period of many days.

The structure of the Van Allen belt

Since 1958, a great deal of experimental data on the radiation belt has been obtained by means of the space vehicles already mentioned, by means of other space vehicles launched subsequently, and also by means of sounding rockets shot into the lower edge of the radiation belt. Among those who made important contributions were American scientists working with Van Allen at the University of Iowa, with John Simpson at the University of Chicago, and with J. R. Winkler at the University of Minnesota and Soviet scientists, including V. I. Krassowsky, S. N. Vernov, A. E. Chudakov, and their associates. What follows is a summary of some of their most significant conclusions.

The radiation belt appears to consist of electrons and protons. The energy spectrum is very steep, which means that the counting rate of an instrument sensitive only to particles with an energy greater than E decreases very rapidly as E increases. In fact the spectrum of the radiation belt is much steeper than the spectrum of ordinary cosmic rays, or, to put it another way, the average energy of the trapped particles is much smaller than that of cosmic rays. Furthermore, the spectrum changes from one region of the radiation belt to another. Consequently, the intensity distribution measured by a given detector depends to a large extent on the manner in which the detector responds to electrons and protons of different energies.

A typical G-M counter detects, with nearly perfect efficiency, electrons of several MeV or more and protons of 30 to 40 MeV or more because these particles are capable of traversing the counter walls. It also detects, but with much lower efficiency, electrons with energies ranging down to some 20 keV. These electrons, upon hitting the counter walls, produce X-rays, some of which discharge the counter by producing Compton electrons.

A G-M counter carried farther and farther from the earth will record two separate maxima in the radiation intensity (Fig. 13–4). Thus there are two distinct zones of high intensity separated by a region of lower intensity. The intensity, as I have already noted, depends on the magnetic latitude as well as on altitude. Figure 13–5 shows a preliminary intensity map, drawn by Van Allen in 1959, in which there appears an *inner belt* in the neighborhood of the equator and an *outer belt* that reaches down toward the poles.

The average energy of the particles is much higher in the inner belt than in the outer belt. The energies of protons in the inner belt range up to about 100 MeV; protons in the outer belt have energies of a few MeV at most. Moreover, the inner belt is comparatively stable, whereas the population of the outer belt appears to fluctuate wildly, especially during periods of high solar activity.

The origin of the Van Allen belt

There is as yet no definite answer to the question concerning the origin of the radiation belt (or, rather, belts). However, it seems

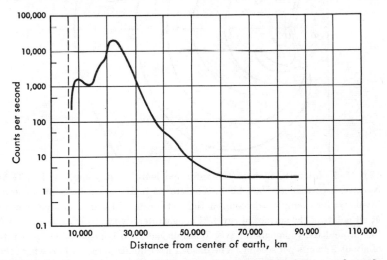

Fig. 13-4 Counting rate of a G-M counter as a function of distance from the center of the earth, according to Van Allen (dotted line corresponds to the earth's surface). The data were obtained with a G-M counter carried by the Pioneer III space probe.

likely that the proton component of the inner belt is largely a secondary effect of cosmic rays. Among the secondary particles arising from the collisions of primary cosmic rays with atomic nuclei in the atmosphere are neutrons. Some of the neutrons are ejected in an "upward" direction. They travel away from the earth undisturbed by the magnetic field because they carry no electric charge. But neutrons are unstable. They decay into protons and electrons after a mean life of about 16.6 minutes. Some of the neutrons will decay on their way out, thus injecting electrons and protons into trapped orbits.

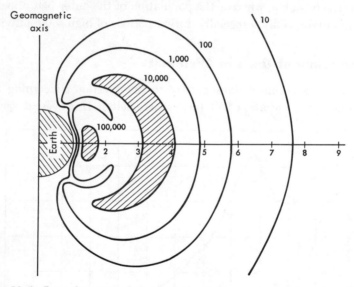

Fig. 13-5 Intensity map of the radiation belts, as measured with a G-M counter, according to Van Allen. The curves represent surfaces of constant intensity; for example, the counter ticks at a rate of 1,000 counts per second at all points of the surface of revolution generated by the rotation of the 1,000 line around the geomagnetic axis. (Cosmic radiation is responsible for a rate of about 2 counts per second.) The dashed areas indicate the regions where the counting rate is greater than 10,000. The scale shows the distance from the center of the earth, in earth radii. (This map is the result of early experiments, which were analyzed under the assumption that the earth's magnetic field was exactly that of a dipole.)

From what is known today about the "upward flux" of neutrons and about the mean life of trapped particles, it appears that this mechanism may account for most of the protons found in the inner belt. It is difficult, however, to account for all of the trapped radiation, and particularly that in the outer belt, in a similar manner. The fact that the structure of this belt is strongly affected by the activity of the sun lends considerable support to the idea that, in one way or another, the sun is involved in the production of the belt radiation. However, it is not clear whether the particles trapped in the outer belt actually come from the sun or whether they are accclerated locally as a result of mangetic disturbances originating from the sun. I shall have more to say about these disturbances in the next chapter.

Cosmic rays
and the sun

14

One of the most striking results of the early work on cosmic rays was the discovery that the radiation intensity appeared to be remarkably constant in time. Whatever small changes occurred were usually related to comparatively trivial atmospheric effects such as changes in atmospheric pressure.

These early observations were carried out at or near sea level. There, because of atmospheric absorption, only primary cosmic-ray particles of rather high energy (several BeV or more) produce observable effects. Later, when systematic measurements were undertaken at altitudes and latitudes where primary cosmic-ray particles of lower energy could also be observed, it became apparent that the low-energy portion of the cosmic radiation was not at all constant in time and that its intensity changes had to do primarily with events in the sun. Even more spectacular changes in the particle flux appeared when satellites and space probes took counters into regions where the shielding effects of the earth's atmosphere and magnetic field play no part.

At the same time, measurements near sea level with instruments of increased accuracy were bringing to light small but significant changes in the cosmic-ray intensity which again were related to the activity of the sun. Moreover, it was found that once in a very great while there occurred, even at sea level, large temporary changes in the cosmic-ray intensity. These changes in the flux of charged particles reaching the earth from outer space are an important element in the broad picture of the sun-earth relationship, which also includes such diverse effects as magnetic storms, aurorae, and blackouts in radio communication.

Solar-flare particles

The most spectacular solar event ever recorded by ground-based instruments took place on February 23, 1956. On that day, a great flare suddenly appeared on the face of the solar disk. A few minutes later the counting rates of cosmic-ray detectors all over the earth began to increase rapidly. In 15 to 20 minutes the counting rates had reached a maximum and had begun to decrease; in a few hours, everything was over and the counting rates had returned to near their normal value.

Various detectors located at stations all over the world gave quite different results. The largest effects were recorded by instruments located at fairly high latitudes and designed to detect the secondary neutrons generated by cosmic radiation (Fig. 14–1). The maximum counting rate of some of these detectors had increased to between 25 and 50 times normal. At the other extreme, μ-meson detectors located near the equator had recorded increases of only a few per cent.

There is no doubt that the observed increases were due to a stream of high-energy particles, presumably protons, ejected by the sun at the time of the solar flare. Since even detectors located at low latitudes had recorded an increase, some of these particles must have had sufficiently high energies to penetrate the earth's magnetic field near the equator, energies greater than 10 to 20 BeV. On the other hand, the effect was much smaller near the equator than at high latitudes, where particles down to one or a few BeV could penetrate the field. This meant the radiation originating from the flare contained comparatively fewer high-energy particles and comparatively more low-energy particles than did the ordinary cosmic radiation. The fact that the neutron detectors had recorded, in general, a much greater increase than had μ-meson detectors pointed to the same conclusion, because μ mesons are produced abundantly only by protons with energies of many BeV, whereas protons of lower energies are quite effective in producing neutrons.

Four solar-flare increases, smaller in magnitude but roughly similar in character to the great increase of 1956, had been observed

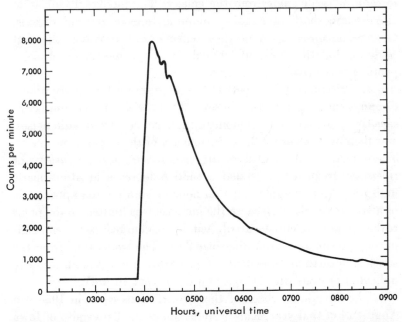

Fig. 14-1 Increase in the counting rate of a neutron detector at Chicago, following the solar flare of February 26, 1956. (From John Simpson, *Proceedings of the National Academy of Sciences of the United States of America*, vol. 43, p. 42, 1957.)

previously, in the years between 1942 and 1956. Several additional events, some fairly large, some quite small, were observed in the following years, at a rate of about one a year. In the meantime, however, it became apparent that while very few solar flares are capable of accelerating protons to energies of several BeV, the production of protons with energies of 100 MeV or less is a much more common event.

Because of the earth's magnetic field, protons of this relatively low energy can approach the earth only near the poles. Even there they do not reach ground-based detectors, because energy losses through collision bring them to a stop in the upper layers of the atmosphere. However, their arrival increases the normal ionization of the upper atmosphere to a considerable extent, making it opaque to radio noises coming from the galaxy. The increased ionization also disrupts short-wave radio communications in the polar regions. It was the observation of these effects that provided the first evidence for the frequent arrival in the atmosphere of solar protons of relatively low energy.

In 1956 and 1957, as part of the program for the International Geophysical Year, scientists in several countries set up a number of sensitive radio receivers to monitor the level of cosmic radio noises, and thereby to measure the radio opacity of the upper atmosphere. These instruments, called *relative ionospheric opacity meters*, or *riometers*, frequently recorded a sudden increase in atmospheric ionization over the polar caps an hour or so after the appearance of a large solar flare. Because the increase was limited to the polar regions, these scientists attributed it to charged particles originating, presumably, from the solar flare. The travel time from the sun to the earth and the depth of penetration into the atmosphere indicated protons with energies up to at least 10 MeV.

The first direct check of these conclusions came in 1958. On August 21 of that year, Kinsey Anderson of the University of Iowa launched a balloon equipped with radiation detectors from Fort Churchill, Canada. The balloon reached a maximum altitude of 32 kilometers at 10:00 P.M. the same day, and it remained at that

altitude until 5:00 P.M. the next day. At first the detectors counted
at the normal rate. At 9:30 A.M. of August 22, however, the counting rate began to increase irregularly to a level about 10 times
greater than normal. A few hours later the counting rate began to
decrease slowly. As Anderson later learned, a large solar flare had
occurred about 75 minutes before the balloon-borne detectors
showed an increase in counting rate. From the thickness of the
atmospheric layer above the balloon, he calculated that the protons
recorded must have had energies greater than 100 MeV.

While these balloon observations were being made, the satellite
Explorer IV was still orbiting the earth and making measurements.
At 300-km altitude in the polar regions, the instruments aboard the
satellite recorded the arrival of even stronger fluxes of solar particles. The effect was greater because the satellite's orbit kept it
outside the earth's atmosphere, where the instruments could therefore detect particles of lower energy than those capable of reaching
Anderson's balloon. On many subsequent occasions, satellite-borne
counters detected the arrival of solar particles after the appearance
of solar flares. There was a close correlation between these observations and those made with riometers on the ground. It thus became
clear that one could confidently take the increased absorption of
cosmic noise, detected by riometers in the polar regions, as an
announcement of the arrival of solar particles.

The observation of solar particles provides very valuable information concerning both the solar atmosphere, where the particles
supposedly originate, and the conditions of interplanetary space,
through which the particles travel on their way to the earth.
Although the discussion of these interesting questions lies beyond
the scope of this book, I should like to mention two very significant
results that have come from the study of many solar events.

First, the particles produced in these events continue to rain
upon the earth for a period of hours after the disappearance of the
flare from which they arose. Apparently the particles cannot escape
directly from the solar system, but are trapped temporarily within
it. Second, the particles observed immediately after the flare often

appear to approach the earth from a fairly well defined direction; toward the end of the event the particles appear to come from all directions. This is exactly what one would expect, because the "early" particles are those coming directly from the sun, whereas the "late" particles have bounced back and forth several times in space before reaching the earth. Even the early particles, of course, do not usually come precisely from the direction of the sun, because the magnetic fields present in interplanetary space bend their trajectories.

Forbush decreases

While the solar-flare increases and the polar-cap absorption provide evidence for the production of high-energy particles by the sun, other observations show that solar activity also affects the flux of high-energy particles entering the solar system from outside. One striking effect is the worldwide decreases in cosmic-ray intensity that occur fairly frequently, especially during periods of high solar activity. The effect was first observed by the American physicist Scott E. Forbush, for whom it is named, in 1937.

Forbush decreases are related to a number of geophysical effects the cause of which appears in every case to be a large solar eruption. Roughly one day after a solar eruption (the period varies from one event to the next), the earth experiences a magnetic "storm." Typically there is a short increase of the order of 1 part in 1,000 in the strength of the earth's magnetic field (*sudden commencement*), followed by a decrease (of the order of several parts in 1,000) that continues for a few hours (*main phase*). The magnetic field then slowly recovers its original strength over a period of days.

Many, though not all, magnetic storms are accompanied by Forbush decreases. When they are, the cosmic-ray intensity begins to decrease at the same time as the magnetic field, reaching a minimum a few per cent below normal. And when the magnetic field subsequently recovers, the cosmic-ray intensity also returns to its normal value (Fig. 14–2). Since Forbush decreases are a world-wide phenomenon, whatever agency produces them must affect both the low-energy primary particles (which can reach the earth's atmosphere only near the magnetic poles) and the high-energy particles (which can arrive at all latitudes).

Simultaneously with the magnetic storms, there often occur large-scale changes in the outer radiation belt. From various

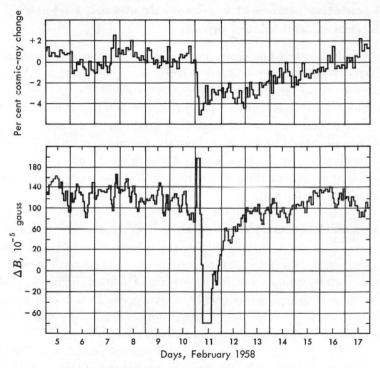

Fig. 14-2 Typical Forbush decrease. The lower curve represents the horizontal component ΔB of the magnetic field measured, from an arbitrary zero, in units of 10^{-5} gauss. The upper curve shows the corresponding variations of cosmic-ray intensity (measured by a neutron monitor in Chicago) as a percentage of the normal intensity. Shown on the horizontal axis is the universal time, in days. (From F. Bachelet, P. Balata, A. M. Conforto, and G. Marini, *Il Nuovo Cimento*, vol. 16, p. 292, 1960.)

satellite observations it appears that the radiation intensity drops sharply at first, particularly in the far region of the outer belt. At the same time, widespread aurorae appear. After a day or two, the outer belt begins to recover. The population of particles overshoots the prestorm level and then decreases gradually. After a few weeks the outer belt has returned to its normal state.

A tentative picture of geomagnetic storms, Forbush decreases, and related effects

A detailed explanation of all these diverse but clearly interrelated effects is still lacking. There is hardly any question that, at the moment of a solar eruption, *something* starts out from the sun and travels through space at such a speed as to reach the earth in about one day. This something is capable of producing magnetic storms, of partially shielding the earth from the oncoming cosmic-ray flux, of causing auroral displays, and of discharging the outer radiation belt. The same something also carries with it the energy needed to rebuild the outer belt.

From a number of arguments based on astronomical observations, on theoretical studies, and, more recently, on direct measurements by means of space vehicles, the following tentative picture has emerged. Out of the sun, or perhaps, more precisely, out of the solar corona, comes a continuous stream of diluted, highly ionized gas, or *plasma*, consisting chiefly of hydrogen. As a consequence, there exists in interplanetary space a more or less steady *solar wind* of plasma. Near the earth this wind has a speed of several hundred kilometers per second and a density of several particles per cubic centimeter. (Incidentally the experimental study of interplanetary plasma, under the direction of Herbert Bridge, is now one of the major activities of the MIT cosmic-ray group.)

The "explosions" responsible for the solar flares occur at the base of the corona, in the region immediately above the *photosphere*, the visible disk of the sun. A sizable part of the energy released by

an explosion appears as additional kinetic energy in the comparatively dense plasma at the base of the corona. As a result, a
cloud of plasma is driven through the corona into interplanetary
space at a speed of roughly 1,000 kilometers per second. As it
pushes against the interplanetary plasma (that is, the solar wind),
which is also moving away from the sun but at a slower speed, the
cloud produces a shock wave. According to this picture, the shock
wave is the something previously referred to.

Presumably upon hitting the earth's magnetic field, the shock
wave at first compresses the lines of force, thus temporarily increasing the strength of the magnetic field (sudden commencement).
Moreover, it may put kinks or wiggles in the distant lines of force
(where the field is weaker, hence more easily disturbed), thus
affording a possibility of escape to the trapped particles of the outer
belt.

The main phase of the magnetic storm may result from the
injection of solar plasma, by the shock wave, into the *magnetosphere*
— the region in which the earth's magnetic field predominates
over the interplanetary field. Alternatively, the shock wave may
"heat" the plasma already present in the magnetosphere, that is,
it may increase the individual energies of the plasma particles.

In either case, the plasma pressure would increase, push the
lines of force apart, and thereby decrease the field strength. This
injection, or heating of the plasma in the magnetosphere, is
probably closely related to the recovery of the outer Van Allen belt.
Indeed, the plasma is thought to consist of ionized hydrogen,
that is, of protons and electrons — the very particles found in the
Van Allen belt. True, the energy of the plasma particles is, on the
average, much lower than that of the particles detected by the
counters used to study the Van Allen belt. But then the plasma
particles and the Van Allen particles in the outer belt might be just
the low-energy and the high-energy portions of a single particle
population.

You will recall that both Singer and Van Allen had suggested
that particles of solar origin might be injected into the mag-

netosphere. Singer had in mind the low-energy plasma particles required to explain the main phase of the magnetic storms; Van Allen was referring to the particles of much higher energy that his counters had revealed. Together the two suggestions form a picture not very different from that favored by the scientific community at the time of this writing — although what is injected into the magnetosphere might be energy, not particles.

Before leaving this subject, I must add a remark to avoid possible misunderstandings. Singer had pictured the main phase of geomagnetic storms as due to the electric currents resulting from the drift of trapped particles around the earth. The explanation given here ascribes the same magnetic disturbance to a pressure effect of the trapped plasma pushing the lines of force apart. The two points of view do not represent two different assumptions, but are two different ways of describing the same physical situation. Unfortunately, any attempt to explain why this is so would lead us into the thorny field of magneto-fluid dynamics.

But what about Forbush decreases? The sun has a general magnetic field of several gauss; much stronger local magnetic fields usually exist in the disturbed regions where solar flares occur. The solar magnetic field induces electric currents in the ionized gases flowing out of the sun. Because these gases behave as nearly perfect electrical conductors, the currents continue to circulate for a long time in the gases as the latter move away from the sun. These currents, in turn, produce magnetic fields. Consequently, the solar wind in interplanetary space normally has a magnetic field, and the plasma immediately behind the shock-wave front resulting from a solar flare has an even stronger field. This field tends to keep cosmic-ray particles away, thus producing Forbush decreases.

If the tentative picture is correct, Forbush decreases should occur not only in the vicinity of the earth but throughout interplanetary space. This expectation has been confirmed by deep-space probes. For example, Pioneer V in 1960 detected a Forbush decrease at a distance of 5 million kilometers from the earth. At the same time, the magnetometer aboard Pioneer V (which had been recording magnetic fields of the order of a few times 10^{-5} gauss in interplanetary space) detected a large increase in the field strength (to about 4×10^{-4} gauss). The decrease in the cosmic-ray flux and the increase of the magnetic field strength probably marked the passage of a shock front. Shortly thereafter, the earth experienced a severe magnetic storm, presumably caused by the same shock front.

Curiously enough, aurorae, although the first effect to be noted by scientists, are still the least understood among the various aspects of the sun-earth relationship. Aurorae appear as a luminescence in the upper layers of the atmosphere. They usually occur at high geomagnetic latitudes and at altitudes ranging from about one hundred to several hundred kilometers. Instruments flown into the auroral regions by means of rockets (by the Iowa group) have detected large fluxes of electrons with energies between 10 and 20 keV and protons with energies greater than about 70 keV (the instruments were not sensitive to particles of lower energy).

On several occasions when artificial satellites were monitoring the Van Allen belt, aurorae were observed to occur simultaneously with the discharge of the outer portion of the belt. This observation seemed to suggest that aurorae might be due to particles escaping from the trapping region along the magnetic lines of force and into the atmosphere below. But further investigations have not supported this view, and to date no other convincing explanation has been offered.

The 11-year cycle

Solar scientists are well acquainted with the fact that the general pattern of solar activity, as evidenced by the number of sun spots, the frequency of solar flares, and other events, follows an 11-year cycle. When accurate records of the cosmic-ray intensity measured over long periods of time near sea level became available, and when the results of extensive balloon observations began to accumulate, it was found that the flux of cosmic rays also changes systematically during the 11-year solar cycle.

For example, the counting rates of μ-meson detectors near sea level are about 6 per cent lower when the solar activity is at a maximum than it is when the solar activity is at a minimum. More spectacular are the results obtained with balloon-borne detectors flown to high altitudes near the magnetic poles, where the cosmic-ray flux is found to be several times smaller during maximum solar

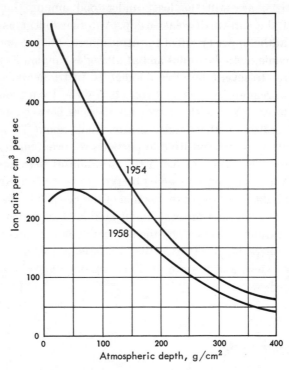

Fig. 14-3 Intensity of cosmic rays as a function of atmospheric depth, measured at a geomagnetic latitude of 88° N at the time of minimum solar activity in 1954 and at the time of maximum solar activity in 1958. The instrument used was an electroscope; the vertical scale gives the number of ion pairs per second produced by cosmic rays in 1 cm³ of air at standard temperature and pressure. The horizontal scale gives the atmospheric depth, in grams per square centimeter. (From H. V. Neher, *Nature*, vol. 184, p. 423, 1959.)

activity. This is shown by the curves in Fig. 14–3, which represents some of the extensive measurements made by H. Victor Neher of the California Institute of Technology.

As I have already mentioned, only primary particles of several BeV or greater energy make their effects felt near sea level. On the other hand, primary particles of energies as low as 100 MeV can reach a balloon-borne instrument flown at high magnetic latitudes. Clearly, then, the agency responsible for the 11-year changes in cosmic-ray intensity has a much stronger effect on particles of comparatively low energy than on those of very high energy. It seems very unlikely that the intensity variations of cosmic rays during the solar cycle are the result of changes in the emission of cosmic rays from the sun. For if they were the result of such changes, the greatest production of cosmic rays would occur at times of least activity. But, as we have seen before, the acceleration of particles is related to increased solar activity.

A more appealing idea is that solar activity modulates the cosmic-ray flux. In agreement with the tentative picture that I presented in the discussion of Forbush decreases, we now believe that the magnetic field found in interplanetary space is, so to speak, carried *materially* away from the sun by the outflowing plasma. The interplanetary magnetic field acts as a partial screen against cosmic-ray particles entering the solar system from the outside. When the solar activity increases, more clouds are ejected from regions of the sun where strong local fields exist. As a consequence, the average magnetic field throughout interplanetary space becomes stronger, the screen becomes more opaque.

Although this general interpretation seems quite plausible, no one can claim to understand in detail what actually happens. An interesting question is why the modulation mechanism responsible for Forbush decreases is about equally effective for high- and low-energy cosmic-ray particles, whereas the modulation mechanism responsible for the 11-year intensity changes acts much more strongly upon particles of lower energy.

The origin of cosmic rays: an unsolved problem

15

Half a century after the discovery of cosmic rays the problem of their origin is still unsolved. We do not know for certain where cosmic rays come from. We do not know for certain how they acquire their tremendous energies.

Cosmic rays from the sun

From the solar flare effects we do know that occasionally the sun accelerates particles up to energies of several BeV and more frequently up to energies of several hundred MeV. We know this acceleration occurs at times of high solar activity, when great eruptions take place and large masses of ionized gases shoot out from the sun into interplanetary space. We also know that magnetic disturbances accompany these eruptions, and we strongly suspect the fast-changing magnetic fields as the agency through which some of the protons in the solar atmosphere acquire high energies. We do not know in detail how this happens; the process may vaguely resemble the processes occurring in some high-energy particle accelerators, such as the betatron.[1]

Since the sun produces cosmic rays, why not assume that all cosmic rays come from the sun? In other words, why not assume that the sun emits high-energy particles continuously, thereby producing the normal cosmic-ray flux observed on the earth, and that the solar flare effects are just temporary increases in its normal activity?

The main argument against this assumption rests on the uniform intensity of the radiation at all hours of the day and night. Cosmic rays come not only from the direction of the sun but from everywhere in the sky.

The argument, however, is not as clear-cut as it may seem. The terrestrial magnetic field bends the trajectories of charged particles coming from the sun, making it possible for some of them to reach the night side of the earth (Chap. 5). Moreover, scientists have for some time suspected the existence of weak magnetic fields throughout the solar system. As noted in the preceding chapter, direct observations by space probes have confirmed their suspicions. Interplanetary magnetic fields will also scatter charged particles about, and these would not appear to come from the sun even if they originated there.

Nonetheless, if cosmic-ray particles actually came from the sun, neither the earth's magnetic field nor the interplanetary magnetic field could account for their almost perfectly uniform flow. This conclusion applies to particles with energies of the order of 10 BeV, which form the bulk of the observed radiation. It applies even more forcefully to the particles of much higher energy

[1] The betatron is used to accelerate electrons to energies in the range of hundreds of MeV. The accelerating force is an electric field induced by a time-varying magnetic field.

responsible for air showers. A proton of 10^{15} eV, for example, has a
magnetic rigidity (see pages 56 and 246)

$$BR = \frac{10^{15}}{300} = 3 \times 10^{12} \text{ gauss} \cdot \text{cm}$$

Since the interplanetary field B is of the order of several times
10^{-5} gauss — say, 3×10^{-5} gauss — the radius of curvature R of
this proton in interplanetary space is somewhere around 10^{17} cm,
which is about 6,500 times the distance from the earth to the sun
(1.5×10^{13} cm). On the other hand, since the earth's magnetic
field is of the order of 0.5 gauss, the radius of curvature in the
vicinity of the earth is approximately 6×10^{12} cm, or 10,000 times
the radius of the earth (6.38×10^{8} cm).

Thus protons with energies of 10^{15} eV or more do not undergo
any appreciable deflection either in the interplanetary or in the
terrestrial magnetic field. If they were produced by the sun, they
would come only from the direction of the sun. On the contrary,
as the air shower experiments have shown, there is no preferred
direction of arrival whatsoever.

Cosmic rays from the stars

If the sun does not contribute a major fraction of the observed
cosmic radiation, then where does one look for the main source of
cosmic rays? There are, of course, billions upon billions of stars
in the universe, and one might think that what reaches the earth is
the combined cosmic-ray emission of all these stars. Considering
the relative nearness of the sun, however, if the average star produced the same number of cosmic rays as the sun does, the total
flux upon the earth of cosmic-ray particles from the sun would be
millions of times greater than that from all other stars together.
This would still mean that practically all cosmic rays had to come
from the sun. And they simply do not.

Of course, there may be stars with special properties that make
them particularly effective sources of cosmic rays. Conceivably,

relatively small numbers of such stars may supply the whole of the observed cosmic-ray flux.

Supernovae have also figured prominently in the speculations on possible cosmic-ray sources. These gigantic explosions of individual stars occur once every few hundred years in our galactic neighborhood (that is, within several thousand light years of the solar system). An explosion releases an amount of energy equivalent, perhaps, to the total mass of the sun.

Nobody knows for sure why the gradual process of nuclear fusion — which supplies the energy continuously radiated into space by ordinary stars — sometimes degenerates into an explosive release of energy. But most astrophysicists agree on the following broad picture. Nuclear fusion occurs predominently near the centers of stars, where the temperature is highest. Eventually, the nuclear furnace in the innermost region runs out of fuel; this means that all primeval hydrogen has fused into helium and helium has fused into progressively heavier nuclei, until the center of the star is practically all iron, the most stable of all nuclei.

At this point the gravitational forces, no longer balanced by the radiation pressure due to the continuous generation of energy, will cause the star to collapse. The *implosion* produces a rapid increase of temperature that is due to the transformation of gravitational energy into heat. The hydrogen and the other light nuclei, which are still present in the peripheral regions of the star, now begin to fuse. And since the rate of fusion increases rapidly with temperature, most of the remaining nuclear fuel burns up nearly at once, and a tremendous explosion results.[1] This catastrophic process is held responsible for the synthesis of the heavier nuclei.

---

[1] Not every star blows up at the end of its life. It has been shown that a supernova explosion can occur only if the star has a mass greater than $1\frac{1}{2}$ times that of the sun. Other properties (such as the speed of rotation and the chemical composition) may play a role. Note that the gravitational collapse will acquire catastrophic proportions only if the heat energy released in the interior of the star escapes fast enough; for otherwise it will create a pressure that slows down the process. It is believed that the energy escapes in the form of neutrinos.

It has been suggested that supernovae also give rise to high-energy particles — that is, cosmic rays, and various ingenious ideas have been put forward to explain how this could happen.

Most scientists believe, however, that cosmic-ray particles are accelerated by electromagnetic processes more or less like those at work in solar flares. Astronomers have observed stars in which eruptions resembling solar flares occur with great frequency. They have also observed double stars that possess large magnetic moments and revolve rapidly around a common center of mass, thus producing strong and varying magnetic fields. Finally, there are some variable stars whose exceedingly strong magnetic fields appear to reverse direction every few days. All of these are possible sources of cosmic rays.

Cosmic rays and radio noise

Several scientists, and particularly the Russian astrophysicist V. L. Ginzburg, have pointed out that radioastronomical observations may offer important clues to the origin of cosmic rays. Their line of reasoning runs as follows. If an electromagnetic field accelerates the protons and heavier nuclei found in cosmic radiation, it presumably accelerates electrons as well. The magnetic field, which is necessarily present in the region where the particles are accelerated, bends the trajectories of the electrons and obliges them to spiral around the lines of force.

Since the motion along a curved path is an accelerated motion, the spiraling electrons must lose energy by emitting electromagnetic radiation (see Chap. 6). This effect is well known to all physicists working with high-energy accelerators. It is responsible for the visible and ultraviolet light emitted by fast electrons as they circle around and around in a synchrotron, and it is known as *synchrotron radiation*. The same name is used to describe the radiation produced by the magnetic bending of fast-electron trajectories in space.

In principle, of course, all charged particles moving in a magnetic field emit synchrotron radiation But the intensity of this radiation is critically dependent on the mass of the particles. Lighter particles, which are more easily deflected by a magnetic field and which move with higher speeds, radiate much more strongly than heavier particles. In fact, the synchrotron radiation of protons and other nuclei is completely negligible under any conditions, either in the laboratory or, from what we know, in the universe.

Synchrotron radiation by electrons, on the other hand, is often a major effect. Its relative intensity in the various parts of the electromagnetic spectrum depends on the strength of the magnetic field and on the energy distribution of the electrons. Synchrotron radiation in the spectral region corresponding to radio waves contributes to the radio noise arriving from outer space. Radio astronomers have learned how to distinguish this type of radio noise from types arising from different sources.

What I have just said makes it appear likely that the sources of cosmic rays and the sources of synchrotron radiation are closely related. Our nearest star, the sun, is a natural subject for a direct experimental test of this view. A number of observations have shown that solar flares that give rise to high-energy protons are almost consistently accompanied by the outbursts of radio noise known as *type IV bursts*. Astrophysicists agree that type IV radio bursts are the result of synchrotron radiation by high-energy electrons spiraling around the magnetic field lines in the solar corona.

Other celestial objects that are strong sources of radio noises have been singled out as likely sources of cosmic rays; among them, in particular, are the gas clouds left behind by supernova explosions. Five or six such remnants of outbursts recorded in historical documents during the last 2,000 years or so are now visible in the sky. The best known is the Crab nebula, a gas cloud about six light years in diameter and about 4,000 light years away, the remnant of a supernova explosion observed by Chinese astronomers in

A.D. 1054 (a light year — the distance traveled by light in a year — is approximately 10^{18} cm). The gas within the cloud is still in a state of violent agitation; the motions are clearly discernible from a comparison of pictures of the nebula taken a few years apart.

Much of the visible light emitted by the Crab nebula shows a continuous spectrum. For many years this was a puzzle, because such dilute gases usually radiate at several sharply defined frequencies. It was later found that this light is also strongly polarized. The Russian astrophysicist I. S. Shklovsky then pointed out, in 1953, that the only sensible explanation of both the continuous spectrum and the polarization lies in the assumption that the light is the product of a synchrotron radiation. In the meantime, radio astronomers had also identified the Crab nebula as a strong source of radio noises. Astrophysicists now attribute the radio emission, as well as the light emission, to a synchrotron radiation.

The great intensity of the synchrotron radiation from the Crab nebula and the appearance of much of this radiation in the visible region of the spectrum indicate the presence of large numbers of electrons, with energies extending up to hundreds of BeV, circling around in relatively strong magnetic fields. Presumably, the mechanism responsible for the acceleration of the electrons also accelerates protons and whatever other nuclei may be present in the nebula. These particles may escape from the Crab nebula into interstellar space. If they do, they may, together with particles originating in the same manner from the remains of the other supernovae, contribute a major portion of the observed cosmic radiation.

The Fermi acceleration mechanism

Protons and nuclei of the heavier elements are found everywhere in the universe. The problem is not to explain their presence in the cosmic radiation, but rather to figure out how they might have acquired their tremendous energies. So far, we have considered acceleration mechanisms operating within restricted regions of space, such as stellar atmospheres or remnants of supernovae. However, it is also possible that cosmic-ray particles are accelerated gradually, while traveling through space, at the expense of electromagnetic fields present in the interstellar medium. In 1933, W. F. G. Swann, director of the Bartol Research Foundation, suggested that the galaxy as a whole might act as a gigantic accelerator of cosmic rays. The principle of the acceleration mechanism proposed by Swann was, in essence, the one later applied in the development of the betatron.

In 1951, Enrico Fermi suggested a more realistic mechanism, based on the general picture of interstellar space that was beginning to emerge from astronomical observations. According to this picture, enormous clouds of ionized gas, mostly hydrogen, wander through space. The clouds contain magnetic fields, just as do the gas clouds ejected from the sun. Fermi pointed out that energy is exchanged between these wandering clouds and fast-moving individual particles and that, on the average, the individual particles gain energy in the exchange.

To understand how this happens, consider the following model, which, although oversimplified, brings out the essential features of the process. Assume the clouds are more or less rigid bodies and that the space between them is free of magnetic fields. Then a particle will travel in a straight path until it strikes a cloud. Once inside a cloud, it describes a complicated path, and it eventually emerges with practically no "memory" of its original direction of motion. Therefore, according to the model, particles scatter back and forth between clouds.

When a particle collides with a cloud coming toward it, it bounces off with increased energy; when it collides with a receding cloud, it loses energy. (Any tennis player knows he can increase or decrease the speed of a ball that hits his racket by moving the racket forward or backward.) On the average, the particle obtains a small net gain of energy, largely because head-on collisons occur more frequently. Fermi thought of this mechanism as operating within our galaxy. A similar mechanism may be at work in a more limited region of space, such as the Crab nebula or the atmospheres of stars. Also, it may be at work, on a more grandiose scale, in the regions of space between galaxies.

Cosmic rays in the solar system, in the galaxy, and beyond

The flux of energy reaching the earth in the form of cosmic rays is approximately the same as that received in the form of light from all stars, excluding the sun. The question of how the cosmic-ray flux found near the earth compares with that in distant parts of the universe is not as easily answered. The problem is much more difficult in the case of cosmic rays than in the case of star light, because light travels in straight lines and cosmic-ray particles, being electrically charged, are deflected by magnetic fields. Magnetic deflection may greatly retard the escape of cosmic-ray particles from the regions of space in which they are produced, and thus cause local concentrations in the particle population. In fact, as the discovery of the radiation belt around the earth has shown, under appropriate circumstances charged particles may remain magnetically trapped for long periods of time.

If very effective trapping fields were present in the solar system, a relatively small supply of high-energy particles from the sun would suffice to maintain the observed flux of cosmic rays. Moreover, since most cosmic rays would reach the earth after bouncing back and forth many times in the surrounding space, they would appear to come from every direction, rather than only from the sun. Then the sun, and presumably other stars as well, would be surrounded by an "atmosphere" of cosmic rays, whereas the cosmic-ray flux in interstellar space would be negligible. But, as we have seen, the magnetic fields in the solar system are not strong enough for this purpose. (Apparently they are only able to store solar-flare particles of energies up to several BeV for a few hours or days.)

This is why physicists were compelled to look beyond the solar system in their search for the source of cosmic rays. Clearly, if cosmic rays do not originate within the solar system, they must fill a large volume of interstellar space around the sun.

Stars and interstellar matter are not distributed uniformly throughout the universe but are condensed in galaxies. Our own galaxy contains about 100 billion (10^{11}) stars. Most of these, particularly most of the younger, more active stars, occupy a flat volume shaped roughly like a grindstone with a bulge at the middle. The diameter of the galactic disk is approximately 100,000 light years, and its thickness is a few thousand light years. Much of the interstellar gas and dust is also condensed in this volume. The disk, however, is surrounded by a halo, roughly spherical in shape, formed by old stars and very dilute gas (Fig. 15–1).

It is natural to assume that cosmic rays are produced in galaxies rather than in the nearly empty space between galaxies. If this is so, then most of the observed cosmic radiation should

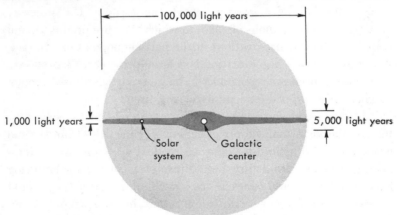

Fig. 15-1 The structure of the Milky Way galaxy, represented schematically. The galactic disk has an average thickness of about 1,000 light years (10^{21} cm); the central bulge in the disk is about 5,000 light years thick. The diameter of the disk is about 100,000 light years (10^{23} cm), and the disk is surrounded by a nearly spherical halo of the same diameter. The solar system is located near the median plane of the disk, about two-thirds of the way from the center.

come from our own galaxy. Other galaxies, because of their great distance, should not contribute more than a small fraction of the cosmic-ray flux, just as they do not contribute more than a small fraction of the light flux in the night sky.

The solar system is located near the median plane of the galaxy, about two-thirds of the way from the center. The distribution of galactic stars and galactic interstellar matter with respect to the earth is therefore very uneven. This, of course, explains the appearance of the great concentration of stars in the Milky Way. Presumably, the sources of cosmic rays are also distributed very unevenly. If there were no magnetic fields in the galaxy, the intensity of cosmic radiation reaching the earth from different directions would vary. One would expect to find most cosmic rays coming from the center of the galaxy. Yet the intensity of cosmic rays from different parts of the sky does not vary by more than a fraction of 1 per cent. Thus, if cosmic rays are of galactic origin, there must be magnetic fields in the galaxy capable of producing a random distribution of cosmic radiation in space.

I have already mentioned the belief that the wandering clouds of ionized gases contain magnetic fields. The crude picture representing cosmic-ray particles as bouncing back and forth between magnetic clouds would explain not only their acceleration but also the random distribution of their directions of motion. Be that as it may, it is quite likely that magnetic fields keep cosmic-ray particles trapped in the galactic volume for long periods of time (compared to the time required to escape along straight lines). Our galaxy, then, and presumably other galaxies as well would have their own cosmic-ray populations, distributed more or less uniformly throughout their volumes, while in the space between galaxies the density of cosmic rays would be almost negligible. If this view is correct, even intermittent sources of cosmic rays within each galaxy (for example, supernovae) might maintain a fairly steady cosmic-ray flux.

Whether cosmic rays are trapped within the galactic disk or within the galactic halo, and how long the actual trapping time is, are still subjects of debate. One important clue is the composition of cosmic rays. The very fact that the cosmic radiation contains nuclei of heavy elements sets an upper limit to the amount of matter traversed by cosmic rays from the moment they are produced to the moment they are detected. For instance, interstellar gas in the galactic disk has an average density of about one atom of hydrogen per cubic centimeter. Considering the known probability for collisions between nuclei of hydrogen and carbon, a carbon nucleus will travel for about 4 million years in the galactic disk before colliding with a hydrogen nucleus of interstellar gas. Such a collision would destroy the carbon nucleus. Consequently, since carbon nuclei are found in cosmic radiation, the radiation cannot remain confined in the galactic disk for more than a few million years on the average.

Another important clue is the small number of high-energy electrons in primary cosmic radiation. This may well result from the fact that electrons moving in a magnetic field emit synchrotron radiation and thereby lose energy fairly rapidly, whereas protons and heavier nuclei do not undergo a corresponding energy loss. Processes such as those occurring in solar flares may not be able to accelerate electrons beyond a certain limit because of the fast rate at which synchrotron radiation robs electrons of their energy. Also, if cosmic rays are magnetically trapped for long periods of time, the energy loss by synchrotron radiation may drastically reduce the flux of high-energy electrons.

Until a few years ago it was generally believed that all cosmic rays arriving at the earth were produced in our own galaxy. This belief has been seriously shaken by the results of air-shower experiments that have gradually pushed the upper limit of the cosmic-ray spectrum to higher and higher energies. The occurrence of primary cosmic rays with energies at least as great as 6×10^{19} eV has been established. If these particles are protons, their magnetic rigidity is

$$BR = \frac{6 \times 10^{19}}{300} = 2 \times 10^{17} \text{ gauss} \cdot \text{cm}$$

Now, several pieces of evidence indicate that the magnetic field in the galactic disk has an average value of about 5×10^{-6} gauss. Presumably the magnetic field in the halo is no stronger. Thus, both in the disk and in the halo the radius of curvature of the particles considered here is at least 4×10^{22} cm. This radius is about 40 times greater than the thickness of the galactic disk (10^{21} cm) and about as large as the radius of the galactic halo (5×10^{22} cm).

It does not seem possible for particles so little affected by the galactic magnetic fields to remain trapped in the galactic disk or even in the galactic halo for any great length of time. If they do not remain trapped, then one must conclude that they are to be found in the space between galaxies, as well as in the space within galaxies, and that most of those observed on earth come from the space beyond our galaxy.[1]

A word of caution is necessary. I have assumed that the high-energy particles responsible for air showers are protons. This is not certain. If they are heavier nuclei, they have, because of their greater electric charge, a smaller magnetic rigidity than protons of the same energy (see pages 57 and 246). For example, in a magnetic field of 5×10^{-6} gauss, an iron nucleus ($Z - 26$) of 6×10^{19} eV energy has a radius of curvature of little more than 10^{21} cm, which is much less than the radius of the galactic halo. These particles, therefore, could conceivably remain trapped in the galactic halo, if not in the galactic disk.

On the other hand, there is no indication that the cosmic-ray spectrum breaks off at 6×10^{19} eV. Any new experimental data showing that the spectrum actually continues well beyond this energy, or any new results showing that the high-energy cosmic-ray particles are protons rather than heavier nuclei, could lead to only one conclusion: these particles are of extragalactic origin.

---

[1] This conclusion is not inconsistent with the view that the *total* cosmic-ray population in the space between galaxies is small compared to that within the galaxies. The evidence for an extragalactic origin applies only to cosmic-ray particles of very great energy, and these form only a minute fraction of the total cosmic-ray flux. As Fig. 11–6 shows, for example, only one primary particle in 10^{16} has an energy greater than 10^{18} eV.

Epilogue

The last pages of this book are written in August, 1962. A few days ago it was the fiftieth anniversary of Hess's flight, with which my story began. The half century covered by this story has been a revolutionary period for science. And cosmic rays, as I have tried to show, have played a major role in the developments that have so greatly enlarged the horizon of our knowledge. Without the wholly unexpected facts and without the tantalizing clues that came to light through the study of cosmic rays, high-energy physics might still be in its infancy. Indeed, physicists might not yet have discovered mesons and all the other particles that have been their major concern during the last decade. And it is certainly not a mere coincidence that the first scientific discoveries of the space age — including the discovery of the Van Allen radiation belt — were made by cosmic-ray physicists.

It is particularly appropriate at this time to pause and look back on the history of cosmic rays, not so much because the fiftieth anniversary of their discovery calls for some sort of celebration, but because, curiously enough, the anniversary comes at a critical moment for cosmic-ray physicists, if not for cosmic-ray physics itself. The interest in cosmic rays is certainly not waning; on the contrary, it is steadily growing. But cosmic-ray research has become such an integral part of many different scientific endeavors that it has almost ceased to exist as a separate and distinct branch of science. The "cosmic-ray physicist," as a specialist, is becoming a figure of the past, while the nuclear physicist, the geophysicist, the astrophysicist, and the cosmologist are turning more and more to the study of cosmic rays for information of vital importance to the solution of their problems. It is quite possible that future historians of science will close the chapter on cosmic rays with the fiftieth anniversary of Hess's discovery. However, they will undoubtedly note that in renouncing its individuality and merging with the main stream of science, cosmic-ray research continued to perform a vital role in advancing man's understanding of the physical world.

Mass per unit area

appendix **A**

The concept of *mass per unit area* appears sufficiently often in this book that a few words of explanation may be useful. When comparing radiation absorbers of different substances, it becomes necessary to consider the density (mass per unit volume), as well as the thickness, of the absorbers. Obviously, 1 meter of air will absorb much less radiation than 1 meter of water, because the density of one is so much smaller than that of the other (0.00129 g/cm³ compared to 1.0 g/cm³ at standard temperature and pressure).

Thus, it is customary to define an absorber not by its geometrical thickness, but by the mass of a column of unit cross-sectional area (Fig. A–1). This quantity — the mass per unit area — is usually measured in grams per square centimeter (g/cm²). For an absorber of constant density, the mass per unit area is just the product of its thickness and its density. For example, a layer of water 1 meter thick has a mass per unit area of 100 g/cm²; the same thickness of air has a mass per unit area of 100 × 0.00129 = 0.129 g/cm². At sea level, the earth's atmosphere has a mass per unit area (which in this instance is numerically equal to the atmospheric pressure) of 1,003 g/cm². The mass per unit area of the atmosphere above a given level is known as the *atmospheric depth.*

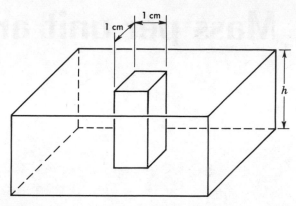

Fig. A-1 Definition of mass per unit area of an absorber. Consider a prism of 1 cm by 1 cm in cross section cut from an absorber slab of thickness h. The mass of this prism is the mass per unit area of the absorber, in grams per square centimeter. The definition applies both to an absorber of uniform density and to an absorber made of layers of different density (such as the earth's atmosphere). In the former case, the mass of the prism is just its volume $(1 \times h = h)$ times the density d, and it is therefore equal to hd.

Powers of ten

appendix B

In the treatment of very large and very small numbers in this book, I have assumed that the reader is more or less familiar with the numerical notation based on positive and negative powers of 10. The following notes, therefore, are intended only as a brief refresher for any reader who may find it useful.

Numbers exactly equal to the products of n terms equal to 10 are represented as the nth power of 10, where n is a positive integer:

$10^1 = 10$
$10^2 = 10 \times 10 = 100$
$10^3 = 10 \times 10 \times 10 = 1,000$
$10^6 = 1,000,000 = 1$ million
$10^9 = 1,000,000,000 = 1$ billion

A number greater than 10 but not equal to a positive power of 10 is represented as the product of a number between 1 and 10 and a power of 10. To take a specific instance, the approximate speed of light in a vacuum is

$1.86 \times 10^5 = 186,000$ miles per second, or
$3 \times 10^5 = 300,000$ kilometers per second, or
$3 \times 10^8 = 300,000,000$ meters per second, or
$3 \times 10^{10} = 30,000,000,000$ centimeters per second

A negative power of 10 is the *reciprocal* of the corresponding positive power:

$10^{-1} = 1/10 = 0.1$
$10^{-2} = 1/10^2 = 1/100 = 0.01$
$10^{-3} = 1/10^3 = 1/1,000 = 0.001$
$10^{-6} = 1/10^6 = 1/1,000,000 = 0.000,001 = 1$ millionth
$10^{-9} = 1/10^9 = 1/1,000,000,000 = 0.000,000,001 = 1$ billionth

A number between 0 and 1, but not equal to a negative power of 10, is represented as the product of a number between 1 and 10 and a negative power of 10. To take a specific instance, the mass of an electron, in grams, is

$$9.11 \times 10^{-28} = \frac{9.11}{10^{28}}$$

$$= 0.000,000,000,000,000,000,000,000,000,911 \text{ gram}$$

Logarithmic scales

appendix **C**

In cosmic-ray physics, more perhaps than in other areas of physics, the quantities of interest vary over a wide range. An extreme example is the measured energy spectrum of primary cosmic rays (Fig. 11-6), where the energy varies from about 10^9 to about 10^{19} eV — that is, by a factor of 10^{10} — and the corresponding intensity from a value of the order of 10^{-1} to a value of the order of 10^{-19} particles per square centimeter per unit solid angle per second — that is, by a factor of the order of 10^{18}. In these cases, the usual (linear) graph — where the distance from the origin is proportional to the magnitude of the number — does not afford a convenient method of representation. If, for example, a horizontal scale 10 cm long represented the energy range from 0 to 10^{19} eV, all measurements in the range, say, from 10^9 to 10^{11} eV, would have to be crowded into a ridiculously small fraction of this scale, precisely into 10^{-7} cm! ($10^{11} - 10^9 = 9.9 \times 10^{10}$; $9.9 \times 10^{10}/10^{19} = 9.9 \times 10^{-9} \approx 10^{-8}$; 10 cm $\times$ $10^{-8} = 10^{-7}$ cm).

Thus, if one wishes to cover a large range of values in a single graph, one must use a scale that "shrinks" as the numbers increase. Such a scale is the *logarithmic scale*, like that used on the horizontal and vertical axes of Fig. 11-6. On a logarithmic scale, the distance from the origin represents the *logarithm* to the base 10 of the number, rather than the number itself. For example, the distance between 10^9 and 10^{11} is the same as the distance between 10^{17} and 10^{19} (because $\log_{10} 10^{11} - \log_{10} 10^9 = 11 - 9 = 2$, and $\log_{10} 10^{19} - \log_{10} 10^{17} = 19 - 17 = 2$). In general, the distance between two points is proportional to the *ratio* of the two corresponding numbers (100 in the example above) rather than to their arithmetical difference.

Energy and momentum

appendix D

The *kinetic energy* of a particle is the energy the particle possesses
as a result of its motion. When a beam of particles (for example,
electrons in a cathode-ray tube) hits a target, the kinetic energy of
the particles is changed into heat; the amount of heat developed
is proportional to the number of particles that hit the target
multiplied by the average kinetic energy of the particles. According
to classical (that is, nonrelativistic) mechanics, the kinetic energy
E is related to the mass of the particle m and to its velocity v by
the equation

$$E = \frac{1}{2}mv^2 \tag{D-1}$$

The equation shows that for a given velocity the kinetic energy is
proportional to the mass; for example, an α particle, which is
nearly 4 times heavier than a proton, has a kinetic energy nearly 4
times that of a proton of the same velocity. The equation also
shows that for a given mass the kinetic energy is proportional to
the square of the velocity; thus, if the velocity of a given particle
is doubled, its kinetic energy becomes 4 times greater.

Albert Einstein showed that Eq. (D-1), once believed to be
rigorously correct, actually represents an approximate expression

of the kinetic energy. The equation is most exact when the velocity
of the particle is very small compared to the velocity of light
($c = 300,000$ km/sec), but it is grossly wrong for velocities comparable to c. The correct equation for the kinetic energy, derived
from Einstein's theory of relativity, reads

$$E = mc^2 \left(\frac{1}{\sqrt{1 - v^2/c^2}} - 1 \right) \tag{D-2}$$

In Eq. (D–2) as well as in the classical equation (D–1), E is
proportional to m. Moreover, one can prove mathematically that
Eq. (D–2) reduces to Eq. (D–1) at the limit for $v \to 0$, as it should.
But Eq. (D–2) shows that, when v is comparable to c, E increases
at a faster rate than the square of the energy. Indeed, as v approaches c, the square root $\sqrt{1 - v^2/c^2}$ approaches zero and the
ratio $1/\sqrt{1 - v^2/c^2}$ approaches infinity, as does the kinetic energy
E. In physical terms this result means that no material particle
can ever travel at the velocity of light, simply because to give a
particle an infinite amount of kinetic energy would require an
infinite amount of work.

The quantity mc^2, which appears as a factor on the right-hand
side of Eq. (D–2), is known as the *rest energy* of the particle.
According to Einstein's equivalence principle which reads

$$\text{Energy} = \text{mass} \times c^2 \tag{D-3}$$

the rest energy mc^2 represents the energy "stored" in the particle's mass. This is the energy released if the particle is annihilated;
thus, when an electron and a positron annihilate each other (Chap.
6), two photons are produced with a total energy equal to c^2 times
their combined mass. Writing Eq. (D–3) in the equivalent form

$$\text{mass} = \frac{\text{energy}}{c^2} \tag{D-4}$$

we see that the equivalence principle assigns a definite mass (that
is, a definite mechanical inertia) to energy. This form of the
equivalence principle has also been verified experimentally. When,
for example, two protons and two neutrons combine to form a
helium nucleus (or α particle; see Appendix G), a certain amount
of energy ΔE is released. Direct measurement shows the α-particle
mass to be slightly less than the combined original mass of the two
protons and two neutrons. This *mass defect* is exactly equal to
$\Delta E/c^2$.

The upper curve in Fig. D–1 provides a graphical representation of Eq. (D–2). The ratio E/mc^2 of the kinetic energy to the rest energy is plotted on a logarithmic scale on the horizontal axis. The vertical (linear) scale represents the ratio v/c of the velocity of the particle to the velocity of light. The graph shows that the particle velocity approaches the velocity of light when E is substantially greater than mc^2 (for example, v becomes greater than $0.95c$ for E greater than 2.2 mc^2). In this case, the particle is said to be *relativistic*. Clearly, light particles (for example, electrons) become relativistic at a lower energy than do heavy particles (for example, protons).

The *momentum* **p** is another property of a moving particle. Unlike the kinetic energy, which is a scalar quantity, the momentum is a vector. The physical significance of the momentum lies in the second law of dynamics, which states that a force **F** acting on a given object during a time t will increase the momentum of the object by an amount **F**t. Thus, the initial momentum of the object $\mathbf{p_1}$, its final momentum $\mathbf{p_2}$, and the force **F** are related by the vector equation

$$\mathbf{p_2} - \mathbf{p_1} = \mathbf{F}t \qquad\qquad (D\text{--}5)$$

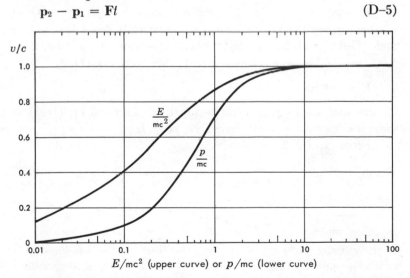

Fig. D-1 The velocity of a particle v, expressed as a fraction of the velocity of light c, as a function of the kinetic energy E divided by the rest energy mc^2, and as a function of the momentum p divided by mc.

Classical mechanics provides the following (approximate) expression for the momentum **p** of a particle of mass m moving with a velocity **v**:

$$\mathbf{p} = m\mathbf{v} \tag{D-6}$$

Here the momentum is seen to be proportional to the mass of the particle and to vary as the first power of the velocity. The correct relativistic equation for the momentum is

$$\mathbf{p} = \frac{m}{\sqrt{1 - v^2/c^2}}\,\mathbf{v} \tag{D-7}$$

Like the kinetic energy, the momentum of a particle approaches infinity as the velocity approaches the velocity of light. The lower curve in Fig. D-1 provides a graphical representation of the momentum-velocity relation. Plotted on the horizontal axis is the quantity $pc/mc^2 (= p/mc)$, that is, the momentum multiplied by the velocity of light and divided by the rest energy of the particle. Plotted on the vertical axis is the ratio v/c. Comparison of the two curves in Fig. D-1 brings out the fact that for relativistic particles the kinetic energy E is nearly equal to pc:

$$E \approx pc \tag{D-8}$$

[One can reach the same conclusion analytically from Eqs. (D-2) and (D-7), considering that, when v is close to c, the ratio $1/\sqrt{1 - v^2/c^2}$ is large compared to 1; therefore, Eq. (D-2)

$$E \approx mc^2/\sqrt{1 - v^2/c^2}$$

On the same assumption, c can be substituted for v in Eq. (D-7) to yield $p = mc/\sqrt{1 - v^2/c^2}$; therefore, $pc \approx E$.]

From Eq. (D-2) we obtain

$$E + mc^2 = \frac{mc^2}{\sqrt{1 - v^2/c^2}}$$

and therefore

$$\frac{mc^2}{E + mc^2} = \sqrt{1 - v^2/c^2}$$

If the mass of the particle is zero, the term on the left-hand side of the equation vanishes. Thus $\sqrt{1 - v^2/c^2} = 0$ and therefore $v = c$. We conclude, then, that *a particle of zero mass* (such as a photon or a neutrino) *must always travel at the velocity of light,* whatever its energy.

The electron volt

The kinetic energy of the individual electrons in a cathode-ray beam depends on the potential difference (number of volts) between the hot negative filament (cathode) and the positive anode. In fact, the kinetic energy is simply proportional to this potential difference and does not depend on the distance between the two electrodes or on the shape of either one. For example, a 20,000-volt potential between the cathode and anode of any cathode-ray tube will always produce electrons of the same kinetic energy, and the energy will always be twice that of electrons generated by a 10,000-volt potential.

This suggests a convenient unit for defining the energies of individual particles. An electron accelerated by a potential difference of 20,000 volts has a kinetic energy of 20,000 *electron volts* (or 20,000 eV for short); an electron accelerated by a potential difference of 10,000 volts has a kinetic energy of 10,000 eV; and so on. In other words, the basic unit of energy (the electron volt) is the energy acquired by an electron when it is accelerated by a potential difference of one volt. The multiples of this unit most commonly used are

1 keV = 1,000 eV (1 thousand electron volts)
1 MeV = 10^6 eV (1 million electron volts)
1 BeV = 10^9 eV (1 billion electron volts)

Thus, the statement that an α particle has an energy of 4.9 MeV means that its kinetic energy equals that of an electron accelerated by a potential difference of 4.9 million volts.

Any electrically charged particle is accelerated by an electric potential difference. From general principles of mechanics, it follows that particles that have the same electric charge and are accelerated by the same potential difference acquire equal kinetic energies even if their masses are different. For instance, a proton accelerated by a potential difference of 10,000 volts will acquire the same kinetic energy (10,000 eV) as an electron accelerated by a potential difference of the same magnitude. On the other hand, particles of different charge accelerated by a given potential difference acquire kinetic energies proportional to their charge. A potential difference of 10,000 volts (which accelerates a singly charged proton to a kinetic energy of 10,000 eV) will accelerate a helium nucleus (which contains two protons and therefore has two elementary charges) to a kinetic energy of 20,000 eV.

The rest energy of a particle is also conveniently expressed in electron volts. For an electron, $mc^2 = 0.51$ MeV, and for a proton, $mc^2 = 938$ MeV.

In the standard system of units, the unit of energy is the *joule*. One joule, which is approximately the energy required to raise a weight of 1.1 kilograms to a height of 10 cm, equals 6.24×10^{18} eV.

Computation of magnetic rigidity

The radius R of the circle described by a charged particle moving in a uniform magnetic field, in the plane perpendicular to the lines of force (Chap. 5), can be obtained from the condition that the centrifugal force and the Lorentz force must balance. If m is the mass of the particle and v its velocity, and if v is small compared to the velocity of light, the centrifugal force is mv^2/R. If B is the strength of the magnetic field and if the electric charge of the particle is Z times the elementary charge e, the Lorentz force is $ZeBv$. Equating the magnitudes of the two forces, we obtain

$$\frac{mv^2}{R} = ZeBv$$

and therefore

$$BR = \frac{mv}{Ze} \qquad \text{(F--1)}$$

Since mv equals the momentum p of the particle, Eq. (F--1) may also be written as

$$BR = \frac{p}{Ze} \qquad \text{(F--2)}$$

245

This equation, which states that the magnetic rigidity equals the ratio of the *momentum* to the *charge* of the particle, was derived from classical mechanics. (The expression used for the centrifugal force is valid only if $v \ll c$.) It turns out (although I shall omit the proof) that Eq. (F–2) is relativistically correct; that is, it is correct for velocities approaching the velocity of light. [This is not true of Eq. (F–1).]

We saw in Appendix D that for relativistic velocities the kinetic energy E approaches the product pc. In this case, Eq. (F–2) yields

$$cBR = \frac{pc}{Ze} = \frac{E}{Ze}$$

From the definition of the electron volt (Appendix E) it follows that the ratio E/e is the energy of the particle measured in electron volts. (A particle of charge e accelerated by a potential difference V acquires a kinetic energy $E = eV$; hence $V = E/e$.) Thus, writing E_{ev} for the energy in electron volts, we have

$$cBR = \frac{E_{ev}}{Z} \tag{F–3}$$

Equation (F–3) is numerically correct if all quantities are measured in the same system of units. We have measured potential differences in volts, and the volt belongs to the mks system of units. In this system, the unit of length (to be used for R) is the meter and the unit of magnetic field strength (to be used for B) is the *weber per square meter*. For consistency, the velocity of light c must be measured in meters per second and therefore has the approximate numerical value of 3×10^8. However, it is customary to measure B in gauss rather than in webers per square meter (1 gauss = 10^{-4} weber/m^2). Also, R is often measured in centimeters rather than meters (1 cm = 10^{-2} meter). The proportionality constant between E_{ev}/Z and BR then becomes $3 \times 10^8 \times 10^{-4} \times 10^{-2} = 300$, and we arrive at the useful formula cited in Chap. 5:

$$300\, B_{gauss}\, R_{cm} = \frac{E_{ev}}{Z} \tag{F–4}$$

The neutron and the structure of atomic nuclei

appendix G

The neutron is a particle with almost exactly the same mass as the proton, but with no electric charge. When it was discovered experimentally by James Chadwick in 1932, the neutron provided the answer to a question about the structure of atomic nuclei that had puzzled physicists for many years. In the early part of the century it had become clear that the masses of all atomic nuclei were approximately whole-number multiples of the proton mass. However, the electric charges of nuclei were less than they would have been if nuclei consisted entirely of protons. For example, experiments had shown the helium nucleus to weigh about as much as four protons, although its charge was equal to that of only two protons.

Physicists considered the possibility that atomic nuclei contained both protons *and* electrons. If, for example, the helium nucleus were made of four protons and two electrons, the negative charge of the latter would cancel that of two protons, leaving a net positive charge of two elementary charges. This idea, however, met with great difficulties. To mention one, the *uncertainty principle*, a basic law of quantum mechanics, stipulates that a particle obliged to remain in a volume with linear dimensions r cannot be at rest, but must possess a momentum of the order of h/r (where h is Planck's constant, equal to 6.61×10^{-27} erg·sec).

From measurements of nuclear radii, it was possible to compute the momentum, and therefore the energy, of the hypothetical electrons in nuclei. This energy turned out to be greater than 100 MeV. It was very hard to accept this conclusion, because electrons with such large kinetic energy could not possibly remain confined within a nucleus.[1] Moreover, the electrons emitted as β rays from radioactive nuclei had much lower energies, ranging from a fraction of one MeV to a few MeV at most.

After the discovery of the neutron, it became clear that nuclei consisted of protons and neutrons, and not protons and electrons. A helium nucleus, then, contains two protons and two neutrons; the nucleus of oxygen contains eight protons and eight neutrons. The total number of protons and neutrons in a nucleus is the *mass number A*, and the number of protons (equal to the number of positive electric charges of the nucleus) is the *charge number Z*. Thus, for a helium nucleus, $A = 4$, $Z = 2$. The same information is frequently given in a more convenient form: $_2\text{He}^4$, where the subscript represents the charge number and the superscript the mass number. By this convention an oxygen nucleus is $_8\text{O}^{16}$ (that is, $A = 16$, $Z = 8$).

Not all nuclei with the same charge number Z have the same mass number A. Atoms whose nuclei have different mass numbers but the same charge number (and therefore the same number of electrons around each nucleus) are called *isotopes*. Isotopes behave in almost identical manners chemically, because chemical reactions depend mainly on the configuration of the electron cloud and are very little influenced by the nuclear mass. Therefore, isotopes occupy the same place in the periodic table of elements (hence their name, derived from the Greek words for "same" and

---

[1] The same difficulty did not arise in the case of protons because, for a given momentum, the energy of a proton is much lower than that of an electron.

"place"). For example, magnesium, the twelfth element in the periodic table ($Z = 12$), has three isotopes, with mass numbers 24, 25, and 26, respectively ($_{12}Mg^{24}$, $_{12}Mg^{25}$, $_{12}Mg^{26}$).

If it is true that nuclei contain only protons and neutrons, the electrons emitted in the β decay of radioactive nuclei must be produced at the moment of the decay. But, because of the law of conservation of electric charge, the birth of an electron must be accompanied by the creation of a positive charge equal in magnitude to that of the negative electron. According to the accepted view, the positive charge appears when one of the neutrons in the nucleus changes into a proton. Free neutrons (that is, neutrons that are not part of a nucleus) have been observed to decay into protons and electrons (see Appendix H).

It should be noted that all nuclei weigh slightly less than their component protons and neutrons would weigh separately. Because protons and neutrons in a nucleus attract one another with large forces (known as *nuclear forces*), a certain amount of energy ΔE is required to separate a given nucleus into its component particles. Conversely, an equal amount of energy is released when free protons and neutrons unite to form a nucleus. This release of energy is accompanied by the loss of a certain amount of mass ΔM given by Einstein's equation

$$\Delta E = \Delta M \, c^2 \tag{G-1}$$

One of the most important experimental data of nuclear physics is the mass defect ΔM of the various nuclei. The first accurate determinations of mass defects were made by the English physicist F. W. Aston in the first quarter of this century. His results are shown, in graphical form, in Fig. G–1. Plotted on the horizontal axis are mass numbers A. Plotted on the vertical axis are the energies $\Delta M \, c^2$ (corresponding to the observed mass defects of various nuclei) divided by the corresponding mass numbers A and expressed in MeV. The quantity $\Delta M \, c^2/A$ is the average energy *per particle* that would be needed to split a nucleus into the individual protons and neutrons of which it is formed. Figure G–1 shows that this energy has a maximum value (of about 8.5 MeV) for nuclei of mass number between 50 and 60. These nuclei, therefore, are the most stable nuclei occurring in nature.

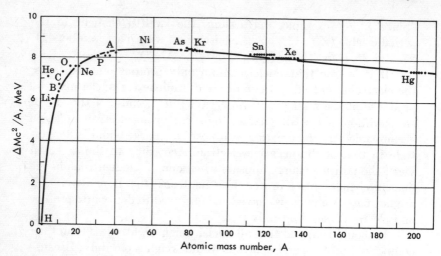

Fig. G-1 Energy per particle ($\Delta M\,c^2/A$) required to split a nucleus into the protons and neutrons of which it is formed, plotted against the mass number A of the nucleus. The dots are experimental points obtained from the measurements of Aston.

The neutrino

The discovery of the *neutrino*, unlike that of the neutron, was the result of theoretical reasoning rather than experiment. It had been known for some time that whereas the α particles emitted by the nuclei of a given radioactive element all have the same energy (or, at most, a few sharply defined energies), β particles have a variety of energies ranging from practically zero to some maximum energy characteristic of the radioactive nucleus from which they came. Physicists were greatly puzzled by this fact, for it was very hard to believe that the β decay of a particular nucleus could occur by a large number of different decay processes, each releasing a different amount of energy. The difficulty was so great that some physicists even began to wonder whether β decay violated the principle of conservation of energy.

In 1931 the theoretical physicist Wolfgang Pauli found a way out of this difficulty by postulating that, in β decay, not one particle (a negative electron) but two particles were emitted simultaneously. One was the electron, the other was an "invisible" particle, or a particle that passed through matter without producing any disturbance by which it could be detected. According to this argument, the decay of a particular nucleus would always release the same amount of energy. The energy could, however, be shared in different proportions between the electron and the

251

hypothetical invisible particle. The particle in question could not carry any electric charge; for it would have betrayed its presence by a trail of ions along its path. Also, in order to account for the known experimental facts about β rays, it was necessary to assume that the mass of the invisible particle was small compared to that of an electron, or perhaps was zero.

Pauli's idea was taken up and developed by Enrico Fermi, who showed in 1934 that the hypothetical particle made it possible to explain the properties of β decay not only qualitatively but quantitatively as well. The particle had first been given the name "neutron." After Chadwick's discovery, the name was changed to *neutrino* (Italian for "the little neutral one"). Neutrinos interact so weakly with matter that physicists did not succeed in detecting them until some 20 years later, after nuclear reactors had made available exceedingly strong sources of neutrinos. (The experiment was performed by F. Reines, C. L. Cowan, and others in 1955.)

Free neutrons n decay spontaneously into protons p, electrons e^-, and neutrinos ν:

$$n \rightarrow p + e^- + \nu \qquad\qquad (H-1)$$

with a mean life of about 16.6 minutes. (The decay was first observed in 1950.) The neutron mass m_n is slightly greater than the proton mass m_p — the difference between the corresponding rest energies $(m_n c^2 - m_p c^2)$ being approximately 1.3 MeV. This energy difference accounts for the rest energy and kinetic energy of the electron and for the energy of the neutrino emitted in the decay. The decay of a neutron bound in a nucleus may be accelerated, retarded, or precluded altogether by the close interaction of the neutron with other neutrons and protons in the nucleus. As noted in Appendix G, the decay of neutrons in radioactive nuclei is the fundamental process responsible for the β-ray emission. In nuclei that are not β active, on the other hand, neutrons are stable; that is, they do not decay.

While free protons are stable (because they have a rest energy smaller than that of neutrons), protons belonging to nuclei of some artificially produced elements decay spontaneously into a neutron, a positron, and a neutrino (or, rather, an antineutrino $\bar{\nu}$; see Appendix I):

$$p \rightarrow n + e^+ + \bar{\nu} \qquad\qquad (\text{H--2})$$

This decay process is responsible for the so-called positive β activity.

Neutrinos are produced not only in the (spontaneous or induced) decay of neutrons and protons but also in the spontaneous decay of other elementary particles such as the μ meson and the π meson (see Chaps. 8 and 9). However, it was shown recently (by L. Lederman, M. Schwartz, and R. J. Steinberg in 1962) that the neutrinos associated with the decay of π mesons into μ mesons (ν_μ) are different from those emitted, together with electrons, when a neutron changes into a proton, or vice versa (ν_e). Thus there exist in nature at least two different kinds of neutrinos (and antineutrinos).

Elementary particles

appendix I

A list of the known elementary particles and a description of some of their properties appear in Table I–1. In this table the particles are subdivided into four families:

1. The *photon* (γ) — the quantum of electromagnetic radiation, that is, the quantum of the electromagnetic field of forces.

2. The *neutrinos* [of which, as noted in Appendix H, there exist two different kinds (ν_e and ν_μ)], the *electrons* [negative (e^-) and positive (e^+)], and the μ *mesons* [negative (μ^-) and positive (μ^+)]. Neutrinos, electrons, and μ mesons are collectively called *leptons*.

3. *Pi mesons* [positive (π^+), negative (π^-), and neutral (π^0)] and *K mesons* [positive (K^+), negative (K^-), and neutral (K^0)]. Pi mesons may be regarded as the quanta of the nuclear field of forces — the cohesive forces between protons and neutrons that hold nuclei together. K mesons are some sort of "heavy" pi mesons.

4. The *nucleons* [that is, protons (p) and neutrons (n)] and the various *hyperons* [lambda particles (Λ), sigma particles (Σ), and xi particles (Ξ)], some of which are neutral and some charged. Collectively these particles are called *baryons*.

All members of the third and fourth families interact strongly with one another by means of the so-called nuclear forces. No such interaction occurs between two leptons, or between a lepton and a particle of another family.

All electrically charged elementary particles have charges equal to the positive or negative elementary charge (1.6×10^{-19} coulomb). In the table, the symbol $+$ in the column under "charge" indicates a positive elementary charge, the symbol $-$ a negative elementary charge, and the symbol 0 no charge. The *law of conservation* of charge states that in an isolated system the total number of positive elementary charges minus the total number of negative elementary charges always remains constant. For example, the creation of a negative electron in the materialization process of a photon is accompanied by the creation of a positive electron (positron) so that the net charge is zero both before and after the event.

To each particle there corresponds an antiparticle with identical mass, so that when a particle and an antiparticle meet, they annihilate each other. The energy released (equal to the combined mass times the square of the velocity of light) appears in the form of photons or of fast-moving particles (for example, the annihilation of a negative electron with a positive electron gives rise to two photons; the annihilation of a proton with an antiproton results in the production of π mesons). Conversely, all particle-antiparticle pairs may be created by materialization of energy.

When a particle is unstable, its antiparticle is also unstable and the two have identical mean lives. Moreover, the decay products of one are the antiparticles of the decay products of the other. If a particle is positively charged, its antiparticle is negatively charged, and vice versa.

In the lepton and baryon families, a neutral particle is physically different from its antiparticle. Thus a neutron (n) is different from an antineutron ($\bar{n}$) because the neutron decay gives rise to a (positively charged) proton and a negative electron, while the antineutron decay gives rise to a (negatively charged) antiproton and a positive electron. In the other two families, however, neutral particles are identical to their antiparticles (for example, the π^0 meson is its own antiparticle).

Leptons and baryons obey two conservation laws that formally resemble the law of conservation of electric charge: the *conservation of leptons* and the *conservation of baryons*.

The first law states that, in an isolated system, the total number of leptons, *minus* the total number of antileptons, remains constant. For example, in the decay process

$$\mu^- \rightarrow e^- + \bar{\nu}_e + \nu_\mu$$

there is one lepton (μ^-) before the event and there are two leptons (e^- and ν_μ) and one antilepton ($\bar{\nu}_e$) after the event.

Similarly, the second law states that, in an isolated system, the total number of baryons minus the total number of antibaryons remains constant. For example, in the simultaneous annihilation of a proton and an antiproton, there are one baryon and one antibaryon before the event and there are no baryons or antibaryons after the event.

In principle, the choice as to which particle of a pair is called a particle and which an antiparticle is an arbitrary one. However, it is customary to regard the negative electron and the proton (which are among the building blocks of ordinary matter) as particles. Consequently the character of all other baryons and leptons is uniquely determined. For example, the ordinary neutron is a baryon, because it decays into a proton and two particles that do not belong to the baryon family.

Conservation of baryons is responsible for the stability of matter; it prevents a proton from changing into, say, five positrons and four electrons, a process not forbidden by the conservation of energy and electric charge.

No conservation law similar to the conservation of leptons and baryons exists for the other two families of particles.

Table I-1 Elementary Particles

Family	Group	Particle	Anti-particle	Mass, electron masses	Charge	Mean life, sec	Decay modes
Photon	Photon	γ	γ	0	0	Stable	
Leptons	Neutrinos	ν_e	$\bar{\nu}_e$	0	0	Stable	
		ν_μ	$\bar{\nu}_\mu$	0	0	Stable	
				0	0	Stable	
				0	0	Stable	
	Electrons	e^-	e^+	1	−	Stable	
				1	+	Stable	
	μ mesons	μ^-	μ^+	206.8	−	2.212×10^{-6}	$e^- + \bar{\nu}_e + \nu_\mu$
				206.8	+	2.212×10^{-6}	$e^+ + \nu_e + \bar{\nu}_\mu$

Table I-1 Elementary Particles—Continued

Family	Group	Particle	Anti-particle	Mass, electron masses	Charge	Mean life, sec	Decay modes
Pi and K mesons	π mesons	π^0	π^0	264	0	2×10^{-16}	$\gamma + \gamma$
		π^+		273	$+$	2.55×10^{-8}	$\mu^+ + \nu_\mu$
		π^-	π^-	273	$-$	2.55×10^{-8}	$\mu^- + \bar{\nu}_\mu$
	K mesons	K_1^0	K_1^0	974	0	1×10^{-10}	$\pi^+ + \pi^-$ $\pi^0 + \pi^0$
		K_2^0	K_2^0	974	0	6×10^{-8}	$\mu^+ + \nu_\mu + \pi^-$ $\mu^- + \bar{\nu}_\mu + \pi^+$ $e^+ + \nu_e + \pi^-$ $e^- + \bar{\nu}_e + \pi^+$ $\pi^+ + \pi^- + \pi^0$ $\pi^0 + \pi^0 + \pi^0$
		K^+		966	$+$	1.22×10^{-8}	$\mu^+ + \nu_\mu$ $\mu^+ + \nu_\mu + \pi^0$ $e^+ + \nu_e + \pi^0$ $\pi^+ + \pi^0$ $\pi^+ + \pi^0 + \pi^0$ $\pi^+ + \pi^+ + \pi^-$
			K^-	966	$-$	1.22×10^{-8}	$\mu^- + \bar{\nu}_\mu$ $\mu^- + \bar{\nu}_\mu + \pi^0$ $e^- + \bar{\nu}_e + \pi^0$ $\pi^- + \pi^0$ $\pi^- + \pi^0 + \pi^0$ $\pi^- + \pi^- + \pi^+$

Table I-1 Elementary Particles—Continued

Family	Group	Particle	Anti-particle	Mass, electron masses	Charge	Mean life, sec	Decay modes
Baryons	Nucleons	n	$\bar{n}$	1,839	0	10^3	$p + e^- + \bar{\nu}_e$
				1,839	0	10^3	$\bar{p} + e^+ + \nu_e$
		p	$\bar{p}$	1,836	+	Stable	
				1,836	−	Stable	
	Hyperons	Λ	$\bar{\Lambda}$	2,183	0	2.2×10^{-10}	$p + \pi^-$; $n + \pi^0$; $p + e^- + \bar{\nu}_e$
				2,183	0	2.2×10^{-10}	$\bar{p} + \pi^+$; $\bar{n} + \pi^0$; $\bar{p} + e^+ + \nu_e$
		Σ^0	$\bar{\Sigma}^0$	2,332	0	$<10^{-11}$	$\Lambda + \gamma$
				2,332	0	$<10^{-11}$	$\bar{\Lambda} + \gamma$
		Σ^+	$\bar{\Sigma}^+$	2,328	+	8×10^{-11}	$p + \pi^0$; $n + \pi^+$
				2,328	−	8×10^{-11}	$\bar{p} + \pi^0$; $\bar{n} + \pi^-$
		Σ^-	$\bar{\Sigma}^-$	2,341	−	1.6×10^{-10}	$n + \pi^-$; $n + e^- + \bar{\nu}_e$
				2,341	+	1.6×10^{-10}	$\bar{n} + \pi^+$; $\bar{n} + e^+ + \nu_e$
		Ξ^0	$\bar{\Xi}^0$	2,566	0	$\sim 10^{-10}$	$\Lambda + \pi^0$
				2,566	0	$\sim 10^{-10}$	$\bar{\Lambda} + \pi^0$
		Ξ^-	$\bar{\Xi}^-$	2,580	−	1.3×10^{-10}	$\Lambda + \pi^-$
				2,580	+	1.3×10^{-10}	$\bar{\Lambda} + \pi^+$

Index

316